# HOLT CALIFORNIA
# Life Science

## Interactive Reader and Study Guide

**HOLT, RINEHART AND WINSTON**

A Harcourt Education Company

Orlando • Austin • New York • San Diego • London

# Contents

**CHAPTER 1** The Nature of Life Science

**SECTION 1** # Asking About Life

**BEFORE YOU READ**

After you read this section, you should be able to answer these questions:

• What is life science?

• Why is life science important for everyday life?

**California Science Standards**

**7.7.b**

## What Is Life Science?

Imagine that it is summer. You are lying on the grass in a park watching dogs play and bees visiting flowers. An ant carries away a crumb from your lunch. Suddenly, questions pop into your head: How do ants find food? Why don't bees visit every flower? Why do dogs play? You have just taken the first steps to becoming a life scientist.

**Life science** is the study of living things. Asking questions about the world around you is the first step in any scientific investigation. What kinds of questions can you ask? ☑

**STUDY TIP**

**Predict** As you read this section, write a list of questions about life science that you think this book will help your answer.

**READING CHECK**

**1. Identify** What is the first step in a scientific investigation?

_____

_____

Part of science is asking questions about the world around you.

## What Kind of Questions Can You Ask in Life Science?

Take a look around your home or neighborhood. Just about anywhere you go, you will find some kind of living organism. The world around us is full of an amazing diversity of life. Single-celled algae, giant redwood trees, and 40-ton whales are all living things. For any living thing you could ask: How does the organism get its food? Where does it live? Why does it behave in a certain way? However, these questions are just the beginning.

# What Do You Do Once You Have a Question?

Once you ask a question, it is time to look for an answer. How do you start your investigation? There are three methods you can use: research, observation, and experimentation. ☑

## RESEARCH

You can find answers to some of your questions by doing research. The following are some ways you can do research:

• Ask someone who knows a lot about the subject.

• Look up information in print resources, such as textbooks, encylopedias, and magazines.

• Use electronic resources such as the World Wide Web.

When you do research, be sure to think about the source of the information you find. Not all information you find in print materials or on the World Wide Web is correct. Scientists use information only from reliable sources.

## OBSERVATION

You can find answers to some questions by observation. When you observe, you watch something and write down what you see. For example, if you wanted to know what birds live in your area, you could go outside and look for them. You could also hang a bird feeder outside your home and observe the birds that use it.

## EXPERIMENTATION

You can answer some questions by doing an experiment. An experiment should be designed carefully to answer a specific question. Making good observations and analyzing data are two important parts of doing an experiment.

**READING CHECK**

**2. List** List three methods of investigation that you could use to answer questions.

_____

_____

_____

**Say It**

**Research** Choose your favorite living thing. Write five questions about that organism. Use three different types of resources to answer those questions. Present to the class what you have learned.

**TAKE A LOOK**

**3. Identify** What type of investigation method is this student using?

_____

_____

This student is trying to find the hardness of a mineral.

**SECTION 1** Asking About Life *continued*

# Why Is Asking Questions Important?

Why do life scientists need to ask questions? Do the answers really matter in everyday life? Absolutely! As you study life science, you will begin to see how important it is to ask and answer questions. Life scientists are looking for answers to many questions. These include fighting disease, producing food, and protecting the environment.

## FIGHTING DISEASE

Before 1955, many people suffered from a disease called polio. *Polio* is caused by a virus that affects the brain and nerves and can cause paralysis. Today, very few people in the world have polio. By asking questions and searching for answers, scientists were able to create a vaccine that protects people from the polio virus.

Today, scientists are looking for ways to stop the spread of the virus that causes *acquired immune deficiency syndrome* (AIDS). By studying how this virus affects the body and how it causes AIDS, scientists hope to find a cure.

## PRODUCING FOOD

How can we produce enough food to feed everyone? How can we make sure that foods are safe to eat? To answer these questions, some scientists design experiments to see what makes plants grow larger or faster. Others are looking for ways to preserve foods better so that they will last longer. ☑

## PROTECTING THE ENVIRONMENT

Many environmental problems are caused by our misuse of natural resources. Life scientists try to understand how we affect the world around us. They are studying things such as pollution, endangered species, and the effects of cutting down too many trees.

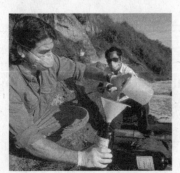

These environmental scientists are testing water quality.

*Critical Thinking*

**4. Infer** Why do you think that more people suffered from polio before 1955 than they do today?

_____

_____

_____

_____

_____

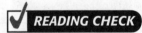 **READING CHECK**

**5. Identify** Give one question about producing food that life scientists are trying to answer.

_____

_____

# Section 1 Review

## SECTION VOCABULARY

| | |
|---|---|
| **life science** the study of living things | |

**1. List** Give three examples of resources you could use to do research.

_____

_____

_____

**2. Write Questions** Write three questions about the animal in this picture. Try to use different ones from the examples given in the text.

_____

_____

_____

**3. Explain** Why do you need to be careful about choosing resources for research?

_____

_____

**4. Identify Relationships** How are observation and experimentation related?

_____

_____

_____

**5. List** List three environmental problems that life scientists are studying.

_____

_____

**6. Apply Concepts** When do you think a life scientist would study a nonliving thing, such as a lake or a rock? Give an example.

_____

_____

CHAPTER 1 | The Nature of Life Science

**SECTION 2** **Scientific Methods**

**California Science Standards**

7.7.c, 7.7.e

## What Are Scientific Methods?

A group of students in Minnesota went on a field trip to a wildlife refuge. They noticed that some of the frogs they saw looked strange. For example, some of the frogs had too many legs or eyes. The frogs were *deformed*. The students wondered what made the frogs deformed. They decided to carry out an investigation to learn what happened to the frogs.

By making observations and asking questions about the observations, the students were using scientific methods. **Scientific methods** are a series of steps that scientists use to answer questions and to solve problems. The figure below shows the steps in scientific methods. ☑

**STUDY TIP**

**Outline** As you read this section, make a chart showing the different steps of scientific methods. In the chart, describe how the students in Minnesota used each step to investigate the deformed frogs.

**READING CHECK**

**1. Define** What are scientific methods?

_____

_____

_____

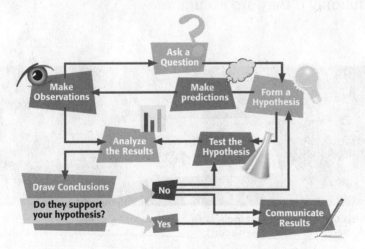

As you can see, the order of steps in scientific methods can vary. Scientists may use all of the steps or just some of the steps during a certain investigation. They may even repeat some of the steps. The order depends on what works best to answer a certain question.

**TAKE A LOOK**

**2. Use Models** Starting with "Ask a question," trace two different paths through the figure to "Communicate results." Use a colored pen or marker to trace your paths.

## Why Is It Important to Ask a Question?

Asking a question helps scientists focus on the most important things they want to learn. The question helps to guide the research that the scientist does. ☑

In many cases, an observation leads to a question. For example, the students in Minnesota observed that some of the frogs were deformed. Then they asked the question, "Why are some of the frogs deformed?" Answering questions often involves making more observations.

## How Do Scientists Make Observations?

The students in Minnesota made careful observations to help them answer their question. The students caught many frogs. Then they counted how many normal and how many deformed frogs they caught. They photographed, measured, and described each frog. They also tested the water the frogs were living in. The students were careful to record their observations accurately.

Like the students, scientists make many different kinds of observations. They may measure length, volume, time, or speed. They may describe the color or shape of an organism. They may also describe how an organism behaves. When scientists make and record their observations, they are careful to be accurate. Observations are useful only if they are accurate.

Scientists use many different tools, such as microscopes, rulers, and thermometers, to make observations.

**READING CHECK**

**3. Explain** Why do scientists ask questions?

_____
_____

*Critical Thinking*

**4. Explain** Why is it important for observations to be accurate?

_____
_____
_____

**TAKE A LOOK**
**5. Identify** Give three kinds of observations that can be made with the tools in the picture.

_____
_____
_____

# What Is a Hypothesis?

After asking questions and making observations, scientists may form a hypothesis. A **hypothesis** (plural, *hypotheses*) is a possible answer to a question. A good hypothesis is based on observations and can be tested. When scientists form a hypothesis, they base it on all of the observations and information that they have. ☑

A single question can lead to more than one hypothesis. The students in Minnesota learned about different things that can cause frogs to be deformed. They used this information to form three hypotheses to answer their question. These hypotheses are shown in the figure below.

Hypothesis 1:
The deformities were caused by one or more chemical pollutants in the water.

Hypothesis 2:
The deformities were caused by attacks from parasites or other frogs.

Hypothesis 3:
The deformities were caused by an increase in exposure to ultraviolet light from the sun.

More than one hypothesis can be made for a single question.

**READING CHECK**

**6. Define** What is a hypothesis?

_____

_____

**Say It**

**Discuss** In a group, talk about some other possible hypotheses that the students could have come up with.

**TAKE A LOOK**
**7. Describe** What are two things that all of the hypotheses have in common?

_____

_____

_____

**SECTION 2** Scientific Methods *continued*

## PREDICTIONS

Before a scientist can test a hypothesis, the scientist must first make predictions. A *prediction* is a statement that explains how something can cause an effect. A prediction can be used to set up a test of a hypothesis. Predictions are usually stated in an if-then format, as shown in the figure below. More than one prediction may be made for a hypothesis.

Hypothesis 1:
Prediction: If a substance in the pond water is causing the deformities, then the water from ponds that have deformed frogs will be different from the water from ponds in which no abnormal frogs have been found.
Prediction: If a substance in the pond water is causing the deformities, then some tadpoles will develop deformities when they are raised in pond water collected from ponds that have deformed frogs.

Hypothesis 2:
Prediction: If a parasite is causing the deformities, then this parasite will be found more often in frogs that have deformities than in frogs that do not have deformities.

Hypothesis 3:
Prediction: If an increase in exposure to ultraviolet light is causing the deformities, then frog eggs exposed to more ultraviolet light in a laboratory will be more likely to develop into deformed frogs than frog eggs that are exposed to less UV light will.

More than one prediction may be made for a single hypothesis.

Scientists can perform experiments to test their predictions. In many cases, the results from the experiments match a prediction for a hypothesis. In other cases, the results do not match any of the predictions. When this happens, the scientist must make a new hypothesis and carry out more tests.

# How Do Scientists Test a Hypothesis?

Scientists plan experiments to show whether a certain factor caused a certain observation. A *factor* is anything in an experiment that can change the experiment's results. Some examples of factors are temperature, the type of organism being studied, and the weather in an area. ☑

To study the effect of each factor, scientists perform controlled experiments. A **controlled experiment** tests only one factor at a time. These experiments have a control group and one or more experimental groups.

The factors for the control group and the experimental groups are the same, except for the one factor being tested. This factor is called the **variable**. Any difference in the results between the control and experimental groups is probably caused by the variable. ☑

## DESIGNING AN EXPERIMENT

Experiments must be carefully planned. Scientists should consider every factor when designing experiments. It is also important for scientists to use ethical guidelines when they design and carry out experiments. These guidelines help to make sure that the scientists do not cause unnecessary harm to the organisms in the experiment.

The table below shows a sample experiment to test whether UV light can cause frogs to be deformed. In the experiment, there is one control group and two experimental groups. All the factors affecting these groups are the same except the amount of UV light exposure. The number of days that the frog eggs are shown UV light changes between the groups. Therefore, amount of exposure to UV light is the variable.

☑ **READING CHECK**

9. **Define** What is a factor?

_____

_____

_____

☑ **READING CHECK**

10. **Compare** How are control groups and experimental groups different?

_____

_____

_____

| Group | Tank | Control Factors | | | Variable |
| | | Kind of frog | Number of eggs | Temperature of water (°C) | UV light exposure (days) |
|---|---|---|---|---|---|
| #1 | A | leopard frog | 50 | 25 | 0 |
| | B | leopard frog | 50 | 25 | 0 |
| #2 | C | leopard frog | 50 | 25 | 15 |
| | D | leopard frog | 50 | 25 | 15 |
| #3 | E | leopard frog | 50 | 25 | 24 |
| | F | leopard frog | 50 | 25 | 24 |

**TAKE A LOOK**

11. **Apply Concepts** Which group (1, 2, or 3) is the control group? Explain your answer.

_____

_____

_____

Name _____ Class _____ Date _____

SECTION 2 | Scientific Methods *continued*

## COLLECTING DATA

Scientists always try to test many individuals. For example, in the UV light experiment, a total of 300 frogs were tested. By testing many individuals, scientists can account for the effects of differences between individuals. They can be more sure that differences between the control and experimental groups are caused by the variable. ☑

Scientists will often repeat an experiment to prove that it produces the same results every time. If an experiment produces the same results again and again, scientists can be more certain that the results are true.

The figure below shows the setup of the UV light experiment. It also shows the results of the experiment.

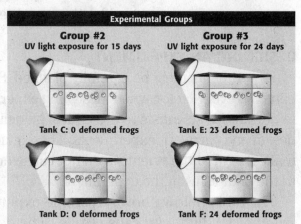

| Control Group | Experimental Groups | |
|---|---|---|
| **Group #1**<br>No UV light exposure | **Group #2**<br>UV light exposure for 15 days | **Group #3**<br>UV light exposure for 24 days |
| Tank A: 0 deformed frogs | Tank C: 0 deformed frogs | Tank E: 23 deformed frogs |
| Tank B: 0 deformed frogs | Tank D: 0 deformed frogs | Tank F: 24 deformed frogs |

## How Do Scientists Analyze Results?

When scientists finish their experiments, they must analyze their results. Analyzing results helps scientists explain their observations. Their explanations are based on the information they collect.

To organize their data, scientists often make tables and graphs. Scientists study organized data to learn how the variable affected the experiment. The data from the UV light experiment is shown in the table below. This table shows that frogs that were exposed to 24 days of UV light developed deformities.

| Number of days of UV exposure | Number of deformed frogs |
|---|---|
| 0 | 0 |
| 15 | 0 |
| 24 | 48 |

---

**READING CHECK**

**12. Explain** Why do scientists try to use many individuals in their experiments?

_____

_____

_____

---

# Math Focus

**13. Make a Graph** Use the information in the table to fill in the graph below.

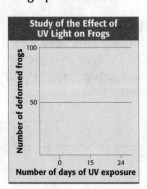

Study of the Effect of UV Light on Frogs

---

**SECTION 2** Scientific Methods *continued*

## What Are Conclusions?

After analyzing results from experiments, scientists must decide if the results support the hypotheses. This is called *drawing conclusions*. Finding out that a hypothesis is not correct can be as valuable as finding out that a hypothesis is correct.

What happens if the results do not support the hypothesis? Scientists may repeat the investigation to check for mistakes. Scientists may repeat experiments hundreds of times. Another option is to look at the original question in a different way. A scientist can then ask another question and make a new hypothesis.

The UV light experiment showed that UV light can cause frogs to be deformed. However, this does not mean that UV light definitely caused the frog deformities in Minnesota. Many other factors may affect the frogs. Some of these factors may be things that scientists have not even thought of yet.

Questions as complicated as why the frogs are deformed are rarely solved with a single experiment. The search for a solution may continue for many years. Finding an answer doesn't always end an investigation. In many cases, the answer begins another investigation. In this way, scientists continue to build knowledge.

## Why Do Scientists Share Their Results?

After finishing a study, scientists share their results with others. They write reports and give presentations. They can also put their results on the Internet.

Sharing information allows others the chance to repeat the experiments for themselves. If other scientists get different results, more studies must be done to find out if the differences are significant.

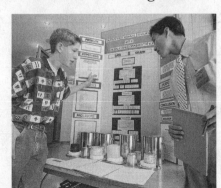

This student scientist is communicating the results of his investigation at a science fair.

*Critical Thinking*

**14. Infer** How can finding out that a hypothesis is not correct be useful for a scientist?

_____

_____

_____

_____

_____

**TAKE A LOOK**

**15. Describe** Why is it important for scientists to share their results?

_____

_____

_____

_____

# Section 2 Review

7.7.c, 7.7.e

## SECTION VOCABULARY

| | |
|---|---|
| **controlled experiment** an experiment that tests only one factor at a time by using a comparison of a control group with an experimental group | **scientific methods** a series of steps followed to solve problems |
| **hypothesis** a testable idea or explanation that leads to scientific investigation | **variable** a factor that changes in an experiment in order to test a hypothesis |
| **Wordwise** The prefix *hypo-* means "under." The root *thesis* means "proposition." Other examples are *hypodermic* and *hypoallergenic*. | |

**1. Describe** What are the main parts of a controlled experiment?

_____

_____

_____

**2. Infer** Why might a scientist need to repeat a step in scientific methods?

_____

_____

_____

**3. Identify** What are two ways that scientists can share the results of their experiments?

_____

_____

_____

**4. Define** What is a prediction?

_____

_____

_____

**5. Explain** Why might a scientist repeat an experiment?

_____

_____

_____

**6. Describe** What can scientists do if the results of an experiment do not support a hypothesis?

_____

_____

_____

**CHAPTER 1** The Nature of Life Science
**SECTION 3** **Tools and Measurement**

---

**BEFORE YOU READ**

**After you read this section, you should be able to answer these questions:**

- How do tools help scientists?
- How do scientists measure length, area, mass, volume, and temperature?

## What Tools Do Scientists Use?

The application of science for practical purposes is called **technology**. Life scientists can use technology to find information and solve problems in new ways. New technology can allow scientists to get information that was not available before.

### CALCULATORS AND COMPUTERS

Scientists use many different tools to analyze, or examine, data. Calculators can help scientists do calculations quickly. Computers are very important tools for collecting, storing, and studying data.

### BINOCULARS

Scientists can use tools to help them see objects clearly. For example, it is not always easy or safe to get close to an organism that you are studying. *Binoculars* are a tool that scientists can use to help them see things that are far away.

Binoculars help scientists make observations when they cannot get close to their subject.

### COMPOUND LIGHT MICROSCOPES

Scientists use microscopes to see things that are very small. One kind of microscope is a **compound light microscope**, which is a tool that magnifies small objects. It has three main parts: a stage, a tube with two or more lenses, and a light. An item is placed on the stage. Light passes through the item. The lenses help to magnify the image of the item.

**STUDY TIP**

**Compare** As you read this section, make a table that compares how scientists measure length, area, mass, volume, and temperature. Include the tools and units of measurement that scientists use.

**TAKE A LOOK**
**1. Explain** Why would a scientist use binoculars?

_____

_____

_____

**7.7.a** Select and use <u>appropriate</u> tools and <u>technology</u> (including calculators, <u>computers</u>, balances, spring scales, microscopes, and binoculars) to perform tests, collect <u>data</u>, and display <u>data</u>.

**Word Help: appropriate**
correct for the use; proper

**Word Help: technology**
tools, including electronic products

**Word Help: computer**
an electronic device that stores, retrieves, and calculates data

**Word Help: data**
facts or figures; information

**2. Identify** A scientist wants to look at a small, living cell. Should the scientist use a compound light microscope or an electron microscope? Explain your answer.

_____
_____
_____
_____
_____

*Critical Thinking*

**3. Predict Consequences**
What could happen if scientists used many different systems of measurement to record their data?

_____
_____
_____

## ELECTRON MICROSCOPES

**Electron microscopes** use tiny particles called *electrons* to produce magnified images. Electron microscopes make clearer and more detailed images than light microscopes do. However, unlike light microscopes, electron microscopes cannot be used to study things that are alive.

## How Do Scientists Measure Objects?

Scientists make many measurements as they collect data. It is important for scientists to be able to share their data with other scientists. Therefore, scientists use units of measurement that are known to all other scientists. One system of measurement that most scientists use is called the International System of Units.

**Transmission Electron Microscope** Electrons pass through the specimen and produce a flat image.

**Scanning Electron Microscope** Electrons bounce off the surface of the specimen and produce a three-dimensional (3-D) image.

**Compound Light Microscope** Light passes through a specimen and produces a flat image.

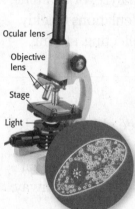
Ocular lens
Objective lens
Stage
Light

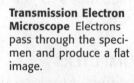

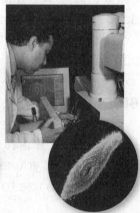

## THE INTERNATIONAL SYSTEM OF UNITS

The *International System of Units*, or *SI*, is a system of measurement that scientists use when they collect data. This system of measurement has two benefits. First, scientists around the world can share and compare their data easily because all measurements are made in the same units. Second, SI units are based on the number 10. This makes it easy to change from one unit to another.

It is important to learn the SI units that are used for different types of measurements. You will use SI units when you make measurements in the science lab.

**SECTION 3** Tools and Measurement *continued*

## LENGTH

*Length* is a measure of how long an object is. The SI unit for length is the meter (m). Centimeters (cm) and millimeters (mm) are used to measure small distances. There are 100 cm in 1 m. There are 1,000 mm in 1 m. Micrometers (μm) are used to measure very small distances. There are 1 million μm in 1 m. Rulers and meter sticks are used to measure length.

| Length Tools: ruler or meter stick | SI unit: meter (m) kilometer (km) centimeter (cm) millimeter (mm) | 1 km = 1,000 m 1 cm = 0.01 m 1 mm = 0.001 m 1 μm = 0.000001 m |
|---|---|---|

**TAKE A LOOK**
**4. Identify** What is the SI unit for length?

## AREA

Area is a measure of how much surface an object has. For most objects, area is calculated by multiplying two lengths together. For example, you can find the area of a rectangle by multiplying its length by its width. Area is measured in square units, such as square meters ($m^2$) or square centimeters ($cm^2$). There are 10,000 $cm^2$ in 1 $m^2$. ☑

There is no tool that is used to measure area directly. However, you can use a ruler to measure length and width. Multiply these measurements to find area.

| Area | square meter ($m^2$) square centimeter ($cm^2$) | 1 $cm^2$ = 0.0001 $m^2$ |
|---|---|---|

**READING CHECK**
**5. Explain** How can you find the area of a rectangle?

_____

_____

## VOLUME

Volume is the amount of space an object takes up. You can find the volume of a box-shaped object by multiplying its length, width, and height together. You can find the volume of objects with many sides by measuring how much liquid they can push out of a container, as shown in the figure on the next page. Beakers and graduated cylinders are used to measure the volume of liquids. ☑

Volume is often measured in cubic units. For example, very large objects can be measured in cubic meters ($m^3$). Smaller objects can be measured in cubic centimeters ($cm^3$). There are 1 million $cm^3$ in 1 $m^3$. The volume of a liquid is sometimes given in units of liters (L) or milliliters (mL). One mL has the same volume as 1 $cm^3$. There are 1,000 mL in 1 L. There are 1,000 L in 1 $m^3$.

| Volume Tools: graduated cylinder or beaker | cubic meter ($m^3$) cubic centimeter ($cm^3$) liter (L) milliliter (mL) | 1 $cm^3$ = 0.000001 $m^3$ 1 L = 0.001 $m^3$ 1 mL = 1 $cm^3$ |
|---|---|---|

**READING CHECK**
**6. Define** What is volume?

_____

_____

You can find the volume of a more complicated object, such as this rock, by measuring how much liquid it pushes out of the way. The graduated cylinder has 70 mL of liquid in it before the rock is added.

The rock made the volume of material in the cylinder go up to 80 mL. The rock pushed 10 mL of liquid out of the way. The volume of the rock is 10 mL. Because 1 mL = 1 cm³, the volume of the rock can also be written as 10 cm³.

## TAKE A LOOK

**7. Explain** How do you know that the rock in the figure has a volume of 10 mL?

_____

_____

_____

_____

## Math Focus

**8. Convert** How many milligrams are there in 1 g?

_____

_____

✓ **READING CHECK**

**9. Compare** How are mass and weight different?

_____

_____

_____

_____

### MASS AND WEIGHT

   **Mass** is the amount of matter in an object. The SI unit for mass is the kilogram (kg). The masses of large objects, such as people, are measured in kilograms. The masses of smaller objects, such as apples, are measured in grams (g) or milligrams (mg). There are 1,000 g in 1 kg. There are 1 million mg in 1 kg. Balances are used to measure mass.

| Mass<br>Tool: balance | SI unit: kilogram (kg)<br>gram (g)<br>milligram (mg) | 1 g = 0.001 kg<br>1 mg = 0.000001 kg |
|---|---|---|

   Weight is different from mass. **Weight** is a measure of the force of gravity on an object. The force of gravity is measured in newtons (N). The force of gravity changes depending on where you are located in the universe. Therefore, a person's weight changes from place to place. For example, you weigh more on Earth than on the moon, even though your mass is the same in both places. Spring scales are used to measure weight. ☑

SECTION 3 Tools and Measurement *continued*

## TEMPERATURE

**Temperature** is a measure of how hot or cold an object is. The SI unit for temperature is the kelvin (K). However, most people are more familiar with other units of temperature. For example, most people in the United States measure temperatures in degrees Fahrenheit (°F). Scientists often measure temperatures in degrees Celsius (°C). Thermometers are used to measure temperature. ☑

| Temperature Tool: thermometer | SI unit: kelvin (K) degrees Celsius (°C) | 0°C = 273 K 100°C = 373 K |
|---|---|---|

It is easy to change a temperature measurement from degrees Celsius to kelvins. You simply add 273 to the Celsius measurement. For example, 200°C + 200 + 273 = 473 K. It is more complicated to change measurements in kelvins or degrees Celsius to degrees Fahrenheit. That is why scientists do not measure temperatures in degrees Fahrenheit. ☑

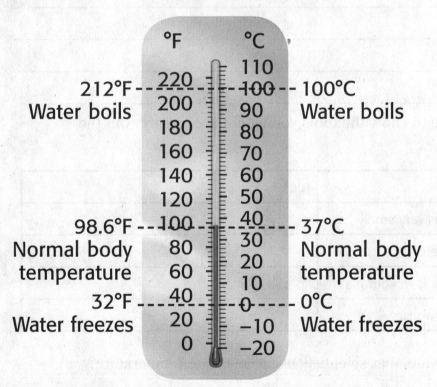

This thermometer shows the relationship between degrees Fahrenheit and degrees Celsius.

☑ **READING CHECK**

**10. Define** What is temperature?

_____

_____

_____

☑ **READING CHECK**

**11. Explain** Why do scientists measure temperature in kelvins or degrees Celsius rather than degrees Fahrenheit?

_____

_____

_____

**TAKE A LOOK**

**12. Identify** What is normal body temperature in degrees Celsius?

_____

# Section 3 Review

## SECTION VOCABULARY

**area** a measure of the size of a surface or a region

**compound light microscope** an instrument that magnifies small objects so that they can be seen easily by using two or more lenses

   <u>Wordwise</u> The root *micro* means "small." The root *scope* means "an instrument for seeing or observing."

**electron microscope** a microscope that focuses a beam of electrons to magnify objects

**mass** a measure of the amount of matter in an object

**temperature** a measure of how hot (or cold) something is; specifically, a measure of the average kinetic energy of the particles in an object

**technology** the application of science for practical purposes; the use of tools, machines, materials, and processes to meet human needs

**volume** a measure of the size of a body or region in three-dimensional space

**weight** a measure of the gravitational force exerted on an object; its value can change with the location of the object in the universe

1. **Describe** You can find the volume of a box-shaped object by multiplying its length, width, and height together. How can you measure the volume of an object if it is not shaped like a box?

_____

_____

_____

_____

2. **Identify** Fill in the table to show the tools you would use to carry out the measurements.

| Task | Tool |
|------|------|
| Looking at something that is very small | |
| Measuring how tall your friend is | |
| Measuring how much water is in your glass | |
| Measuring the weight of a mouse | |

3. **Identify** What are two units that scientists use to measure temperature?

_____

_____

**SECTION 4**

# Scientific Models and Knowledge

**California Science Standards**

7.7.c, 7.7.d

## BEFORE YOU READ

**After you read this section, you should be able to answer these questions:**

- How do scientists use models?
- What are scientific theories and laws?

## What Are Models?

You need a microscope to see inside most cells. How can you learn about the parts of a cell if you don't have a microscope? Scientists use models to learn about things that they cannot see or touch.

A **model** is something scientists use to represent an object or event in order to make it easier to study. Scientists study models to learn how things work or are made in the natural world. However, you cannot learn everything by studying a model, because models are not exactly like the objects they represent. Some types of scientific models are physical models, mathematical models, and conceptual models. ☑

### PHYSICAL MODELS

A toy rocket and a plastic skeleton are examples of physical models. *Physical models* are models that you can see or touch. Many physical models look like the things they represent. The figure shows students using a model of a human body to learn how the body works. However, because the model is not alive, the students cannot learn exactly how the body functions.

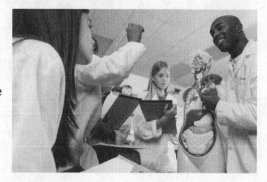

This physical model looks a lot like a real human body. But it is easier to see inside this model than to see inside a real human body.

**STUDY TIP**

**Compare** As you read, make a table to show the features of physical models, mathematical models, and conceptual models.

**READING CHECK**

**1. Explain** Why can't you learn everything about an object or event by studying a model?

_____

_____

_____

## TAKE A LOOK

**2. Compare** Give two ways that the model is like a person and two ways the model is not like a person.

_____

_____

_____

_____

## MATHEMATICAL MODELS

A mathematical model is made up of mathematical equations and data. Some mathematical models are simple. These models help you to calculate things such as how far a car will travel in an hour. Other models are more complicated. These models can have many different parts related by complicated equations. ☑

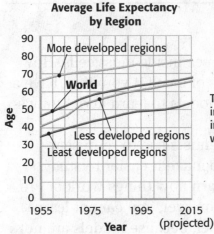

**Average Life Expectancy by Region**

This mathematical model measures the increase in life expectancy in the past. This information is used to predict, or project, what life expectancy will be in the future.

☑ **READING CHECK**

**3. Define** What is a mathematical model?

_____

_____

## CONCEPTUAL MODELS

A *conceptual model* is a diagram, drawing, or spoken description of how something works or is put together. The conceptual model below describes how mercury is released when coal is burned. It traces how the mercury travels through the environment and affects humans. Scientists often use conceptual models to show how one part of a system affects another part. ☑

☑ **READING CHECK**

**4. Explain** Why do scientists use conceptual models?

_____

_____

_____

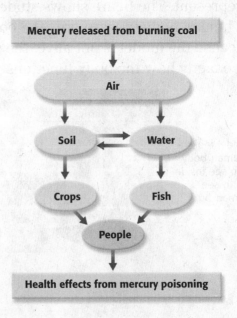

**TAKE A LOOK**
**5. Use a Model** Use a colored pen or marker to trace two different paths between mercury in the air and mercury in people.

**SECTION 4** Scientific Models and Knowledge *continued*

## WHY SCIENTISTS USE MODELS

Scientists use models to study things that are very small, such as atoms, or things that are very large, such as Earth. Some scientists use models to predict things that haven't happened yet or to study events that happened long ago. For example, some scientists use computers to produce models of dinosaurs. These models are based on information from fossils and other observations. They can show how dinosaurs may have looked and moved.

## How Are Sizes Shown in Models?

Imagine that you see a model of your school with a new addition for a swimming pool. In the model, the building that will house the swimming pool is the same size as the cafeteria. You expect that a large pool will be built. However, when the addition is finished, the pool is only as large as the principal's office. Why is the pool so small?

The model that you saw was not drawn to scale. **Scale** shows how the size of a model is related to the size of the object it represents. In a scale model of your school, the new pool would be the same size as the principal's office.

Maps and diagrams should also be drawn to scale. Scale is always shown on a map. The figure shows a map of California. The scale is 1 cm:100 miles. This means that 1 cm on the map represents 100 miles in California. Because the map is drawn to scale, it shows accurate information about the relative locations of places in California.

This map of California is drawn with a scale of 1 cm:100 miles.

---

**CALIFORNIA STANDARDS CHECK**

**7.7.d** Construct scale models, maps, and appropriately labeled diagrams to communicate scientific knowledge (e.g., motion of Earth's plates and cell structure).

**Word Help: construct**
to build; to make from parts

**Word Help: appropriately**
in a correct or proper way

**Word Help: labeled**
marked with a name or a description

**Word Help: communicate**
to make known; to tell

**Word Help: structure**
the arrangement of the parts of a whole

**6. Describe** You want to make a drawing of a room in your school. The room is 7 m long and 10 m wide. You want to make your drawing with a scale of 2 cm:1 m. Give the length and width of your scale drawing.

_____

_____

---

*Critical Thinking*

**7. Infer** Why can two scientists study the same data but come to different conclusions about it?

_____

_____

_____

_____

## How Does Scientific Knowledge Grow?

Science is always changing. Two scientists can study the same data and have different conclusions. When new technology is developed, scientists often review old data and come to new conclusions. By observing patterns in the world, scientists can create scientific theories and laws.

A scientific **theory** is a scientific explanation that connects and explains many observations. Scientific theories are based on observations. They explain all of the observations about a topic that scientists have at a certain time. Theories are conceptual models that help organize scientific thinking. They are used to explain and predict situations.

A scientific **law** is a statement or equation that can predict what will happen in certain situations. Unlike theories, scientific laws do not explain why something happens. They only predict what will happen. Many people think that scientific theories become scientific laws, but this is not true. Actually, many scientific laws provide evidence to support scientific theories.

**TAKE A LOOK**

**8. Identify** Fill in the blanks in the table with the terms *scientific theory* and *scientific law.*

| Name | What it is |
|------|-----------|
|  | an explanation that connects and explains evidence and observations |
|  | a statement or equation that predicts what will happen in a certain situation |

## How Do Scientific Ideas Change?

Sometimes, new technology changes how scientists think about a topic. For example, scientists use to think that the dinosaur *Apatosaurus* could hold its head high up on its long neck. To test this idea, the scientists used a computer model to study how *Apatosaurus* may have moved.

The model showed that *Apatosaurus* could not have held its head up. Instead, it must have stood and moved with its head held horizontally. The figure on the next page shows the new idea about how *Apatosaurus* moved.

**SECTION 4** Scientific Models and Knowledge *continued*

## An Example of How Scientific Ideas Can Change

Scientists used to think that *Apatosaurus* used its long neck to reach leaves high in trees.

Computer models show that *Apatosaurus* could not hold its head high. It probably held its head out horizontally.

### Say It

**Investigate** Use the Internet or the library to learn about a scientific idea that interests you. Study how the idea has changed with time. Share your findings with your class.

### TAKE A LOOK
**9. Infer** Why did scientists have to use computer models to study how *Apatosaurus* moved?

_____

_____

_____

### EVALUATING SCIENTIFIC THEORIES

Scientists are always discovering new information. This new information may show that a theory is incorrect. When this happens, the theory must be changed so that it explains the new information. Sometimes, scientists have to develop a totally new theory to explain the new and old information.

Sometimes, more than one new theory is given to explain the new information. How do scientists know that a new theory is accurate? They use scientific methods to test the new theory. They also examine all the evidence to see if it supports the new theory. Scientists accept a new theory when many tests and pieces of evidence support it. ☑

### READING CHECK
**10. Explain** When do scientists decide that a new theory is accurate?

_____

_____

_____

# Section 4 Review

7.7.c, 7.7.d

## SECTION VOCABULARY

| | |
|---|---|
| **law** a descriptive statement or equation that reliably predicts events under certain conditions | **scale** the relationship between the measurements on a model, map, or diagram and the actual measurement of distance |
| **model** a pattern, plan, representation, or description designed to show the structure or workings of an object, system, or concept | **theory** a system of ideas that explains many related observations and is supported by a large body of evidence acquired through scientific investigation |

**1. Identify**  How are scientific theories related to observations and evidence?

_____

_____

_____

**2. Explain**  Why do scientists use models?

_____

_____

_____

**3. Describe**  Why is scale important in models and maps?

_____

_____

**4. Describe**  What effect can new observations have on a scientific theory?

_____

_____

**5. Identify**  Give three types of models and an example of each type.

_____

_____

_____

**6. Compare**  How is a scientific theory different from a scientific law?

_____

_____

_____

_____

# SECTION 5 Safety in Science

**California Science Standards**

7.7.a

## BEFORE YOU READ

**After you read this section, you should be able to answer these questions:**

• Why should you follow safety rules when learning science?

• What are the elements of safety?

• What should you do if there is an accident?

## Why Are Safety Rules Important?

All safety rules have two purposes. Safety rules help prevent accidents. They also help prevent injuries if an accident does happen.

### PREVENTING ACCIDENTS

So that you'll be safe while doing science activities, it is a good idea to learn some safety rules. The most important safety rule is to follow directions. The directions of a science activity are made to help you prevent accidents. Following directions will also make your work easier, which will help you get better results. ☑

### PREVENTING INJURIES

If an accident takes place, you or someone nearby can get hurt. Following safety rules after an accident can help prevent injuries. For example, you should never touch or try to clean up a spilled chemical unless you know how to do it safely. If you are using chemicals in a lab, you should learn how to use them safely.

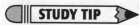

**STUDY TIP**

**Prepare** As you read this section, look around your classroom and try to find examples of proper safety equipment and procedures.

**READING CHECK**

**1. Describe** Why should you follow directions in science?

_____

_____

_____

_____

**TAKE A LOOK**

**2. Explain** How can goggles help to keep you safe in science class?

_____

_____

_____

**SECTION 5** Safety in Science *continued*

## What Are the Elements of Safety?

Safety has many parts. To be safe, you need to recognize safety symbols. You also must follow directions, be neat, use equipment correctly, and clean up after experiments.

### SAFETY SYMBOLS

Signs and symbols have special meanings when they are used in science. Some of these symbols are safety symbols. They tell you what to do to prevent injuries or accidents.

Look at the safety symbols in the figure below. Each symbol tells you something important. For example, the symbol for animal safety means that you should be careful when you work with live animals. Always follow your teacher's directions on how to handle animals. Never bring wild animals into the classroom, because they might carry a disease. Remember to always wash your hands after touching a lab animal.

**TAKE A LOOK**
**3. Investigate** Look around your classroom for safety symbols like the ones in the figure. Give two examples of places where safety symbols are found in your classroom.

_____

_____

**Safety Symbols**

| Eye protection | Clothing protection |  Hand safety |  Heating safety |  Electrical safety |

Chemical safety    Animal safety    Sharp object    Plant safety

### READING AND FOLLOWING DIRECTIONS

If you want to bake cookies, you use a recipe. The recipe provides all the directions on how to make cookies. When scientists work in a lab, they also follow directions.

Before starting a science activity, read the directions very carefully. If you do not understand them, ask your teacher to explain them. If you can't finish some of the directions, you should stop your experiment and ask your teacher for help.

When you read, understand, and follow directions, you get better results. You also reduce the chance of causing an accident.

**SECTION 5** Safety in Science *continued*

## NEATNESS

Before starting any experiment, you should clear your work area of anything you don't need for the lab. Some objects can get in the way and can cause an accident. Long hair and loose clothing can get in the way, too. They should be tied back.

During an experiment, keep your table or desk clean. Gather all the equipment you need for the activity before you start. Arrange your equipment and materials so that they are easy to find and pick up.

Label your materials clearly. Some lab materials look alike and can get mixed up if they are not labeled.

As you collect data, you should record your findings carefully in your data table or notebook. Neatly recorded data are easier to read and analyze.

| What to do | Why to do it |
|---|---|
| Tie back loose hair and clothing. | |
| | This will keep your books or backpack from getting in the way during the activity. |
| Gather all of your equipment before you start the activity. | |
| | This will prevent materials that look alike from getting mixed up. |

## USING PROPER SAFETY EQUIPMENT

Goggles, gloves, and aprons are all pieces of safety equipment that you may use. Some of the safety symbols tell you what safety equipment you need.

For example, when you see the symbol for eye protection, you must put on safety goggles. Your goggles should be clean and fit properly. Your teacher can help you adjust them for a proper fit.

The chemicals that you use may not always be dangerous. However, you should always wear aprons, goggles, and protective gloves whenever you use chemicals. ☑

You should wear protective gloves when handling animals, too. Different gloves are available for different uses. For example, if you are handling warm or hot objects, you should wear heat-resistant gloves.

**TAKE A LOOK**
**4. Explain** In the table, fill in the blank spaces with things you should do in a lab experiment and the reasons for doing them.

✓ **READING CHECK**
**5. Identify** Give three pieces of safety equipment that you should use when you handle chemicals.

_____

_____

_____

**SECTION 5** Safety in Science *continued*

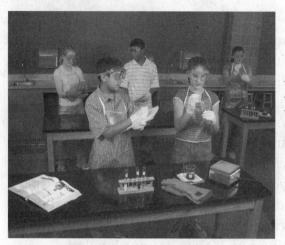

These students are wearing protective gloves when they work with chemicals. They put on heat-resistant gloves before lifting the beakers off the hot plates.

**PROPER CLEANUP PROCEDURES**

At the end of a science activity, always clean up your work area. Put caps back on bottles or jars. Return everything to its proper place. Spills and accidents are less likely to happen when everything is put away correctly. ☑

Wash your glassware, and check for chips and cracks. If you find any damaged glassware, notify your teacher. It should be carefully thrown away in a special container.

If you have extra chemicals, follow your teacher's directions for throwing them away. Once your work area is clear, you should wipe it with a wet paper towel. Finally, wash your hands carefully with soap and water.

## What Should You Do If There Is an Accident?

Even when all the safety rules are followed, accidents may still happen. If an accident happens, try to remain calm. You may be scared, but staying in control will help keep you and others safe. Being prepared and having a plan of action will help you do the right things if an emergency happens.

**THINGS TO KNOW BEFORE AN ACCIDENT**

The figure on the next page shows some items that you may need to use if an accident happens. Look around your classroom or work area to locate these items. In addition, find out where the exits from the room are and where the telephone is.

Before an accident happens, find out when and how to use the fire extinguisher, the emergency shower, and the eyewash station. Find out what phone number you can call in case there is an emergency. Make sure that the number is clearly written on or near the phone.

☑ **READING CHECK**

**6. Explain** Why is it important to clean up correctly after a lab activity?

_____

_____

_____

*Critical Thinking*

**7. Identify** Why is it important to plan ahead for an accident?

_____

_____

_____

_____

**SECTION 5** Safety in Science *continued*

## Emergency Equipment

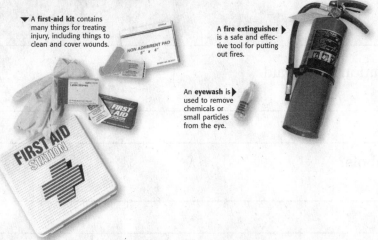

▼ A **first-aid kit** contains many things for treating injury, including things to clean and cover wounds.

A **fire extinguisher** ▶ is a safe and effective tool for putting out fires.

An **eyewash** is ▶ used to remove chemicals or small particles from the eye.

**TAKE A LOOK**
**8. Identify** What is an eyewash used for?

_____

_____

_____

### STEPS TO FOLLOW AFTER AN ACCIDENT

If an accident happens, first, remain calm. Try to stay calm and figure out what happened. Look around you for clues, but do not touch anything. Second, make sure that no one (including you!) is in danger. If other students are coming over to see what happened, tell them to stay away so that they don't get hurt.

Third, tell your teacher that an accident happened, even if the accident was small. Explain exactly what happened. If you can't find your teacher, call for help. Finally, ask your teacher if there is anything you can do to help. If not, stay out of your teacher's way.

### CARING FOR INJURIES

If an accident happens, someone may need first aid. **First aid** is emergency care for someone who has been hurt. Find the first-aid kit in your classroom. Become familiar with the items in it, such as bandages and protective gloves.

If an accident happens, you can help your teacher give first aid to someone who is hurt. In most cases, you should not give first aid to someone unless you have first-aid training. However, you can provide first aid for some minor injuries. These are given in the table below.

*Critical Thinking*

**9. Design a Plan** You are heating water on a hot plate. You suddenly notice that some papers near the hot plate have caught fire. What should you do? What could you have done to prevent this accident?

_____

_____

_____

_____

_____

| Injury | First-aid procedure |
|--------|---------------------|
| Minor burn from heat | Hold the affected area under cold, running water for at least 15 minutes. |
| Small cut | Clean the area, cover with a clean cloth or gauze pad, and apply pressure. |
| Chemicals on the skin | Rinse the area with running water. |
| Chemicals in the eye | Rinse the eye with running water or in an eyewash. |

# Section 5 Review

7.7.a

## SECTION VOCABULARY

| first aid emergency medical care for someone who has been hurt or who is sick | |
|---|---|
| | |

**1. Define** Write your own definition of first aid.

_____

_____

**2. Explain** What are safety symbols?

_____

_____

**3. Identify** What are five elements of safety?

_____

_____

_____

_____

**4. List** What should you do if an accident happens? List four steps.

_____

_____

_____

**5. Explain** Why are safety rules important?

_____

_____

**6. Describe** What should you do if you see an animal safety symbol in the directions for a lab?

_____

_____

**CHAPTER 2** It's Alive!! Or Is It?

# Characteristics of Living Things

**BEFORE YOU READ**

After you read this section, you should be able to answer these questions:

• What are all living things made of?

• What do all living things have in common?

## What Are All Living Things Made Of?

If you saw a bright yellow, slimy blob in the grass, would you think it was alive? How could you tell? All living things, or *organisms*, share several characteristics. What does a dog have in common with a bacterium? What do *you* have in common with a bright yellow slime mold?

All living things are made of one or more cells. A **cell** is the smallest unit that can carry out all the activities of life. All cells are surrounded by a cell membrane. The *cell membrane* separates the cell from the outside environment.

Some organisms are made of trillions of cells. In these organisms, different kinds of cells do different jobs. For example, muscle cells are used for movement. Other organisms are made of only one cell. In these organisms, different parts of the cell have different jobs.

 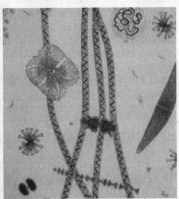

Some organisms, such as the California quail on the left, are made up of trillions of cells. The protists on the right are made up of one or a few cells. They are so small they can only be seen with a microscope.

## How Do Living Things Respond to Change?

All organisms can sense changes in their environment. Each organism reacts differently to these changes. A change that affects how an organism acts is called a *stimulus* (plural, *stimuli*). Stimuli can be chemicals, light, sounds, hunger, or anything that causes an organism to react. ☑

**STUDY TIP**

**Organize** As you read this section, make a list of the six characteristics of living things.

**CALIFORNIA STANDARDS CHECK**

**7.1.a** Students know cells function similarly in all living organisms.

**Word Help: function** to work

**1. Identify** What are all living things made of?

_____

_____

**READING CHECK**

**2. List** Give three examples of stimuli.

_____

_____

_____

**SECTION 1** Characteristics of Living Things *continued*

The touch of an insect is a stimulus for a Venus' flytrap. The stimulus causes the plant to close its leaves quickly.

## TAKE A LOOK

**3. Complete** For a Venus' flytrap, the touch of an insect is a _____.

Even when things outside the body change, an organism must keep the conditions inside its body the same. The act of keeping a constant environment inside an organism is called **homeostasis**. When an organism maintains homeostasis, all the chemical reactions inside its body can work correctly.

### RESPONDING TO EXTERNAL CHANGES

If it is hot outside, your body starts to sweat to cool down. If it is cold outside, your body starts to shiver to warm up. In each situation, your body reacts to the changes in the environment. It tries to return itself to normal.

Different kinds of organisms react to changes in the environment in different ways. For example, crocodiles lie in the sun to get warm. When they get too warm, they open their mouths wide to release heat.

## *Critical Thinking*

**4. Predict** What would happen if your body couldn't maintain homeostasis?

_____

_____

_____

_____

_____

## How Do Organisms Have Offspring?

Every type of organism has *offspring*. The two ways to make offspring are by sexual reproduction or asexual reproduction. In **sexual reproduction**, two parents make offspring. The offspring get traits from both parents. In **asexual reproduction**, one parent makes offspring. The offspring are identical to the parent. ☑

Most plants and animals make offspring by sexual reproduction. However, most single-celled organisms and some multicellular organisms make offspring by asexual reproduction. For example, hydra make offspring by forming buds that break off and grow into new hydra.

**READING CHECK**

**5. Identify** How many parents are needed to produce offspring by sexual reproduction?

_____

Like most animals, bears produce offspring by sexual reproduction. However, some animals, such as hydra, can reproduce asexually.

**TAKE A LOOK**
**6. Identify** How do most animals reproduce?

_____
_____

## Why Do Offspring Look Like Their Parents?

All organisms are made of cells. Inside each cell, there is information about all of the organism's traits. This information is found in DNA (**d**eoxyribo**n**ucleic **a**cid). *DNA* carries instructions for the organism's traits. Offspring look like their parents because they get copies of parts of their parent's DNA. Passing traits from parent to offspring is called *heredity*. ☑

## Why Do Organisms Need Energy?

All organisms need energy to live. Most organisms get their energy from the food they eat. Organisms use this energy to carry out all the activities that happen inside their bodies. For example, organisms need energy to break down food, to move materials in and out of cells, and to build cells. An organism uses energy to keep up its metabolism. An organism's **metabolism** is all of the chemical reactions that take place in its body.

**READING CHECK**
**7. Define** What is the function of DNA?

_____
_____
_____

## How Do Organisms Grow?

All organisms grow during some part of their lives. In a single-celled organism, the cell gets bigger and divides. This makes new organisms. An organism made of many cells gets bigger by making more cells. As these organisms grow, they get new traits. These traits often change how the organism looks. For example, as a tadpole grows into a frog, it develops legs and loses its tail.

# Section 1 Review

7.1.a, 7.2.a

## SECTION VOCABULARY

**asexual reproduction** reproduction that does not involve the union of sex cells and in which one parent produces offspring that are genetically identical to the parent.

**cell** the smallest functional and structural unit of all living organisms

**homeostasis** the maintenance of a constant internal state in a changing environment

**metabolism** the sum of all chemical processes that occur in an organism

**sexual reproduction** reproduction in which the sex cells from two parents unite to produce offspring that share traits from both parents

1. **Summarize** Complete the Spider Map to show the six characteristics of living things. Add lines to give details on each characteristic.

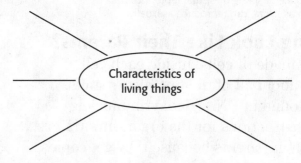

Characteristics of living things

2. **Compare** How does sexual reproduction differ from asexual reproduction?

_____

_____

_____

3. **Explain** How do the buds of an organism such as hydra compare to the parent?

_____

_____

4. **Identify Relationships** How is a bear's fur related to homeostasis?

_____

_____

_____

5. **Compare** How does growth differ in single-celled organisms and those made of many cells?

_____

_____

_____

# SECTION 2 | The Necessities of Life

**California Science Standards**

7.1.a

## BEFORE YOU READ

After you read this section, you should be able to answer these questions:

- What things do almost all organisms need?
- Why do living things need food?

## What Do Living Things Need?

Would it surprise you to learn that you have the same basic needs as a tree, a frog, and a fly? Almost every organism has the same basic needs: water, air, a place to live, and food.

### WATER

Your body is made mostly of water. The cells that make up your body are about 70% to 85% water. Cells need water to keep their inside environments stable. Most of the chemical reactions that happen in cells need water.

Organisms get water from the fluids they drink and the foods they eat. However, organisms need different amounts of water. You could survive only three days without water. A kangaroo rat never drinks. It lives in the desert and gets all the water it needs from its food.

### AIR

Oxygen, nitrogen, and carbon dioxide are some of the gases in air. Most organisms use oxygen to help them break down food for energy. Other organisms, such as green plants, use carbon dioxide to make food.

Some organisms do not need air. These are called *anaerobic organisms*. Most anaerobic organisms are single-celled organisms, such as bacteria. Air can actually kill these organisms.

### STUDY TIP

**Organize** As you read, make a table of the basic needs of most organisms. Fill in examples of how different organisms meet those needs.

### CALIFORNIA STANDARDS CHECK

**7.1.a** Students know cells <u>function</u> similarly in all living organisms.

**Word Help: <u>function</u>** to work

**1. Explain** Why do cells need water?

_____

_____

_____

_____

_____

### TAKE A LOOK

**2. Infer** Why do you think this diving spider surrounds itself with a bubble in the water?

_____

_____

## A PLACE TO LIVE

Just as you do, all living things need a place to live. Organisms look for an area that has everything they need to survive. Often, many organisms live in the same area. They all must use the same resources, such as food and water. Many times, an organism will try to keep others out of its area. For example, some birds keep other birds away by singing.

## FOOD

All organisms need food. Food gives organisms energy and nutrients to live and grow. However, not all organisms get food in the same way. There are three ways in which organisms can get food. ☑

Some organisms, such as plants, are producers. **Producers** make their own food using energy from their environment. For example, plants use the sun's energy to make food from carbon dioxide and water. This process is called *photosynthesis*.

Many organisms are consumers. **Consumers** eat other organisms to get food. For example, a frog is a consumer because it eats insects.

A mushroom is a decomposer. **Decomposers** break down dead organisms and animal wastes to get food. Decomposers are also consumers because they get their food from other organisms.

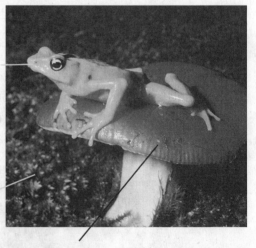

**READING CHECK**

**3. Explain** Why do living things need food?

_____

_____

_____

*Critical Thinking*

**4. Identify** Are you a producer, consumer, or decomposer? Explain your answer.

_____

_____

_____

_____

## TAKE A LOOK

**5. Label** On the picture, label the producer, consumer, and decomposer.

## What Do Organisms Get from Food?

As you just read, organisms can get their food in three different ways. However, all organisms must break down their food to use the nutrients.

Nutrients are molecules. *Molecules* are made of two or more atoms joined together. Most molecules in living things are combinations of carbon, nitrogen, oxygen, phosphorus, and sulfur. Proteins, nucleic acids, lipids, carbohydrates, and ATP are some of the molecules needed by living things.

### PROTEINS

Proteins are used in many processes inside a cell. **Proteins** are large molecules made up of smaller molecules called *amino acids*. Living things break down the proteins in food and use the amino acids to make new proteins. ☑

An organism uses proteins in many different ways. Some proteins are used to build or fix parts of an organism's body. Some proteins stay on the outside of a cell, to protect it. Proteins called *enzymes* help to start or speed up reactions inside a cell.

Some proteins help cells do their jobs. For example, a protein called *hemoglobin* is found in red blood cells. It picks up oxygen and delivers it through the body.

Spider webs, horns, and feathers are made from proteins.

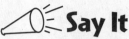 **Say It**

**Discuss** With a partner, name 10 organisms and describe what foods they eat. Discuss whether these organisms are producers, consumers, or decomposers.

---

**READING CHECK**

**6. Complete** Proteins are made up of _____

_____ .

## Math Focus

**7. Calculate** Each red blood cell carries about 250 million molecules of hemoglobin. If every hemoglobin molecule is attached to four oxygen molecules, how many oxygen molecules could one red blood cell carry?

_____

**SECTION 2** The Necessities of Life *continued*

## NUCLEIC ACIDS

When you bake a cake, you follow instructions to make sure the cake is made correctly. When cells make new molecules, such as proteins, they also follow a set of instructions. The instructions for making any part of an organism are stored in *DNA*.

DNA is a nucleic acid. **Nucleic acids** are molecules made of smaller molecules called *nucleotides*. The instructions carried by DNA tell a cell how to make proteins. The order of nucleotides in DNA tells cells which amino acids to use and which order to put them in.

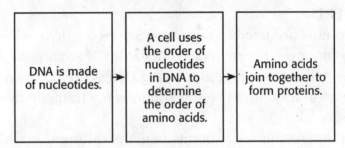

*Critical Thinking*

**8. Identify Relationships** What is the relationship between amino acids and nucleotides?

_____

_____

_____

_____

_____

## LIPIDS

**Lipids** are molecules that cannot mix with water. They are a form of stored energy. When lipids are stored in an animal, they are usually solid. These are called *fats*. When lipids are stored in a plant, they are usually liquid. These are called *oils*. When an organism has used up other sources of energy, it can break down fats and oils for more energy.

Lipids also form cell membranes. Cell membranes surround and protect cells. They are made of special lipids called **phospholipids**. When phospholipids are in water, the tails come together and the heads face out. This is shown in the figure below.

**TAKE A LOOK**

**9. Describe** Describe the structure of a phospholipid, and how it behaves in water.

_____

_____

_____

_____

_____

**Phospholipid Membranes**

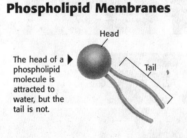

The head of a phospholipid molecule is attracted to water, but the tail is not.

Head

Tail

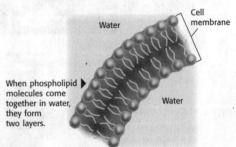

When phospholipid ▶ molecules come together in water, they form two layers.

Water

Cell membrane

Water

## CARBOHYDRATES

**Carbohydrates** are molecules made of sugars. They provide and store energy for cells. An organism's cells break down carbohydrates to free energy. There are two types of carbohydrates: simple and complex. ☑

*Simple carbohydrates* are made of one or a few sugar molecules. Both table sugar and sugar in fruits are examples of simple carbohydrates. The simple carbohydrate *glucose* is the most common source of energy for cells. The body breaks down simple carbohydrates more quickly than complex carbohydrates.

*Complex carbohydrates* are made of hundreds of sugar molecules linked together. When organisms such as plants have more sugar than they need, they can store the extra sugar as complex carbohydrates. For example, potatoes store extra sugar as starch. You can also find complex carbohydrates in foods such as whole-wheat bread, pasta, oatmeal, and brown rice.

**READING CHECK**

**10. Identify** What are two types of carbohydrates?

_____

_____

| Type of carbohydrate | Structure | Example |
|---|---|---|
| | made of one or a few sugar molecules | |
| complex | | |

## ATP

After carbohydrates and fats have been broken down, how does their energy get to where it is needed? The cells use adenosine triphosphate, or ATP. **ATP** is a molecule that carries energy in cells. The energy released from carbohydrates and fats is passed to ATP molecules. ATP then carries the energy to where it is needed in the cell. ☑

**TAKE A LOOK**

**11. Complete** Complete the table to explain the two types of carbohydrates.

**READING CHECK**

**12. Identify** What molecule carries energy in cells?

_____

_____

# Section 2 Review

## SECTION VOCABULARY

| | |
|---|---|
| **ATP** adenosine triphosphate, a molecule that acts as the main energy source for cell processes. | **nucleic acid** a molecule made up of subunits called nucleotides |
| **carbohydrate** a class of molecules that includes sugars, starches, and fiber | **phospholipid** a lipid that contains phosphorus and that is a structural component in cell membranes |
| **consumer** an organism that eats other organisms or organic matter | <u>Wordwise</u> The root *phospho* means "containing phosphorus." The root *lip* means "fat." |
| **decomposer** an organism that gets energy by breaking down the remains of dead organisms or animal wastes and consuming or absorbing the nutrients | **producer** an organism that can make its own food by using energy from its surroundings |
| **lipid** a fat molecule or a molecule that has similar properties | **protein** a molecule that is made up of amino acids and that is needed to build and repair body structures and to regulate processes in the body |

**1. List** Name four things that organisms need to survive.

_____

**2. Explain** Why are decomposers also consumers?

_____

_____

**3. Identify** What two nutrients store energy?

_____

**4. Describe** Describe the structure of a cell membrane.

_____

_____

_____

**5. Compare** Name two ways that simple carbohydrates differ from complex carbohydrates.

_____

_____

**6. Explain** Why is ATP important to cells?

_____

_____

**CHAPTER 3** Light and Living Things

**SECTION 1**
# The Electromagnetic Spectrum

## BEFORE YOU READ

**After you read this section, you should be able to answer these questions:**

• What is light?

• What is the electromagnetic spectrum?

• How is light important to life on Earth?

## What Is Light?

Light is a form of energy that travels as a wave. You can see the things around you because they reflect a type of light called visible light. You also may have heard of ultraviolet light. You can't see ultraviolet light, but some animals, like bees, can.

Light travels as a wave called an electromagnetic (EM) wave. An **electromagnetic wave** is a wave made of changing electric and magnetic field strengths. EM waves can travel through empty space and through matter.

## What Is the Electromagnetic Spectrum?

Visible light waves and ultraviolet light waves are both kinds of EM waves. Other kinds of EM waves include radio waves, infrared waves, and X rays. The entire range of electromagnetic waves is called the **electromagnetic spectrum**, shown in the figure below. ☑

As you can see, visible light is only a small part of the electromagnetic spectrum. There is no sharp cutoff between one kind of wave and the next. Some types of waves even run into each other.

**STUDY TIP**

**Illustrate Concepts** Copy the chart of the electromagnetic spectrum into your science notebook. As you read about the different types of light, locate each on your chart.

**READING CHECK**

**1. List** What are five different types of electromagnetic waves?

_____

_____

_____

**TAKE A LOOK**

**2. Identify** Which type of wave has the longest wavelength? Which type has the shortest wavelength?

_____

_____

_____

### The Electromagnetic Spectrum

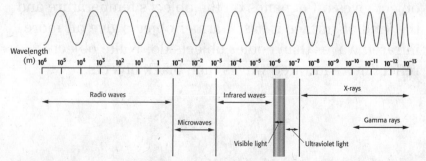

The electromagnetic spectrum shows waves with the longest wavelengths on the left, radio waves, to the shortest wavelengths on the right, gamma rays.

## What Is Wavelength?

You probably know how different kinds of EM waves
are used. For example, microwave ovens use microwaves
to cook food. Radio waves send TV and radio signals.
X-ray machines use X rays to make images of tissues and
bones.

An important difference between kinds of EM waves is
their wavelength. A *wavelength* is the distance from any
point on a wave to an identical point on the next wave.
The figure below shows how wavelength can be measured
on a wave. Notice that the wavelength of the wave is the
same no matter where it is measured. You can see the
range of wavelengths for the different kinds of EM waves
in the figure on the previous page.

## Math Focus

**3. Infer** If you were told
that the wavelength of a
particular wave is $10^{-7}$ m,
what kind of EM wave would
it be?

_____

_____

Wavelength can be measured from any two corresponding points
that are adjacent on a wave.

## What Are Infrared Waves?

Infrared waves are one kind of EM wave that is important to living things. Infrared waves have wavelengths
between 700 nm and 1 mm. A nanometer (nm) is equal to
0.000000001 m, or $10^{-9}$ m.

On a sunny day, infrared waves from the sun warm
you. The sun also warms other things on Earth and even
warms Earth itself. In fact, infrared waves from the sun
keep the temperatures on Earth suitable for life. ☑

All things give off infrared waves, including buildings,
trees, animals, and you! The amount of infrared waves an
object gives off depends on the object's temperature and
the kind of surface it has. Warmer objects give off more
infrared waves than cooler objects do. White objects
reflect more infrared waves than black objects.

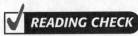

**READING CHECK**

**4. Describe** What keeps the
temperatures on Earth suitable for life?

_____

_____

# Visible Light

*Visible light* is the very narrow range of wavelengths in the EM spectrum that humans can see. Visible light waves have wavelengths between 400 nm and 700 nm. Visible light energy is important to life on Earth. It is changed into chemical energy by green plants during photosynthesis, as shown in the figure below. The chemical energy is stored in food that you can eat.

**From Light Energy to Chemical Energy**

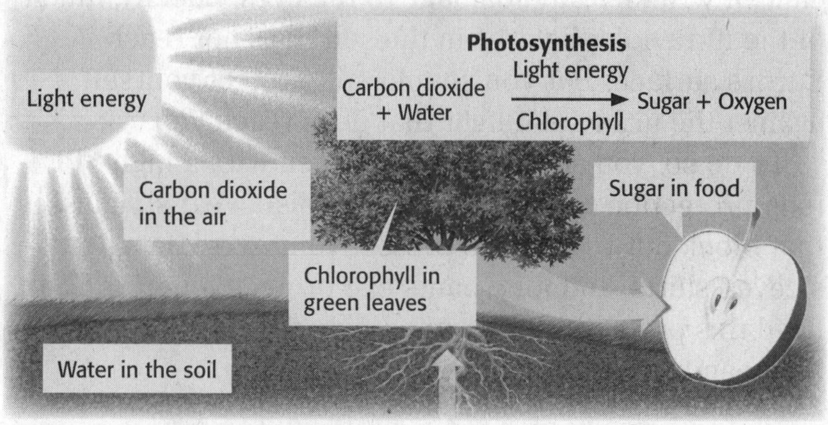

**Photosynthesis**

Light energy

Carbon dioxide + Water → (Light energy / Chlorophyll) → Sugar + Oxygen

Light energy

Carbon dioxide in the air

Chlorophyll in green leaves

Sugar in food

Water in the soil

**CALIFORNIA STANDARDS CHECK**

**7.6.a** Students know visible light is a small band within a very broad electromagnetic spectrum.

**5. Describe** Where is visible light in the EM spectrum?

_____

_____

_____

## VISIBLE LIGHT FROM THE SUN

Some of the energy that reaches Earth from the sun is visible light called white light. *White light* is visible light of all wavelengths, or colors, combined. Light from lamps in your home and from the fluorescent bulbs in your school is also white light. ☑

## THE MANY COLORS OF VISIBLE LIGHT

Cells in the human eye react differently to the wavelengths of light. As a result, we see the different wavelengths of visible light as different colors. The range of colors is called the visible spectrum.

To help you remember the colors, remember the name *ROY G. BIV*. The capital letters in Roy's name represent the first letter of each color of visible light: red, orange, yellow, green, blue, indigo (dark blue), and violet. When you look at the visible spectrum, each color changes smoothly into the next color. ☑

**READING CHECK**

**6. Describe** What is white light? What are three sources of white light?

_____

_____

_____

**READING CHECK**

**7. Describe** How can we see different colors?

_____

_____

_____

## What Is Ultraviolet Light?

*Ultraviolet light* (UV light) is another type of electromagnetic wave. Ultraviolet waves have shorter wavelengths than visible light does. The wavelengths of ultraviolet light waves vary between 60 nm and 400 nm. Ultraviolet light affects your body in both bad and good ways. ☑

### HARMFUL EFFECTS OF UV LIGHT

Too much ultraviolet light can cause sunburn, skin cancer, wrinkles, and damage to the eyes. Luckily, much of the ultraviolet light from the sun does not reach Earth's surface. But you should still protect yourself against the ultraviolet light that does reach you.

To do so, you should use sunscreen with a high SPF (sun protection factor). You should also wear sunglasses that block out UV light to protect your eyes. Hats, long-sleeved shirts, and long pants can protect you, too. You need this protection even on cloudy days because UV light can travel through clouds. ☑

### GOOD EFFECTS OF UV LIGHT

UV light can be helpful. Ultraviolet light produced by ultraviolet lamps is used to kill bacteria on food and surgical tools. In addition, small amounts of ultraviolet light are good for your body. When exposed to UV light, skin cells produce vitamin D. This vitamin allows your body to absorb calcium. Calcium helps build strong bones and teeth. ☑

Healthy teeth need calcium. Vitamin D produced when your skin is exposed to ultraviolet light helps your body absorb calcium. Those with light-colored skin must be careful about being in the sunshine for too much time.

**✓ READING CHECK**

**8. Explain** Does ultraviolet light have a longer or shorter wavelength than visible light?

_____

_____

**✓ READING CHECK**

**9. Explain** Why should you wear sun protection, even on cloudy days?

_____

_____

_____

**✓ READING CHECK**

**10. List** What are two helpful effects of UV light?

_____

_____

_____

_____

# Section 1 Review

## SECTION VOCABULARY

| **electromagnetic spectrum** all of the frequencies or wavelengths of electromagnetic radiation | **electromagnetic wave** a wave that consists of electric and magnetic fields that vibrate at right angles to each other |
|---|---|

**1. Compare** How much of the electromagnetic spectrum is occupied by visible light?

_____

_____

Use the figure below to answer questions 2 and 3.

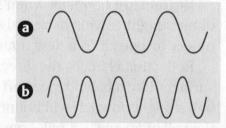

**2. Apply Concepts** Which wave has the longest wavelength?

_____

**3. Analyze Relationships** Suppose that one of the waves represents infrared light and one wave represents visible light. Which wave represents visible light?

_____

**4. List** Which colors of light make up white light?

_____

_____

**5. Explain** How are we able to see different colors?

_____

_____

_____

**6. Describe** What can electromagnetic waves travel through?

_____

_____

_____

CHAPTER 3 | Light and Living Things
SECTION
**2** # Interactions of Light with Matter

## California Science Standards

7.6.b, 7.6.c, 7.6.e, 7.6.f, 7.6.g

### BEFORE YOU READ

**After you read this section, you should be able to answer these questions:**

• How does light interact with matter?
• What determines the color of objects we see?
• How does light travel?

---

### STUDY TIP

**Clarify Concepts** In your science notebook, draw figures that show regular reflection and diffuse reflection. Write one or two sentences to summarize each figure.

### ☑ READING CHECK

**1. Identify** According to the law of reflection, what two angles are equal?

_____

_____

_____

### TAKE A LOOK

**2. Identify** Color the angle of incidence one color and the angle of reflection another color.

## What Is Reflection?

**Reflection** happens when light waves bounce off an object. Light travels in a straight line unless it hits an object or goes into a new material.

Reflection changes the direction of light. Light reflects off surfaces like a ball bounces off the ground. If you throw the ball straight down, it will bounce straight up. If you throw the ball at an angle, it will bounce away at an angle.

Light acts according to the *law of reflection*. The law of reflection states that the angle made by light hitting a surface equals the angle of light reflected. ☑

The figure below shows a beam of light hitting a mirror. This beam of light is called incident light and the angle it makes is called the *angle of incidence*. A dashed line, called a *normal*, is drawn perpendicular to the mirror. The angles of incidence and reflection are on either side of the line.

**The Law of Reflection**

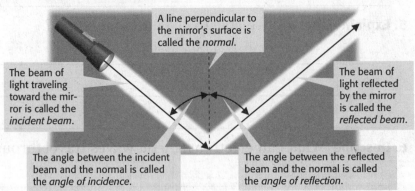

A line perpendicular to the mirror's surface is called the *normal*.

The beam of light traveling toward the mirror is called the *incident beam*.

The beam of light reflected by the mirror is called the *reflected beam*.

The angle between the incident beam and the normal is called the *angle of incidence*.

The angle between the reflected beam and the normal is called the *angle of reflection*.

# What Are the Types of Reflection?

Why can you see your image in a mirror but not in a wall? The two surfaces are different. A mirror's surface is very smooth and shiny. Thus, light beams reflect off all points of the mirror at the same angle. This kind of reflection is called *regular reflection*.

A wall's surface is slightly rough. Light beams will hit the wall's surface and reflect at many different angles. So, the light scatters as it is reflected. This kind of reflection is called *diffuse reflection*. The figure below shows the difference between the two kinds of reflection.

**Regular Reflection vs. Diffuse Reflection**

**Regular reflection** occurs when light beams are reflected at the same angle. When your eye detects the reflected beams, you see a reflection on the surface.

**Diffuse reflection** occurs when light beams reflect at many different angles. You can't see a reflection because not all of the reflected light comes straight toward your eyes.

# What Are Light Sources?

A light source is an object that produces light. Flames, light bulbs, the sun, and firefly tails are all light sources. Objects that produce visible light are called *luminous*.

Most things around you are not light sources. But you can still see them because light from light sources reflects off the objects into your eyes. We say the light *illuminates* the object.

If you look at a TV set in a bright room, you see the cabinet surrounding the TV and the image on the screen. But if you look at the same TV in the dark, you see only the image on the screen. That's because the screen is a light source, but the cabinet is not. The cabinet needs to reflect light in order for you to see it. ☑

---

*Critical Thinking*

**3. Compare** Explain the difference between regular and diffuse reflection.

_____

_____

_____

_____

_____

_____

📢 **Say It**

**Clarify Concepts** Working with a partner, take turns reading aloud the captions in the figure. Explain to each other why you can't see your reflection in a sweater.

✓ READING CHECK

**4. Explain** Why can't you see the cabinet surrounding a TV in a dark room? Use the words "light source" and "illuminates" in your answer.

_____

_____

_____

_____

---

**SECTION 2** Interactions of Light with Matter *continued*

## What Is Absorption of Light?

When a beam of light shines through the air, particles in the air gain some of the energy from the light. This transfer of energy is called **absorption**. This causes the light to lose some of its energy. Because of this, the beam of light becomes dim. The farther the light travels from its source, the more energy is absorbed by air particles. So, the light that reaches your eye is dimmer than the light was at the source. ☑

## What Is Scattering of Light?

**Scattering** occurs when light moves in all directions after colliding with particles of matter. Light scatters when it strikes a rough surface, like a wall.

Light from the ship shown below is scattered out of the beam by particles in the fog. This scattered light allows you to see things that are outside the beam. But, because light is scattered out of the beam, the beam becomes dimmer.

**Regular Reflection vs. Diffuse Reflection**

A beam of light is dimmer when it is far from its source. This is partly because it is scattered by particles in the air.

Scattering makes the sky look blue. Sunlight is made up of many different colors of light. Light with shorter wavelengths is scattered more by air particles than light with longer wavelengths. Blue light, which has a very short wavelength, is scattered more than any other color. So, when you look at the sky, you see a background of blue light. ☑

---

**READING CHECK**

**5. Explain** How does absorption explain why light becomes dimmer as it travels through the air?

_____
_____
_____
_____
_____

**TAKE A LOOK**

**6. Describe** As the two light beams move farther from the ship, they get dimmer. What else happens to the light beams?

_____
_____
_____

**READING CHECK**

**7. Explain** Why is the sky blue? Your answer should include the word "scattered."

_____
_____
_____

---

**SECTION 2** Interactions of Light with Matter *continued*

# How Does Light Interact with Matter?

When light hits any form of matter, it can interact with the matter in different ways. The light can be reflected, absorbed, or transmitted.

Reflection happens when light bounces off an object. Reflected light allows you to see things. Absorption is the transfer of light energy to matter. Absorbed light can make things feel warmer. **Transmission** is the passing of light through matter. In order for you to see, light must be transmitted to your eyes. When it gets to your eyes, it is transmitted to the back of each eye.

Light interacting with glass is shown in the figure below.

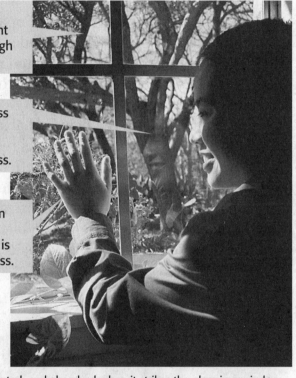

You can see objects outside because light is transmitted through the glass.

You can see the glass and your reflection in it because light is reflected off the glass.

The glass feels warm when you touch it because some light is absorbed by the glass.

Light is transmitted, reflected, and absorbed when it strikes the glass in a window.

## TRANSPARENT, TRANSLUCENT, OR OPAQUE

Transparent matter easily transmits visible light. Air, glass, and water are transparent matter. You can see objects clearly when you view them through transparent matter.

Translucent matter transmits light but also scatters the light as it passes through the matter. Wax paper is an example of translucent matter.

Opaque matter does not transmit any light. You cannot see through opaque objects. Metal, wood, and this book are opaque.

🐻 **CALIFORNIA STANDARDS CHECK**

**7.6.f** Students know light can be reflected, refracted, transmitted, and absorbed by matter.

**8. List** What are three ways light can interact with matter?

_____

_____

_____

**Say It**

**Discuss** Work with a partner and brainstorm different opaque, translucent and transparent objects you see every day.

**SECTION 2** Interactions of Light with Matter *continued*

## How Is an Object's Color Determined?

We see different wavelengths of light as different colors. For example, we see long wavelengths as red and short wavelengths as violet. Colors like pink and brown are seen when certain colors of light mix with each other. ☑

The color that something appears to be is determined by the wavelengths of light that reach your eyes. Light can reach your eyes after being reflected off an object, transmitted through an object, or emitted by an object. When your eyes receive the light, they send signals to your brain. Your brain interprets the signals as colors.

### REFLECTING AND ABSORBING LIGHT

When white light strikes a colored opaque object, some colors of light are absorbed, and some are reflected. Only the light that is reflected reaches your eyes. The colors of light reflected by an opaque object determine the color you see. ☑

A strawberry reflects red light and absorbs all other colors. This is why a strawberry looks red. What colors of light does the cow shown below reflect? White light includes all colors of light. So, white objects—such as the cow's white hair—appear white because all the colors of light are reflected. On the other hand, black is the absence of color. When light strikes a black object, all the colors are absorbed.

This cow's white hair reflects all of the colors of light, but the black hair absorbs all of the colors.

---

**READING CHECK**

**9. Identify** How do we see different wavelengths of light?

_____

_____

**READING CHECK**

**10. Explain** What determines the color you see when you look at an opaque object?

_____

_____

_____

*Critical Thinking*

**11. Infer** Which parts of the cow shown in the figure will feel warmer on a sunny day—the black spots or the white areas? Explain.

_____

_____

_____

_____

---

# What Determines Color in Non-Opaque Objects?

The colors of transparent and translucent objects are determined differently than the colors of opaque objects. Ordinary window glass is colorless in white light because it transmits all the colors that strike it. In other words, all the colors of light that make up white light pass through window glass. ☑

Some transparent or translucent objects are colored, such as stained-glass windows. When you look at a stained-glass window, you see the color of light that was transmitted or reflected. The other colors are absorbed, so you don't see them.

**READING CHECK**

**12. Explain** Why does ordinary window glass look colorless in white light?

_____

_____

_____

# How Do Pigments Produce Color?

A pigment is a material that gives a substance its color by absorbing some colors of light and reflecting others. Almost everything contains pigments. ☑

Melanin is a pigment that gives your skin its color. Chlorophyll is the pigment that gives plants a green color. Chlorophyll absorbs light energy, which is converted into chemical energy during photosynthesis. Some tree leaves have other pigments that make leaves look orange, red, or yellow in the fall.

**READING CHECK**

**13. Describe** What is a pigment?

_____

_____

Some leaves contain orange and yellow pigments. However, you can't see them if chlorophyll is present. In the fall, chlorophyll breaks down and other pigments in the leaves can be seen.

**TAKE A LOOK**

**14. Identify** Use colored pencils to show that the leaves on the left-hand side of the figure contain chlorophyll. Use colored pencils to show that the leaves on the right-hand side of the figure have lost their chlorophyll.

# What Happens If You Mix Pigments?

Each pigment absorbs at least one color of light. When you mix pigments together, more colors of light are absorbed, or taken away. The primary pigments are yellow, cyan (a blue shade), and magenta. These are the colors of ink used in a color printer. These pigments can be combined to make any other color. ☑

**READING CHECK**

**15. Explain** What happens when you mix pigments?

_____

_____

# Section 2 Review

**7.6.b, 7.6.c, 7.6.e, 7.6.f, 7.6.g**

## SECTION VOCABULARY

| | |
|---|---|
| **absorption** in optics, the transfer of light energy to particles of matter | **scattering** an interaction of light with matter that causes light to change its energy, direction of motion, or both |
| **reflection** the bouncing back of a ray of light, sound, or heat when the ray hits a surface that it does not go through | **transmission** the passing of light or other form of energy through matter. |
| <u>Wordwise</u> The prefix *re-* means "again" or "back." The root *flect* means "to bend." | |

**1. Identify** For an object to be seen, it must do one of two things. What must the object do?

_____

**2. Describe** What is the path that light travels if it does not hit an object or travel through a new medium?

_____

**3. Describe** What is sunlight composed of? Why is the sky blue?

_____

_____

_____

**4. Identify** What are three things that light can do when it interacts with matter?

_____

**5. Draw** Using two arrows and a dashed line, show the law of reflection in the figure below.

| Mirror |
|---|

**6. Apply Concepts** Complete the table below applying the concepts discussed in this section.

| Description | What light will do |
|---|---|
| A beam of light reflected from a rough surface | Light will show diffuse reflection. |
| A beam of light passing through a fog | |
| A beam of light shining on a glass window | |

# Refraction

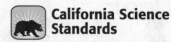
**California Science Standards**
7.6.c, 7.6.d, 7.6.e, 7.6.f

## BEFORE YOU READ

After you read this section, you should be able to answer these questions:

• What is refraction?

• What is a lens?

• How are lenses used in some common optical instruments?

## What Is Refraction?

**Refraction** is the bending of a wave as it passes from one medium into another. A *medium* is a substance a wave can travel through. Light changes speed when it enters a new medium. This causes it to bend, or refract. ☑

Usually, when you look at an object, the light reflecting off the object travels in a straight line from the object to your eye. But when you look at something that is underwater, the light reflecting off it does not travel in a straight line. Instead, it refracts. This refraction makes a ruler inside a beaker of water appear to be bent.

In the figure below, a beam of light hits a piece of glass called a *prism*. The prism refracts the light beam because the speed of light is slower in glass than in air.

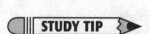
**STUDY TIP**

**Clarify Concepts** In your science notebook, draw the figures in this section that show how refraction works. Write one or two sentences to summarize each figure.

✓ **READING CHECK**

**1. Define** What is refraction?

_____

_____

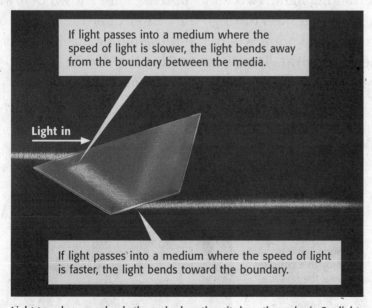

If light passes into a medium where the speed of light is slower, the light bends away from the boundary between the media.

Light in →

If light passes into a medium where the speed of light is faster, the light bends toward the boundary.

Light travels more slowly through glass than it does through air. So, light refracts as it passes at an angle from air to glass or from glass to air.

## TAKE A LOOK

**2. Compare** How does the direction of the light beam coming out of the prism compare to its direction before hitting the prism?

_____

_____

## What Can Refraction Cause?

Refraction causes white light to separate into different colors. Color separation causes rainbows to form. Rainbows form when water drops refract sunlight. ☑

White light is made up of all the wavelengths, or colors, of visible light. When white light is refracted, waves with short wavelengths bend more than waves with long wavelengths do.

The figure below shows an *optical illusion*. Optical illusions are caused by refraction.

*Critical Thinking*

**4. Explain** Which colors of light bend the most when refracted? Explain.

_____

_____

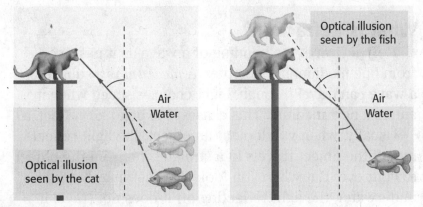

Because of refraction, the cat and the fish see optical illusions. To the cat, the fish seems closer than it really is. To the fish, the cat seems farther away than it really is.

## How Do Lenses Refract Light?

A **lens** is a transparent object that can form an image by refracting light. Two kinds of lenses are shown below. Light rays that pass through the center of any lens are not refracted. The point where the refracted beams intersect is the *focal point*. The distance from the middle of the lens to the focal point is the *focal length*.

### How Lenses Refract Light

When light rays pass through a **convex lens**, the rays are refracted toward each other.

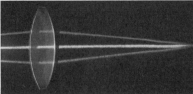

When light rays pass through a **concave lens**, the rays are refracted away from each other.

**TAKE A LOOK**

**5. Identify** Circle the beams in each figure that are not refracted. Label the focal point, F, and the focal length, f, in the image of the convex lens.

## CONVEX LENSES

A lens that is thick in the middle and thin at the edges is a **convex lens**. ☑

The lens of the eye is a convex lens. This lens refracts light and focuses the light on the back surface, or *retina*, of the eye, as shown below. The muscles that hold the lens of the eye can change the shape of the lens to help it focus images. The cornea of the eye also refracts light.

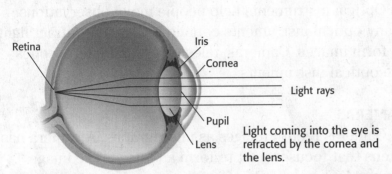

Light coming into the eye is refracted by the cornea and the lens.

A magnifying glass has a convex lens. A magnifying glass can form images of an object that are larger or smaller than the object is. The figure below shows how the lens in a magnifying glass forms two kinds of images, *virtual* and *real*. A real image can be put onto a screen, like at a movie theater. A virtual image can be seen, but not projected onto a screen.

### How Convex Lenses Form Images

If an object is less than one focal length away from a convex lens, a **virtual image** is formed. The image is larger than the object.

If an object is more than two focal lengths away from the lens, a **real image** is formed. The image is inverted, or upside-down. It is also smaller than the object.

**6. Identify** What is a convex lens?

_____

_____

_____

## TAKE A LOOK

**7. Describe** How do the cornea and lens affect the light that enters the eye?

_____

_____

_____

📢 **Say It**

**Discuss** Read the captions in the figure to yourself, silently. Then take turns explaining to a partner how a magnifying glass forms images.

## CONCAVE LENSES

A **concave lens** is a lens that is thin in the middle and thick at the edges. Light rays entering a concave lens are refracted and bend away from each other. Because the refracted rays bend away from each other, concave lenses can only form virtual images. ☑

# What Are Optical Instruments?

Optical instruments help people make observations. Many optical instruments contain lenses that refract light to form images. Cameras, telescopes, and microscopes are optical instruments.

## CAMERAS

Cameras record images as photographs. A camera has a lens that focuses light to form an image. The image formed by a camera lens is focused and recorded on film.

A digital camera uses light sensors instead of film to record images. A tiny computer in the camera stores the images. The figure below explains how a camera works.

**How a Camera Works**

The shutter opens and closes behind the lens to control how much light enters the camera. The longer the shutter is open, the more light enters the camera.

The film is coated with chemicals that react when they are exposed to light. The result is an image stored on the film.

The lens of a camera is a convex lens that focuses light on the film. Moving the lens focuses light from objects at different distances.

The aperture is an opening that lets light into the camera. The larger the aperture is, the more light enters the camera.

---

✔ **READING CHECK**

**8. Describe** What is a concave lens?

_____

_____

---

🐻 **CALIFORNIA STANDARDS CHECK**

**7.6.d** Students know how simple lenses are used in a magnifying glass, the eye, a camera, a telescope, and a microscope.

**9. Compare** How is the lens of a camera similar to the lens of the eye?

_____

_____

---

## TELESCOPES

Telescopes are used to see images of large, distant objects such as planets and stars. The image you see through a telescope is *magnified*, or made larger. Refracting telescopes use lenses to focus light. A simple refracting telescope has two convex lenses. One lens points toward the object being studied. Another is the lens you look through, as you see below. ☑

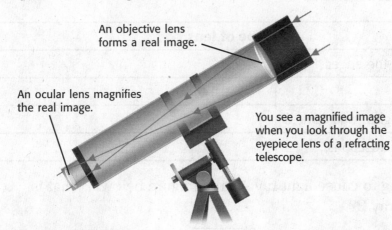

An objective lens forms a real image.

An ocular lens magnifies the real image.

You see a magnified image when you look through the eyepiece lens of a refracting telescope.

**✓ READING CHECK**

**10. Explain** Describe how a refracting telescope works.

_____

_____

_____

_____

## LIGHT MICROSCOPES

Simple light microscopes are similar to refracting telescopes. These microscopes also have two convex lenses. Biologists use microscopes to see magnified images of tiny, nearby objects, such as cells and microscopic organisms. The figure below explains how a microscope works.

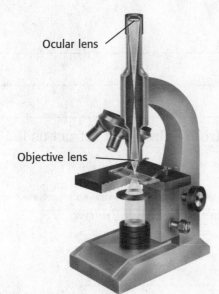

Ocular lens

Objective lens

The objective lens of a microscope forms a real image. The eyepiece lens then produces a larger virtual image. This is the image you see when you look through the microscope.

## Math Focus

**11. Calculate** Microscopes use more than one lens to magnify objects. The power of each lens tells the amount of magnification the lens gives. For example, a 10× lens magnifies objects 10 times. To find the amount of magnification given by two or more lenses used together, multiply the powers of the lenses. So a 5× lens used with a 20× lens will magnify an object 100×. What is the magnification given by a 10× lens used with a 40× lens?

_____

Name _____ Class _____ Date _____

# Section 3 Review

## SECTION VOCABULARY

| | |
|---|---|
| **concave lens** a lens that is thinner in the middle than at the edges<br><br>**convex lens** a lens that is thicker in the middle than at the edges | **lens** a transparent object that refracts light waves such that they converge or diverge to create an image<br><br>**refraction** the bending of a wavefront as the wavefront passes between two substances in which the speed of the wave differs |

**1. Identify** Complete the table for lenses

| Description | Type of lens |
|---|---|
| Thin in the middle, thick on the edges | |
| Forms only virtual images | |
| Found in the eye, magnifying glass, and camera | |
| Found in telescopes and microscopes | |

**2. Identify** What is happening to cause light ray A in the figure below? What is happening to cause light ray B?

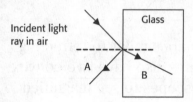

Incident light ray in air

Glass

A          B

_____

**3. Compare** How are microscopes and telescopes alike? How are they different? Your answer should use the word "lens."

_____

_____

_____

**4. Apply Concepts** Why don't you see a beam of light from a flashlight refract as it travels across a room?

_____

**5. Use Graphics** Draw the light rays after they leave the lens shown below.

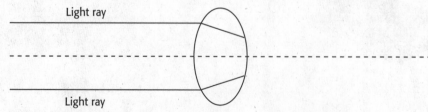

Light ray

Light ray

CHAPTER 4 | Cells: The Basic Units of Life

SECTION 1

# The Characteristics of Cells

 **California Science Standards**

7.1.a, 7.1.c

## BEFORE YOU READ

After you read this section, you should be able to answer these questions:

- What is a cell?
- What is the cell theory?
- What structures are found in all cells?
- What are the two kinds of cells?

## What Is a Cell?

All living things are made of tiny structures called cells. A **cell** is the smallest unit that can perform all the functions needed for life. Most cells are so small you need a microscope to see them. More than 50 human cells can fit on the dot in this letter *i*.

Some living things are made of only one cell. Others are made of millions of cells. Cells from two organisms can be very different from one another. Even cells from different parts of the same organism can be very different from one another. However, all cells have some basic things in common.

**STUDY TIP**

**Organize** As you read this section, make lists of things found in prokaryotic cells, things found in eukaryotic cells, and things found in both.

## What Is the Cell Theory?

Scientists first saw cells through a microscope in 1665. Since then, we have learned a lot more about cells. Scientists have learned that all cells have some important things in common. These things make up the cell theory. The cell theory has three parts:

1. All organisms are made of one or more cells.
2. The cell is the basic unit of all living things.
3. All cells come from existing cells. ☑

## What Structures Are Found in All Cells?

Cells come in many shapes and sizes and can have different jobs. All cells have three parts in common, however: a cell membrane, genetic material, and organelles.

**READING CHECK**

1. **Identify** What is the basic unit of all living things?

_____

_____

## CELL MEMBRANE

Every cell has a cell membrane. The **cell membrane** is a layer that covers and protects the cell. Much like the skin covering your body, the cell membrane separates the cell from its surroundings. The cell membrane also controls what goes in and out of the cell. Inside the cell is a fluid called *cytoplasm*.

## GENETIC MATERIAL

Almost all cells contain DNA (deoxyribonucleic acid). DNA is the genetic material that holds information needed to make new cells and new organisms. DNA passes from parent cells to new cells. It tells the cell what job to do. In some cells, the DNA is found inside a structure called the **nucleus**. Almost every cell in your body has a nucleus.

## ORGANELLES

Cells have parts called **organelles** that do different jobs in the cell. Many organelles are covered with membranes. Different types of cells have different organelles.

**TAKE A LOOK**
**3. Identify** Use the information in the text to fill in the blank labels in the figure.

**Parts of a Cell**

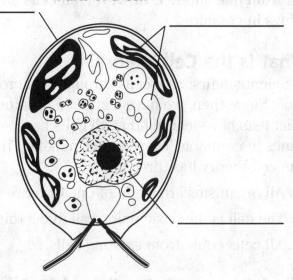

## What Are the Two Kinds of Cells?

There are two basic kinds of cells—one kind has a nucleus and the other kind doesn't. A cell without a nucleus is called a *prokaryotic cell*. A cell with a nucleus is called a *eukaryotic cell*.

## What Are Prokaryotes?

A **prokaryote** is a single-celled organism that does not have a nucleus. Even though they have no nuclei, prokaryotes do have DNA. Bacteria and archaea are prokaryotes. Many prokaryotes have *flagella* (singular, *flagellum*) that help them move.

These are some characteristics of prokaryotes:

• no nucleus

• DNA shaped like a twisted rubber band

• no membrane-covered (or membrane-bound) organelles

• a cell wall outside the cell membrane

**Prokaryotic Cell**

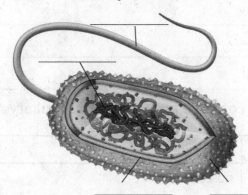

_____   _____

## What Are Eukaryotes?

Eukaryotic cells are about 10 times larger than bacteria cells. Eukaryotic cells are still very small, and you need a microscope to see most of them.

**Eukaryotes** are organisms made of eukaryotic cells. They can have one cell or many cells. Yeast, which makes bread rise, is an example of a eukaryote with one cell. Plants are eukaryotes with many cells.

**Eukaryotic Cell**

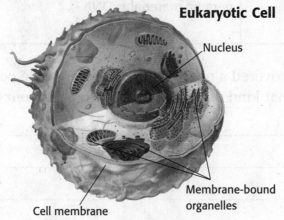

Nucleus

Membrane-bound organelles

Cell membrane

**TAKE A LOOK**
**4. Identify** Label the parts of the prokaryote with the following terms: DNA, flagellum, cell membrane, cell wall.

## Math Focus
**5. Calculate** Most of the smallest prokaryotic cells have diameters of about 1 micron. What do you expect is the diameter of the smallest eukaryotic cell?

_____

**TAKE A LOOK**
**6. Identify** What does this cell have that a prokaryotic cell does not?

_____

_____

_____

# Section 1 Review

7.1.a, 7.1.c

## SECTION VOCABULARY

| | |
|---|---|
| **cell** the smallest functional and structural unit in all living organisms; usually consists of a nucleus, cytoplasm, and a membrane | **nucleus** in a eukaryotic cell, a membrane-bound organelle that contains the cell's DNA and that has a role in processes such as growth, metabolism, and reproduction |
| **cell membrane** a phospholipid layer that covers a cell's surface and acts as a barrier between the inside of a cell and the cell's environment | **organelle** one of the small bodies in a cell's cytoplasm that are specialized to perform a specific function |
| **eukaryote** an organism made up of cells that have a nucleus enclosed by a membrane; eukaryotes include protists, animals, plants, and fungi but not archaea or bacteria | **prokaryote** a single-celled organism that does not have a nucleus or membrane-bound organelles; examples are archaea and bacteria<br><br>**Wordwise** The prefix *pro-* means "before." The root *karyon* means "nut" or "kernel." |

**1. Identify** What are the three parts of the cell theory?

_____

_____

**2. Compare** Complete the chart below to compare prokaryotes and eukaryotes.

| Prokaryotes | Eukaryotes |
|---|---|
| | no cell wall |
| no nucleus | |
| | membrane-bound organelles |
| one cell | |
| | genetic material is DNA |

**3. Apply Concepts** You have just discovered a new organism. It is a single cell and has a cell wall but no nucleus. What kind of organism is it? Explain your answer.

_____

_____

_____

CHAPTER 4 Cells: The Basic Units of Life
SECTION
2 **Eukaryotic Cells**

BEFORE YOU READ

**After you read this section, you should be able to answer these questions:**

- What are the parts of a eukaryotic cell?
- What is the function of each part of a eukaryotic cell?
- How do plant cells differ from animal cells?

## What Are the Parts of a Eukaryotic Cell?

Plant cells and animal cells are two types of eukaryotic cells. A eukaryotic cell has many parts that help it stay alive.

### CELL WALL

All plant cells have a cell wall. The **cell wall** is a stiff structure that supports the cell and surrounds the cell membrane. The cell wall of a plant cell is made of a type of sugar called cellulose.

*Fungi* (singular, *fungus*), such as yeasts and mushrooms, also have cell walls. The cell walls of fungi are made of a sugar called chitin. Prokaryotic cells such as bacteria and archaea also have cell walls. ☑

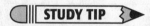
**STUDY TIP**

**Organize** As you read this section, make a chart comparing plant cells and animal cells.

**READING CHECK**

**1. Identify** Name two kinds of eukaryotes that have cell walls.

_____

_____

**Plant Cell**

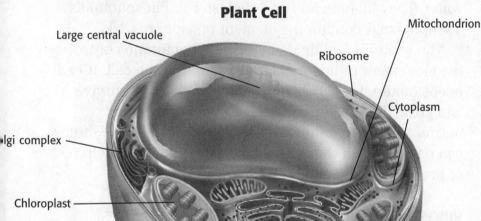

Large central vacuole

Mitochondrion

Ribosome

Cytoplasm

Golgi complex

Chloroplast

Cytoskeleton

Endoplasmic reticulum

Nucleus

Cell membrane

Cell wall

**TAKE A LOOK**

**2. Identify** Where is the cell wall located?

_____

_____

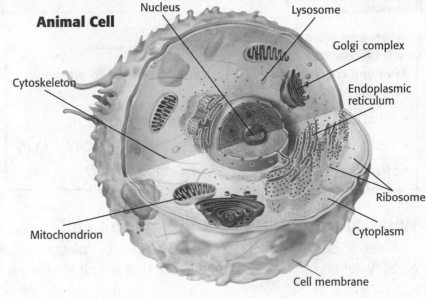

**Animal Cell**

Nucleus
Lysosome
Golgi complex
Cytoskeleton
Endoplasmic reticulum
Ribosome
Cytoplasm
Mitochondrion
Cell membrane

## TAKE A LOOK

**3. Compare** Compare the pictures of an animal cell and a plant cell. Name three parts that both the plant cell and the animal cell have.

_____

_____

_____

## CELL MEMBRANE

Every cell has a cell membrane. The cell membrane surrounds and protects the cell. It separates the cell from the outside environment. In a cell that has a cell wall, the cell membrane is found just inside the cell wall.

The cell membrane is made of many kinds of materials. It contains proteins and lipids, including phospholipids. Proteins are molecules made by cells for a variety of functions. Lipids are compounds that do not dissolve in water. They include fats and cholesterol. Phospholipids are lipids that contain the element phosphorus. ☑

The proteins and lipids in the cell membrane control the movement of materials into and out of the cell. A cell needs materials such as nutrients and water to survive and grow. The proteins in the cell membrane allow nutrients to go in and wastes to go out of the cell. Water can pass through the cell membrane without the help of proteins.

☑ **READING CHECK**

**4. List** What is the cell membrane made of?

_____

_____

## RIBOSOMES

**Ribosomes** are organelles that make proteins. They are the smallest organelles. A cell can have many ribosomes. Some float freely inside the cell. Others are attached to membranes or to other organelles. Unlike most organelles, ribosomes are not covered by membranes. ☑

☑ **READING CHECK**

**5. Compare** How are ribosomes different from other organelles?

_____

_____

## NUCLEUS

The nucleus is a large organelle in a eukaryotic cell. It contains DNA, the cell's genetic material. DNA has the instructions that tell a cell how to make proteins.

The nucleus is covered by two membranes. Materials pass through pores in the double membrane. In many cells, the nucleus contains a dark area called the *nucleolus*.

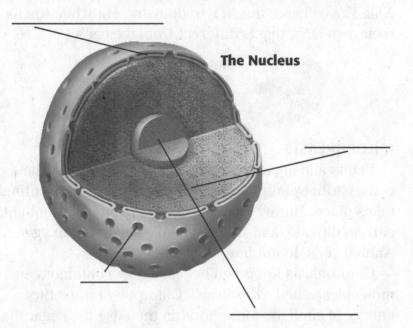

**The Nucleus**

**TAKE A LOOK**
**6. Identify** Label the diagram of a nucleus with these terms: pore, DNA, nucleolus, double membrane.

## ENDOPLASMIC RETICULUM

Many chemical reactions take place in the cell. Many of these reactions happen on or inside the endoplasmic reticulum. The **endoplasmic reticulum** (ER) is a system of membranes with many folds in which proteins, lipids, and other materials are made.

The ER is also part of the cell's delivery system. Its folds have many tubes and passageways. Materials move through the ER to other parts of the cell.

There are two types of ER: rough and smooth. Smooth ER makes lipids and helps break down materials that can harm the cell. Rough ER has ribosomes attached to it. The ribosomes make proteins. The proteins are then delivered to other parts of the cell by the ER. ☑

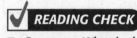 **READING CHECK**

**7. Compare** What is the difference between smooth ER and rough ER?

_____

_____

_____

_____

_____

**Endoplasmic reticulum**
This organelle makes lipids, breaks down drugs and other substances, and packages proteins for the Golgi complex.

## MITOCHONDRIA

A **mitochondrion** (plural, *mitochondria*) is an organelle that breaks down sugar to make energy. It is the main power source for a cell.

A mitochondrion is covered by two membranes. Most of a cell's energy is made in the inside membrane. Energy released by mitochondria is stored in a molecule called ATP. The cell uses the ATP to do work. Mitochondria have their own DNA that is different from the cell's DNA. ☑

**Mitochondrion**
This organelle breaks down food molecules to make ATP.

## CHLOROPLASTS

Plants and algae have chloroplasts in some of their cells. **Chloroplasts** are organelles where photosynthesis takes place. During *photosynthesis*, plants use sunlight, carbon dioxide, and water to make sugar and oxygen. Animal cells do not have chloroplasts.

Chloroplasts are green because they contain green molecules called *chlorophyll*. Chlorophyll traps the energy of sunlight. Mitochondria then use the sugar made in photosynthesis to make ATP.

**Chloroplast**
This organelle uses the energy from sunlight to make food.

## CYTOSKELETON

The **cytoskeleton** is a web of proteins inside the cell. It acts as both a skeleton and a muscle. The cytoskeleton helps the cell keep its shape. It also helps some cells, such as bacteria, to move.

## VESICLES

A **vesicle** is a small sac that surrounds material to be moved. The materials are moved to another part of the cell or out of the cell. Vesicles are made from the membrane of the Golgi complex or from the cell membrane. All eukaryotic cells have vesicles.

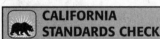

**READING CHECK**

**8. Explain** How do mitochondria differ from other organelles?

_____

_____

**CALIFORNIA STANDARDS CHECK**

**7.1.d** Students know that mitochondria <u>liberate</u> <u>energy</u> for the work that cells do and that chloroplasts capture sunlight

**Word Help: <u>liberate</u>**
to release; to set free

**Word Help: <u>energy</u>**
the capacity to do work

**9. Infer** Why don't animal cells need chloroplasts?

_____

_____

_____

_____

## GOLGI COMPLEX

The **Golgi complex** is the organelle that packages and distributes proteins. It is the "post office" of the cell. The Golgi complex looks like the smooth ER.

The ER delivers lipids and proteins to the Golgi complex. The Golgi complex can change the lipids and proteins so that they can do different jobs. The final products are then enclosed in pieces of the Golgi complex's membrane. This membrane pinches off to make vesicles. The vesicles transport the materials to other parts of the cell or out of the cell. ☑

**Golgi Complex**
This organelle processes and transports proteins and other materials.

✔ READING CHECK

**10. Define** What is the function of the Golgi complex?

_____

_____

_____

## LYSOSOMES

**Lysosomes** are organelles that are responsible for digestion in a cell. They destroy worn-out or damaged organelles, get rid of wastes, and protect the cell from harmful particles.

Lysosomes are found mainly in animal cells. The cell wraps membrane around a particle and encloses it in a vesicle. Lysosomes bump into the vesicle and pour enzymes into it. The enzymes break down the particle inside the vesicle. This removes old or dangerous materials so they do not build up inside the cell.

**Lysosome**
This organelle digests food particles, wastes, cell parts, and foreign invaders.

## VACUOLES

A vacuole is a vesicle. In plant and fungal cells, some vacuoles act like lysosomes. They contain enzymes that help a cell digest particles. The large central vacuole in a plant cell stores water and other liquids. Large vacuoles full of water help support the cells. Some plants wilt when their vacuoles lose water. ☑

✔ READING CHECK

**11. Identify** What types of eukaryotic cells have vacuoles that act like lysosomes?

_____

_____

# Section 2 Review

7.1.a, 7.1.b, 7.1.c, 7.1.d

## SECTION VOCABULARY

| | |
|---|---|
| **cell wall** rigid structure that surrounds the cell membrane and provides support to the cell | **Golgi complex** a cell organelle that helps make and package materials to be transported out of the cell |
| **chloroplast** an organelle found in plant and algae cells where photosynthesis occurs | **lysosome** a cell organelle that contains digestive enzymes |
| **cytoskeleton** the cytoplasmic network of protein filaments that plays an essential role in cell movement, shape, and division | **mitochondrion** in eukaryotic cells, the cell organelle that is surrounded by two membranes and that is the site of cellular respiration |
| **endoplasmic reticulum** a system of membranes that is found in a cell's cytoplasm and that assists in the production, processing, and transport of proteins and in the production of lipids | **ribosome** a cell organelle composed of RNA and protein; the site of protein synthesis |
| | **vesicle** a small cavity or sac that contains materials in a eukaryotic cell |

**1. Compare** Name three parts of a plant cell that are not found in an animal cell.

_____

_____

_____

**2. Explain** How does a cell get water and nutrients?

_____

_____

_____

**3. Predict** What would happen to a eukaryotic cell if all its mitochondria were destroyed?

_____

_____

_____

**4. Apply Concepts** What kind of cell in the human body do you think would have more mitochondria—a muscle cell or a skin cell?

_____

_____

_____

_____

**5. List** What are two functions of the cytoskeleton?

_____

_____

CHAPTER 4 | Cells: The Basic Units of Life

## SECTION 3 | The Organization of Living Things

After you read this section, you should be able to answer these questions:

- What are the benefits of being multicellular?
- What are the four levels of organization in living things?
- How are structure and function related in an organism?

 **California Science Standards**

7.1.f, 7.5.a

## What Is an Organism?

An **organism** is any living thing. An organism made of a single cell is called a *unicellular* organism. An organism made of many cells is a *multicellular* organism. The cells in a multicellular organism depend on each other to survive and to keep the organism alive.

## What Are the Benefits of Having Many Cells?

Three benefits of being multicellular are: larger size, longer life, and specialization of cells.

### LARGER SIZE

Most multicellular organisms are bigger than one-celled organisms. In general, a large organism, such as an elephant, has fewer predators than a small animal. ☑

### LONGER LIFE

A multicellular organism usually lives longer than a one-celled organism. A one-celled organism is limited to the life span of its one cell. A multicellular organism, however, is not limited to the life span of any one of its cells. Multicellular organisms can replace most of their cells as the cells die off.

### SPECIALIZATION

In a multicellular organism, each type of cell has a particular job. No cell has to do every job for the organism. Specialization makes the organism more efficient.

**STUDY TIP**

**Outline** As you read, make an outline of this section. Use the heading questions from the section in your outline.

**READING CHECK**

**1. Identify** What is one benefit to an organism of being large?

_____

_____

_____

**CALIFORNIA STANDARDS CHECK**

**7.1.f** Students know that as multicellular organisms develop, their cells <u>differentiate</u>.

**Word Help: <u>differentiate</u>** to become specialized in structure and function

**2. Explain** Why is cell specialization important?

_____

_____

_____

**7.5.a** Students know plants and animals have levels of organization for structure and function, including cells, tissues, organs, organ systems

**Word Help: structure**
the arrangement of the parts of a whole

**Word Help: function**
use or purpose

**3. List** What are the four levels of organization for an organism?

_____
_____
_____
_____

# What Are the Four Levels of Organization of Living Things?

Multicellular organisms have four levels of organization:

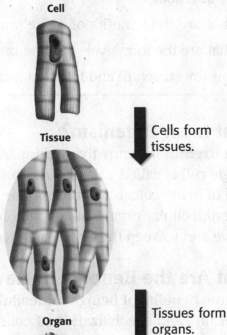

Cell

Cells form tissues.

Tissue

Tissues form organs.

Organ

Organs form organ systems.

Organ system

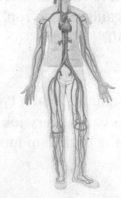

Organ systems form organisms such as you!

 **Say It**

**Discuss** With a partner, name some of the major organs in the human body. Talk about what organ systems they are part of.

**SECTION 3** The Organization of Living Things *continued*

## 1. CELLS

Cells in a multicellular organism can be specialized. A specialized cell has a specific function. The **function** of a cell is the job it does. For example, a brain cell would not do the same job as a heart muscle cell.

The function of a cell is related to its structure. **Structure** is the arrangement of parts in an organism. The structure of a brain cell is different from the structure of a heart muscle cell. Structure includes shape and the material a part is made of.

## 2. TISSUES

A **tissue** is a group of cells that work together to do a specific job. Heart muscle tissue, for example, is made of many heart muscle cells. Animals have four basic kinds of tissue: nerve tissue, muscle tissue, connective tissue, and protective tissue. Plants have three kinds of tissue: transport tissue, protective tissue, and ground tissue.

## 3. ORGANS

A structure made of two or more tissues that work together to do a job is called an **organ**. Your heart, for example, is an organ made of different tissues. The heart has both muscle tissue and nerve tissue. ☑

Plants also have different tissues that act together as organs. Leaves, stems, and roots are all plant organs.

☑ **READING CHECK**

**4. Define** What is an organ?

_____

_____

_____

_____

## 4. ORGAN SYSTEMS

A group of organs working together to do a job is called an **organ system**. An example of an organ system is your digestive system. Organ systems depend on each other to help the organism function. For example, the digestive system depends on the cardiovascular and respiratory systems for oxygen.

Plants also have organ systems. They include leaf systems, root systems, and stem systems.

# Section 3 Review

7.1.f, 7.5.a

## SECTION VOCABULARY

| | |
|---|---|
| **function** the special, normal, or proper activity on an organ or part | **organism** a living thing; anything that can carry out life processes independently |
| **organ** a collection of tissues that carry out a specialized function of the body | **structure** the arrangement of parts in an organism |
| **organ system** a group of organs that work together to perform body functions | **tissue** a group of similar cells that perform a common function |

**1. List** What are three benefits of being multicellular?

_____

_____

_____

**2. Contrast** Fill in the chart below to contrast the levels of organization in an organism.

| Level of organization | Description | Example |
|---|---|---|
| | the smallest unit that can perform all life processes | |
| | | heart muscle |
| | a collection of tissues that carry out a specialized function | |
| Organ system | | circulatory system |

**3. Compare** How are structure and function different?

_____

_____

_____

**4. Explain** What does "specialization of cells" mean?

_____

_____

_____

_____

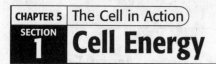

CHAPTER 5 | The Cell in Action

SECTION
1 **Cell Energy**

**BEFORE YOU READ**

**After you read this section, you should be able to answer these questions:**

• How does a plant make food?

• How do plant cells differ from animal cells?

• How do plant and animal cells get energy from food?

## How Does a Plant Make Its Own Food?

The sun is the major source of energy for Earth. Plants use carbon dioxide, water, and the sun's energy to make food in a process called **photosynthesis**. The food that plants make gives them energy. Animals get the energy stored in plants when they eat them.

Plant cells have molecules called *pigments* that absorb light energy. Chlorophyll is the main pigment used in photosynthesis. It is found in *chloroplasts*, where photosynthesis takes place. The food plants make is in the form of a simple sugar called *glucose*. Photosynthesis also produces oxygen. ☑

**STUDY TIP**

**Compare** As you read this section, make a Venn Diagram to compare cellular respiration and fermentation.

**READING CHECK**

**1. Complete** Photosynthesis takes place in

_____.

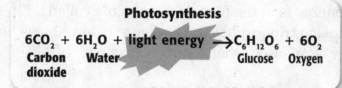

**Photosynthesis**

$6CO_2 + 6H_2O +$ light energy $\longrightarrow C_6H_{12}O_6 + 6O_2$
Carbon    Water                    Glucose    Oxygen
dioxide

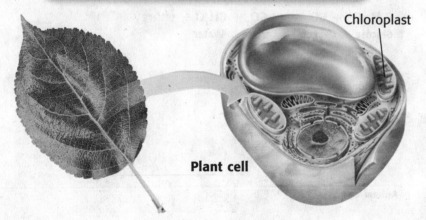

Chloroplast

Plant cell

**TAKE A LOOK**
**2. Identify** What two things are made during photosynthesis?

_____

_____

**SECTION 1** Cell Energy *continued*

**Word Help:** <u>liberate</u>
to release; to set free

**3. Explain** Why do animal cells have mitochondria but no chloroplasts?

_____

_____

_____

_____

_____

_____

_____

## How Do Organisms Get Energy from Food?

Animals cannot make their own food as plants can. However, both plant and animal cells must break down food to get energy from it. There are two ways cells get energy: cellular respiration and fermentation.

**Cellular respiration** uses oxygen to break down food. **Fermentation** does not use oxygen to break down food. Cellular respiration releases more energy from food than fermentation. Most eukaryotes, such as plants and animals, use cellular respiration to free the energy stored in food.

## What Happens in Cellular Respiration?

When you hear the word *respiration*, you might think of breathing. However, cellular respiration is different from breathing. Cellular respiration is a chemical process that happens in cells. In eukaryotic cells, such as plant and animal cells, cellular respiration takes place in *mitochondria*.

Recall that to get energy, plants make their food and animals eat food. Most organisms store the energy as glucose. To use this energy, cells must break down glucose. In cellular respiration, glucose is broken down into carbon dioxide and water. Energy is also released. This energy is in the form of a molecule called *ATP* (adenosine triphosphate). The figure below shows how energy is released when a cow eats grass.

## TAKE A LOOK
**4. Identify** What two things are needed for cellular respiration?

_____

_____

**5. List** What three things are made during cellular respiration?

_____

_____

_____

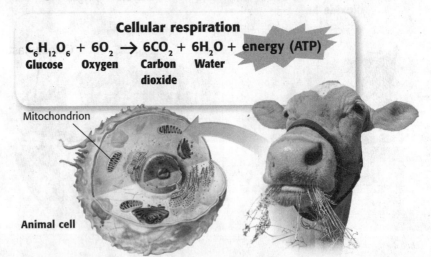

**Cellular respiration**

$$C_6H_{12}O_6 + 6O_2 \rightarrow 6CO_2 + 6H_2O + \text{energy (ATP)}$$

**Glucose**    **Oxygen**    **Carbon dioxide**    **Water**

Mitochondrion

Animal cell

The mitochondria in the cells of this cow will use cellular respiration to release energy stored in the grass.

**SECTION 1** Cell Energy *continued*

## The Connection Between Photosynthesis and Cellular Respiration

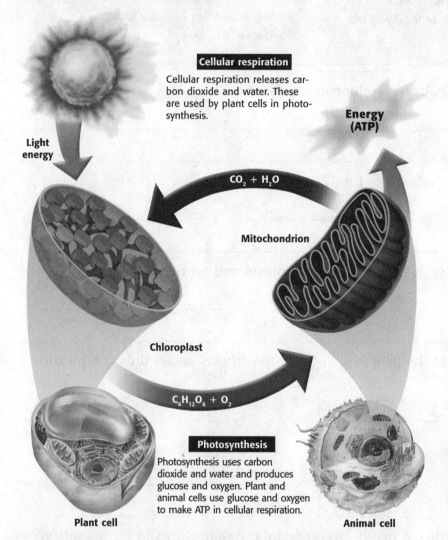

**Cellular respiration**
Cellular respiration releases carbon dioxide and water. These are used by plant cells in photosynthesis.

Energy (ATP)

$CO_2 + H_2O$

Light energy

**Mitochondrion**

**Chloroplast**

$C_6H_{12}O_6 + O_2$

**Photosynthesis**
Photosynthesis uses carbon dioxide and water and produces glucose and oxygen. Plant and animal cells use glucose and oxygen to make ATP in cellular respiration.

Plant cell

Animal cell

*Critical Thinking*

**6. Apply Concepts** What would happen if oxygen was not produced during photosynthesis?

_____

_____

_____

_____

_____

_____

**TAKE A LOOK**

**7. Complete** Plant and animal cells use glucose and oxygen to make

_____.

 **Say It**

**Research** Use the school library or the internet to research an organism that uses fermentation. What kind of organism is it? Where is it found? Is this organism useful to humans? Present your findings to the class.

## How Is Fermentation Different from Cellular Respiration?

In fermentation, cells break down glucose without oxygen. Some bacteria and fungi rely only on fermentation to release energy from food. However, cells in other organisms may use fermentation when there is not enough oxygen for cellular respiration.

When you exercise, your muscles use up oxygen very quickly. When cells don't have enough oxygen, they must use fermentation to get energy. Fermentation creates a byproduct called *lactic acid*. This is what makes your muscles ache as they tire.

# Section 1 Review

7.1.b, 7.1.d

## SECTION VOCABULARY

| | |
|---|---|
| **cellular respiration** the process by which cells use oxygen to produce energy from food<br><br>**fermentation** the breakdown of food without the use of oxygen | **photosynthesis** the process by which plants, algae, and some bacteria use sunlight, carbon dioxide, and water to make food.<br><br><u>Wordwise</u> The root *phot-* means "light." |

**1. Identify** What kind of cells have chloroplasts?

_____

_____

**2. Explain** How do plant cells make food?

_____

_____

_____

**3. Explain** Why do plant cells need both chloroplasts and mitochondria?

_____

_____

**4. Apply Concepts** How do the processes of photosynthesis and cellular respiration work together?

_____

_____

_____

_____

**5. Compare** What is one difference between cellular respiration and fermentation?

_____

_____

_____

_____

**6. Explain** Do your body cells always use cellular respiration to break down glucose? Explain your answer.

_____

_____

_____

CHAPTER 5 | The Cell in Action

## SECTION 2 | The Cell Cycle

**BEFORE YOU READ**

After you read this section, you should be able to answer these questions:

• How are new cells made?

• What is mitosis?

• What happens when cells divide too quickly?

**California Science Standards**

7.1.b, 7.1.e, 7.2.e

## How Are New Cells Made?

As you grow, you pass through different stages in your life. Cells also pass through different stages in their life cycle. These stages are called the **cell cycle**. The cell cycle starts when a cell is made, and ends when the cell divides to make new cells.

Before a cell divides, it makes a copy of its DNA (deoxyribonucleic acid). *DNA* is the molecule that contains all the instructions for making new cells. The DNA is stored in structures called **chromosomes**. The chromosomes are copied to make sure that each new cell has all the DNA of the parent cell. Although all cells pass through a cell cycle, the process differs in prokaryotic and eukaryotic cells. ☑

## How Do Prokaryotic Cells Divide?

Prokaryotes are made of only one cell. Prokaryotic cells have no nucleus. They also have no organelles that are surrounded by membranes. The DNA for prokaryotic cells, such as bacteria, is found on one circular chromosome. The cell divides by a simple process called *binary fission*. Binary fission splits the cell into two parts. Each part has one copy of the cell's DNA.

**STUDY TIP**

**Summarize** As you read this section, make a diagram showing the stages of the eukaryotic cell cycle.

**READING CHECK**

**1. Explain** What must happen before a cell can divide?

_____

_____

_____

Bacteria reproduce by binary fission.

**TAKE A LOOK**

**2. Complete** Prokaryotic cells divide by _____

_____.

## How Do Eukaryotic Cells Divide?

Cell division in eukaryotic cells is more complex than in prokaryotic cells. The cell cycle of a eukaryotic cell has three stages: interphase, mitosis, and cytokinesis.

The first stage of the cell cycle is called *interphase*. During interphase, the cell grows and makes copies of its chromosomes and organelles. The two copies of a chromosome are called *chromatids*. The two chromatids are held together at the *centromere*.

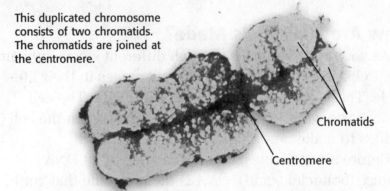

This duplicated chromosome consists of two chromatids. The chromatids are joined at the centromere.

Chromatids

Centromere

The second stage of the cell cycle is called **mitosis**. During this stage, the chromatids separate. This allows each new cell to get a copy of each chromosome. Mitosis happens in four phases: prophase, metaphase, anaphase, and telophase.

The third stage of the cell cycle is called **cytokinesis**. During this stage, the cytoplasm of the cell divides to form two cells. These two cells are called *daughter cells*. The new daughter cells are exactly the same as each other. They are also exactly the same as the original cell.

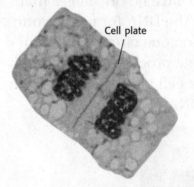

Cell plate

When a plant cell divides, a cell plate forms. The cell then divides into two cells. After the cell divides, a new cell wall forms where the cell plate was.

## How Does the Cell Cycle Work?

The figure on the following page shows the cell cycle. In this example, the stages of the cell cycle are shown in a eukaryotic cell that has only four chromosomes.

*Critical Thinking*

**3. Compare** What is the difference between a chromosome and a chromatid?

_____

_____

_____

_____

---

**CALIFORNIA STANDARDS CHECK**

**7.1.e** Students know cells divide to increase their numbers through a <u>process</u> of mitosis, which results in two daughter cells with identical sets of chromosomes.

**Word Help: process**
a set of steps, events, or changes

**4. Identify** After one cell goes through mitosis and cytokinesis, how many cells are there?

_____

---

**SECTION 2** The Cell Cycle *continued*

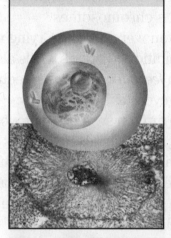

**Interphase** Before mitosis begins, chromosomes are copied. Each chromosome is then made of two chromatids.

**Mitosis Phase 1 (Prophase)** Mitosis begins. Chromatids condense from long strands to thick rods.

**Mitosis Phase 2 (Metaphase)** The nuclear membrane dissolves. Chromosome pairs line up around the equator of the cell.

**Mitosis Phase 3 (Anaphase)** Chromatids separate and move to opposite sides of the cell.

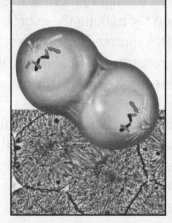

**Mitosis Phase 4 (Telophase)** A nuclear membrane forms around each set of chromosomes. The chromosomes unwind. Mitosis is complete.

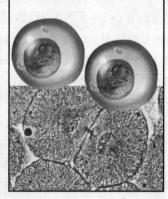

**Cytokinesis** In cells with no cell wall, the cell pinches in two. In cells with a cell wall, a cell plate forms and separates the new cells.

## TAKE A LOOK
**5. List** What are the four phases of mitosis?

_____

_____

_____

**6. Identify** What structure do plant cells have during cytokinesis that animal cells do not have?

_____

## What Tells a Cell When to Divide?

After cytokinesis is complete, each new cell is an exact copy of the parent cell. How did the parent cell know when to start copying its chromosomes?

As a baby, you cried when you were hungry. Crying was your way of reporting your condition to others. Cells also report conditions. This is called *feedback*. Cells use feedback to control the stages of the cell cycle, as shown below.

In a cell, feedback is used to turn on switches that work like red and green traffic lights. A cell spends most of its life in interphase, when it is not dividing. During this time, the cell grows. When feedback messages report that the cell is large and healthy, proteins in the cell get the "green light." The cell starts to copy its organelles and chromosomes. ☑

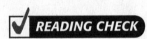

**7. Identify** In which stage of the cell cycle does a cell spend most of its life?

_____

_____

The cell cycle in eukaryotes is controlled at three points. Feedback at each point determines whether the cell will get a "red light" or a "green light" to continue cell division.

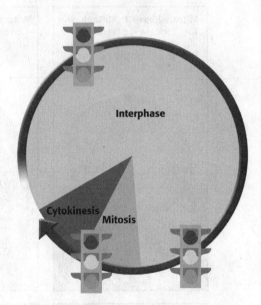

Interphase

Cytokinesis

Mitosis

## What Happens When Cell Division Is Not Controlled?

The molecules that control the "red light-green light" signals are proteins. The information for making these proteins is found in a cell's DNA. If the DNA mutates, or changes, the proteins the cell makes could be changed. The changed protein may not control the cell correctly. This can cause cancer to occur. **Cancer** is the uncontrolled growth of cells.

There are different ways cancer can begin in a cell. Some mutations in DNA cause too many molecules that make a cell grow. This speeds up the cell cycle. Other mutations turn off the proteins that stop a cell from dividing. This would allow cells to divide constantly.

## Math Focus

**8. Calculate** Cell A normally divides once every two days. If its control mechanisms aren't working correctly, cell A divides six times faster than normal. How many hours does it take cell A to divide when its control mechanisms aren't working correctly?

_____

_____

# Section 2 Review

7.1.b, 7.1.e, 7.2.e

## SECTION VOCABULARY

| | |
|---|---|
| **cancer** a tumor in which the cells begin dividing at an uncontrolled rate and can become invasive | **cytokinesis** the division of cytoplasm of a cell |
| **cell cycle** the life cycle of a cell | **mitosis** in eukaryotic cells, a process of cell division that forms two new nuclei, each of which has the same number of chromosomes |
| **chromosome** in a eukaryotic cell, one of the structures in the nucleus that are made up of DNA and protein; in a prokaryotic cell, the main ring of DNA | |

**1. Compare** How does the the DNA of prokaryotic and eukaryotic cells differ?

_____

_____

**2. Summarize** Complete the Process Chart to explain the three stages of the cell cycle. Include the four phases of mitosis.

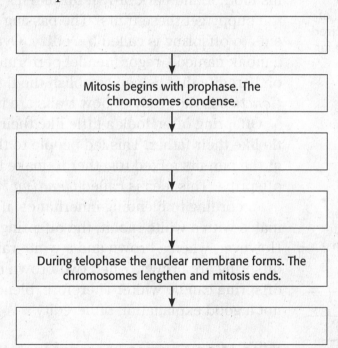

Mitosis begins with prophase. The chromosomes condense.

During telophase the nuclear membrane forms. The chromosomes lengthen and mitosis ends.

**3. Explain** Why does a cell make a copy of its DNA before it divides?

_____

_____

**4. Explain** Why does cancer occur?

_____

_____

_____

**SECTION 1** # Mendel and His Peas

**California Science Standards**

7.2.d

---

**BEFORE YOU READ**

After you read this section, you should be able to answer these questions:

- What is heredity?
- Who was Gregor Mendel?
- What experiments did Mendel conduct on pea plants?
- What did Mendel learn about heredity?

---

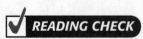
**STUDY TIP**

**Define** As you read this section, make a list of all of the underlined and italicized words. Write a definition for each of the words.

## What Is Heredity?

Imagine a puppy. The puppy has long, floppy ears like his mother and dark brown fur like his father. How did the puppy get these traits? The passing of traits from parents to offspring is called **heredity**. Over 100 years ago, a monk named Gregor Mendel performed experiments on heredity that helped establish the field of genetics. *Genetics* is the study of how traits are inherited.

Offspring often look a little like their mother and a little like their father. This led people to think that the traits of the parents mixed together to make the traits of the offspring. This idea is called *blending inheritance.* ☑

According to blending inheritance, if a brown rabbit mates with a white rabbit, the offspring should be tan. However, when a brown and a white rabbit do mate, the offspring are brown. When two brown rabbits mate, the offspring can be white! Therefore, blending inheritance is not a good explanation of heredity.

---

☑ **READING CHECK**

**1. Explain** Why did people think that blending inheritance was a good explanation of heredity?

_____
_____
_____
_____

## Who Was Gregor Mendel?

Gregor Mendel was born in Austria in 1822. He grew up on a farm and learned a lot about flowers and fruit trees. Mendel studied at a university and then entered a monastery. A monastery is a place where monks study religion.

Mendel examined pea plants in the monastery garden to study how traits are passed from parent to offspring. He used garden peas because they grow quickly. They also have many traits that are easy to see. His experiments showed why blending inheritance does not explain how traits are passed from parents to offspring. His results changed the way people think about inheritance. ☑

---

☑ **READING CHECK**

**2. Explain** Why did Mendel choose to study pea plants?

_____
_____
_____
_____

SECTION 1 | Mendel and His Peas *continued*

## REPRODUCTION IN PEAS

Pea plants, like many flowering plants, have both male and female reproductive parts. Many flowering plants reproduce by cross-pollination. In *cross-pollination*, sperm in the pollen of one plant fertilize eggs in the flower of a different plant. Pollen can be carried by organisms, such as insects. Pollen can also be carried by the wind from one flower to another.

Some flowering plants must use cross-pollination. They need another plant to reproduce. However, a pea plant can also reproduce by self-pollination. In *self-pollination*, sperm from one plant fertilize the eggs of the same plant. ☑

Mendel used self-pollination in pea plants in order to grow true-breeding plants for his experiments. When a *true-breeding* plant self-pollinates, its offspring all have the same traits as the parent. For example, a true-breeding plant with purple flowers always has offspring with purple flowers.

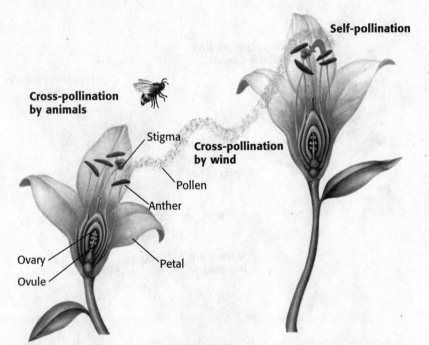

During pollination, pollen from the anther (male part) is carried to the stigma (female part). Fertilization happens when a sperm from the pollen moves through the stigma and enters an egg in an ovule.

☑ **READING CHECK**

**3. Compare** How is cross-pollination different from self-pollination?

_____

_____

_____

_____

## TAKE A LOOK

**4. Identify** What are two ways pollen can travel from one plant to another during cross-pollination?

_____

_____

_____

_____

*Critical Thinking*

**5. Infer** How do you think pollen might move during self-pollination?

_____

_____

_____

_____

## CHARACTERISTICS

Mendel studied one characteristic of peas at a time. A *characteristic* is a feature that has different forms. For example, hair color is a characteristic of humans. The different forms, or colors, such as brown or red hair, are called *traits*. ☑

Mendel used plants that had different traits for each characteristic he studied. One pea characteristic he studied was flower color. He chose plants that had purple flowers and plants that had white flowers. He also studied other characteristics, such as seed shape, pod color, and plant height.

## CROSSING PEA PLANTS

Mendel was careful to use true-breeding plants in his experiments. By choosing these plants, he would know what to expect if his plants were to self-pollinate. He decided to find out what would happen if he crossed, or bred, two plants that had different traits.

**Say It**

**Describe** How would you describe yourself? Make a list of your physical traits, such as height, hair color, and eye color. List other traits you have that you weren't born with. Share this list with your classmates. Which of these traits did you inherit?

## TAKE A LOOK

**7. Describe** How did Mendel make sure that the plant with round seeds did not self-pollinate?

_____
_____
_____
_____

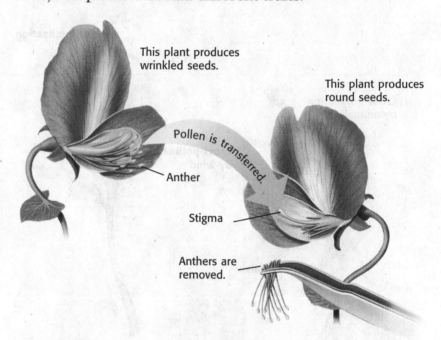

This plant produces wrinkled seeds.

This plant produces round seeds.

Pollen is transferred.

Anther

Stigma

Anthers are removed.

Mendel removed the anthers from a plant that made round seeds. Then, he used pollen from a plant that made wrinkled seeds to fertilize the plant that made round seeds.

# What Happened in Mendel's First Experiment?

Mendel studied seven different characteristics in his first experiment with peas. For example, he crossed plants that were true-breeding for purple flowers with plants that were true-breeding for white flowers. The offspring from such a cross are called *first-generation plants*. All the first-generation plants in this cross had purple flowers. What happened to the trait for white flowers?

Mendel got similar results for each cross. One trait was always present in the first generation, and the other trait seemed to disappear. Mendel called the trait that appeared the **dominant trait**. He called the other trait the **recessive trait**. To *recede* means "to go away or back off." To find out what happened to the recessive trait, Mendel did another set of experiments. ☑

# What Happened in Mendel's Second Experiment?

Mendel let the first-generation plants self-pollinate. When a first-generation plant with purple flowers self-pollinated, the recessive trait for white flowers showed up again in the second generation.

Mendel did the same experiment on seven different characteristics. Each time, some of the second-generation plants had the recessive trait.

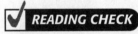

**READING CHECK**

**8. Identify** What kind of trait appeared in the first generation?

_____

_____

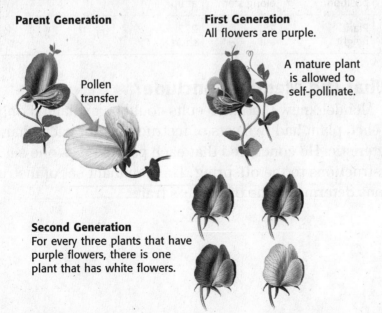

**Parent Generation**

Pollen transfer

**First Generation**
All flowers are purple.

A mature plant is allowed to self-pollinate.

**Second Generation**
For every three plants that have purple flowers, there is one plant that has white flowers.

**TAKE A LOOK**
**9. Identify** What type of trait reappeared in the second generation?

_____

_____

## RATIOS IN MENDEL'S EXPERIMENTS

Mendel counted the number of plants that had each trait in the second generation. He hoped that this would help him explain his results.

As you can see, the recessive trait did not show up as often as the dominant trait. Mendel decided to figure out the ratio of the dominant traits to the recessive traits. A *ratio* is a relationship between two different numbers. It is often written as a fraction. For example, the second generation produced 705 plants with purple flowers and 224 plants with white flowers. Mendel used this formula to calculate the ratios:

$$705/224 = 3.15/1 \text{ or } 3.15:1$$

| Characteristic | Dominant trait | Recessive trait | Ratio |
|---|---|---|---|
| Flower color | 705 purple | 224 white | 3.15:1 |
| Seed color | 6,002 yellow | 2,001 green | |
| Seed shape | 5,474 round | 1,850 wrinkled | |
| Pod color | 428 green | 152 yellow | |
| Pod shape | 882 smooth | 299 bumpy | |
| Flower position | 651 along stem | 207 at tip | |
| Plant height | 787 tall | 277 short | |

## Math Focus

**10. Find Ratios** Calculate the missing ratios of the pea plant characteristics in the table.

**11. Round** Round off all the numbers in the ratios to whole numbers. What ratio do you get?

## What Did Mendel Conclude?

Mendel knew that his results could be explained only if each plant had two sets of instructions for each characteristic. He concluded that each parent gives one set of instructions to the offspring. The dominant set of instructions determines the offspring's traits.

# Section 1 Review

7.2.d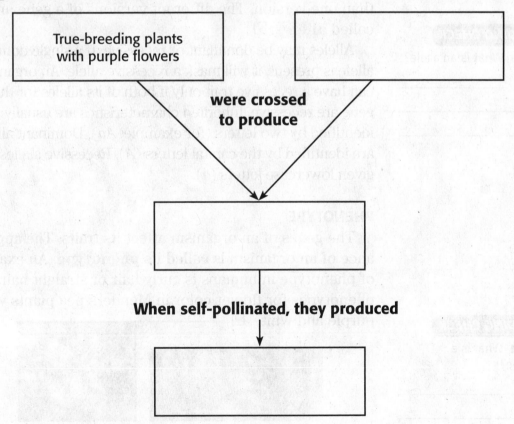

## SECTION VOCABULARY

| | |
|---|---|
| **dominant trait** the trait observed in the first generation when parents that have different traits are bred<br>**heredity** the passing of genetic traits from parent to offspring | **recessive trait** a trait that reappears in the second generation after disappearing in the first generation when parents with different traits are bred |

**1. Explain** Why isn't blended inheritance a good explanation of heredity?

_____

_____

_____

**2. Apply Concepts** Cats may have straight or curly ears. A cat with curly ears mated with a straight-eared cat. All the kittens had curly ears. Are curly ears a dominant or recessive trait? Explain your answer.

_____

_____

**3. Summarize** Complete the Cause-and-Effect Map to summarize Mendel's experiments on flower color in pea plants.

```
┌─────────────────────┐        ┌─────────────────────┐
│  True-breeding plants│        │                     │
│  with purple flowers │        │                     │
└─────────────────────┘        └─────────────────────┘
            │                              │
            │        were crossed          │
            │         to produce           │
            └──────────────┬───────────────┘
                           ▼
                ┌─────────────────────┐
                │                     │
                │                     │
                └─────────────────────┘
                           │
              When self-pollinated, they produced
                           │
                           ▼
                ┌─────────────────────┐
                │                     │
                │                     │
                └─────────────────────┘
```

**CHAPTER 6** Heredity

**SECTION 2** Traits and Inheritance

**California Science Standards**

7.2.c., 7.2.d

**BEFORE YOU READ**

After you read this section, you should be able to answer these questions:

• What did Mendel's experiments tell him about heredity?

• Are there exceptions to Mendel's laws of heredity?

• What causes differences among organisms?

**STUDY TIP**

**Organize** As you read, make combination notes. Explain genes, alleles, phenotype, and genotype in both words and pictures or diagrams.

**READING CHECK**

**1. Define** What is an allele?

_____

_____

_____

**READING CHECK**

**2. Define** What is a phenotype?

_____

_____

_____

## What Did Mendel Learn About Heredity?

Mendel knew from his pea plant experiments that there must be two sets of instructions for each characteristic. All of the first-generation plants showed the dominant trait. However, they could give the recessive trait to their offspring. Today, scientists call these instructions for inherited characteristics **genes**. Offspring have two sets of genes—one from each parent.

The two sets of genes that parents give to offspring are never exactly the same. The same gene might have more than one version. The different versions of a gene are called **alleles**. ☑

Alleles may be dominant or recessive. If a single dominant allele is present, it will mask a recessive allele. An organism can have a recessive trait only if both of its alleles for the gene are recessive. Inherited characteristics are usually identified by two letters (for example, *Aa*). Dominant alleles are identified by the capital letters (*A*). Recessive alleles are given lowercase letters (*a*).

### PHENOTYPE

The genes of an organism affect its traits. The appearance of an organism is called its **phenotype**. An example of phenotype in humans is curly hair or straight hair. The phenotypes for flower color in Mendel's pea plants were purple and white. ☑

Purple flowers and white flowers are the two possible phenotypes for the characteristic of flower color in pea plants

**SECTION 2** Traits and Inheritance *continued*

## GENOTYPE

The two alleles present for a trait make up an organism's **genotype**. A plant with two dominant or two recessive alleles (*PP* or *pp*) is said to be *homozygous*. *Homo* means "the same." A plant that has the genotype *Pp* is said to be *heterozygous*. *Hetero* means "different." Because the allele for purple flowers (*P*) is dominant, only one *P* allele is needed for a plant to have purple flowers. ☑

## PUNNETT SQUARES

A Punnett square is used to predict the possible genotypes of offspring from certain parents. In a Punnett square, the alleles for one parent are written along the top of the square. The alleles for the other parent are written along the side of the square. The possible genotypes of the offspring are found by combining the letters at the top and side of each square.

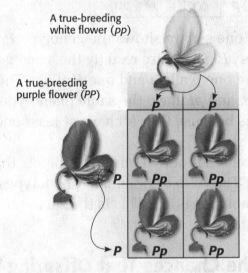

A true-breeding
white flower (*pp*)

A true-breeding
purple flower (*PP*)

|  | *P* | *P* |
|---|---|---|
| *P* | *Pp* | *Pp* |
| *P* | *Pp* | *Pp* |

All of the offspring for this cross have the same genotype—*Pp*.

The figure shows a Punnett square for a cross of two true-breeding plants. One has purple flowers and the other has white flowers. The alleles for a true-breeding purple-flowered plant are written as *PP*. The alleles for a true-breeding white flowered plant are written as *pp*. Offspring get one of their two alleles from each parent. All of the offspring from this cross will have the same genotype: *Pp*. Because they have a dominant allele, all of the offspring will have purple flowers.

### READING CHECK

**3. Identify** What kind of alleles does a heterozygous individual have?

_____

_____

_____

### TAKE A LOOK

**4. Identify** Is the plant with white flowers homozygous or heterozygous? How can you tell?

_____

_____

_____

## MORE EVIDENCE FOR INHERITANCE

In his next experiments, Mendel let the first-generation plants self-pollinate. He did this by covering the flowers of the plant. This way, no pollen from another plant could fertilize its eggs. The Punnett square below shows a cross of a plant with the genotype *Pp* that self-pollinated.

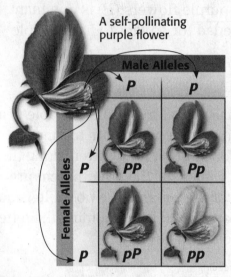

A self-pollinating purple flower

This Punnett square shows the possible results from the cross *Pp × Pp*.

## TAKE A LOOK
**5. List** What are the possible genotypes of the offspring in this cross?

_____

_____

Notice that one square shows the genotype *Pp* and another shows *pP*. These are exactly the same genotype. They both have one *p* allele and one *P* allele. The combinations *PP*, *Pp*, and *pP* have the same phenotype—purple flowers. This is because they all have at least one dominant allele, *P.* ☑

Only one combination, *pp*, produces plants that have white flowers. The ratio of dominant phenotypes to recessive phenotypes is 3:1. This is the same ratio Mendel found.

## READING CHECK
**6. Explain** Why do the genotypes *PP, Pp,* and *pP* all have the same phenotype?

_____

_____

_____

## What Are the Chances That Offspring Will Receive a Certain Allele?

Each parent has two alleles for each gene. When it reproduces, it will pass one of them to its offspring. When these alleles are different, as in *Pp*, offspring are equally likely to receive either of the alleles. Think of a coin toss. When you toss the coin, there is a 50% chance you will get heads and a 50% chance you will get tails. The chance of the offspring receiving one allele or the other is as random as a coin toss.

**SECTION 2** Traits and Inheritance *continued*

## PROBABILITY

The mathematical chance that something will happen is known as **probability**. Probability is usually written as a fraction or percentage. If you toss a coin, the probability of getting tails is 1/2, or 50%. You will get tails half of the time.

To find the probability that you will get two heads in a row, multiply the probability of tossing the first head (1/2) by the probability of tossing the second head (1/2). The probability of tossing two heads in a row is 1/4.

## GENOTYPE PROBABILITY

Finding the probability of certain genotypes for offspring is like predicting the results of a coin toss. To have white flowers, a pea plant must receive a *p* allele from each parent. Each offspring of a *Pp* × *Pp* cross has a 50% chance of receiving either allele from either parent. So, the probability of inheriting two *p* alleles is 1/2 × 1/2, which equals 1/4, or 25%.

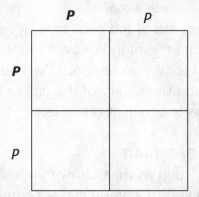

## Are There Exceptions to Mendel's Principles?

Mendel's experiments helped show the basic principles of how genes are passed from one generation to the next. Mendel studied sets of traits such as flower color and seed shape. The traits he studied in pea plants are easy to predict because there are only two choices for each trait. ☑

Traits in other organisms are often harder to predict. Some traits are affected by more than one gene. A single gene may affect more than one trait. As scientists learned more about heredity, they found exceptions to Mendel's principles.

## Math Focus
**7. Complete** Fill in the Punnett square to show the cross between two heterozygous parents. What percentage of the offspring are homozygous?

_____

_____

**✓ READING CHECK**

**8. Explain** Why were color and seed shape in pea plants good traits for Mendel to study?

_____

_____

_____

## ONE GENE, MANY TRAITS

In Mendel's studies, one gene controlled one trait. However, some genes affect more than one trait. For example, the genetic disorder known as sickle cell anemia is caused by an allele of a single gene. This gene carries instructions for the shape of a protein in red blood cells. When a person has an allele for sickle cell disease, this protein has the wrong shape. This causes the red blood cells to be a different shape than normal red blood cells.

*Critical Thinking*

**9. Explain** How is the gene involved in sickle cell anemia different from the genes for pea plant traits that Mendel studied?

_____

_____

_____

_____

_____

_____

Sickle-shaped red blood cells cannot carry oxygen as well as normal red blood cells. Also, they tend to get stuck in small blood vessels. Both the ability of the cell to carry oxygen and the ability of the cell to move through the body is affected by just one allele.

## MANY GENES, ONE TRAIT

Some traits, such as the color of your skin, hair, or eyes, are the result of several genes acting together. Another characteristic affected by more than one gene is your height. In humans, different combinations of many alleles can result in a variety of heights. ☑

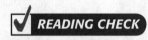
**READING CHECK**

**10. Identify** Give an example of a single trait that is affected by more than one gene.

_____

## IMPORTANCE OF ENVIRONMENT

Genes are not the only things that affect traits in organisms. Traits are also affected by factors in the environment. For example, human height is affected by many genes, but it is also influenced by nutrition. An individual who has plenty of food to eat may be taller than one who does not.

**SECTION 2** Traits and Inheritance *continued*

Would you believe that these grasshoppers are from the same species? They have a different color pattern because they ate different food when they were young. Some grasshoppers eat certain plants that make them poisonous to predators. These grasshoppers have a yellow and black color pattern. Grasshoppers that eat other kinds of plants are not poisonous. They have a green coloration.

## Do the Same Kinds of Organisms Have the Same Set of Genes?

How many genes do you have? Would you guess that you have a hundred or a thousand genes? Scientists estimate that humans have around 30,000 genes! For most genes, a person has two versions, or alleles. There are many ways these alleles can combine in a single person. One reason people look different from each other is that they do not have the same set of alleles. ☑

The differences between the sets of alleles in individuals in a population are called *genetic variation*. Genetic variation is found in many organisms. The many breeds of dogs are an example of this variation. Genetic variation in corn snakes is shown below.

Genetic variation explains why these corn snakes are different colors.

**TAKE A LOOK**
**11. Infer** One of these grasshoppers is poisonous and one is not. Circle the grasshopper you think is poisonous. Explain your answer.

_____
_____
_____
_____
_____

**READING CHECK**
**12. Explain** What is one reason people look different from each other?

_____
_____
_____

# Section 2 Review

7.2.c, 7.2.d

## SECTION VOCABULARY

| | |
|---|---|
| **allele** one of the alternative forms of a gene that governs a characteristic, such as hair color | **phenotype** an organism's appearance or other detectable characteristic |
| **gene** one set of instructions for an inherited trait | **probability** the likelihood that a possible future event will occur in any given instance of the event |
| **genotype** the entire genetic makeup of an organism; also the combination of genes for one or more specific traits | |

**1. Identify Relationships** How are genes and alleles related?

_____

_____

**2. Explain** How is it possible for two individuals to have the same phenotype but different genotypes for a trait?

_____

_____

_____

**3. Complete** Mendel allowed a pea plant that was heterozygous for yellow seeds (*Yy*) to self-pollinate. Fill in the Punnett square below for this cross. *Y* identifies yellow seeds, and *y* identifies green seeds. What percentage of the offspring will have green seeds?

_____

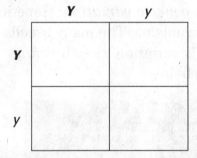

**4. Discuss** Why is human height an exception to Mendel's principles of heredity?

_____

_____

_____

_____

## BEFORE YOU READ

After you read this section, you should be able to answer these questions:

• What is a sex cell?

• How are sex cells made?

• How does meiosis help explain Mendel's results?

**California Science Standards**

7.2.b, 7.2.e

## How Do Offspring Get Their Genetic Information?

When organisms reproduce, their genetic information is passed on to their offspring. This information is in the form of a chemical called DNA.

In sexual reproduction, two parents each give genetic information to their offspring. Before this happens, both parents must reduce their genetic information by half. That way, when the genetic information of the two parents is combined, the offspring will have the same amount as each parent. Genetic information is located on structures called *chromosomes*.

**STUDY TIP**

**Summarize** As you read, make a diagram that shows the steps of meiosis.

### CHROMOSOME NUMBERS

Most species have a certain number of chromosomes in their body cells. For example, human cells usually have 46 chromosomes. Corn cells usually have 20 chromosomes. Dog cells usually have 78 chromosomes. Most of the time, the chromosomes are spread out in long, thin strands. They cannot be seen with a microscope. However, when a cell divides, the chromosomes get shorter and thicker. Then they can be seen with a microscope.

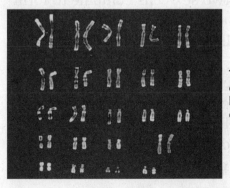

This image shows the chromosomes in a human body cell during cell division.

## TAKE A LOOK

**1. Identify** How many pairs of chromosomes are in each human body cell?

_____

**2. Identify** How many total chromosomes are in each human body cell?

_____

**SECTION 3** Meiosis *continued*

## Homologous Chromosomes

Organisms that reproduce sexually have two kinds of cells, body cells and sex cells. Most of your cells are body cells. In body cells, the chromosomes are found in pairs. Each member of the pair has a similar structure. They carry similar genetic information.

Chromosomes that carry the same set of genes are called **homologous chromosomes**. These chromosomes carry the same genes, but they may have different versions, or alleles, for those genes. ☑

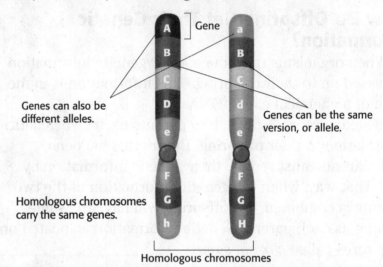

Genes can also be different alleles.

Genes can be the same version, or allele.

Homologous chromosomes carry the same genes.

Homologous chromosomes

## What Is a Sex Cell?

Cells that have pairs of homologous chromosomes are called **diploid**. Body cells are diploid cells. However, before an organism can reproduce sexually, it must make *sex cells*. Sex cells do not have homologous chromosomes.

When sex cells are made, homologous chromosomes separate from one another. So, each sex cell has only one copy of each gene, instead of two. A cell that does not have homologous chromosomes is called **haploid**. Sex cells are haploid cells.

In sexual reproduction, two sex cells combine to form a new individual. Males produce sex cells called *sperm*. Females make sex cells called *eggs*. Sperm and eggs are haploid cells.

Fertilization happens when a sperm cell and an egg cell join. When the two haploid cells join, a diploid cell is formed. This new diploid cell has homologous chromosomes. The diploid cell can divide and produce more diploid cells by mitosis. These cells can grow into a new organism.

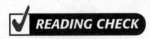

**READING CHECK**

**3. Define** What are homologous chromosomes?

_____

_____

_____

_____

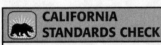

**CALIFORNIA STANDARDS CHECK**

**7.2.b** Students know that <u>sexual</u> reproduction produces offspring that inherit half their genes from each parent.

**Word Help: <u>sexual</u>** having to do with sex

**4. Explain** Where do the homologous chromosomes in a diploid cell come from?

_____

_____

_____

_____

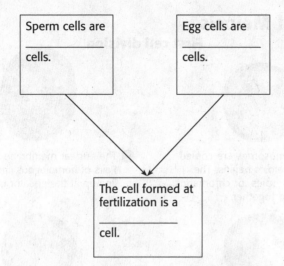

Sperm cells are
_____
cells.

Egg cells are
_____
cells.

The cell formed at
fertilization is a
_____
cell.

**TAKE A LOOK**
**5. Complete** Use the words
"haploid" and "diploid" to
complete the organizer.

## How Are Sex Cells Made?

Sex cells are made during meiosis. **Meiosis** is a copying process that produces cells with half the usual number of chromosomes. In meiosis, each sex cell that is
made gets only one chromosome from each homologous
pair. For example, a human egg cell has 23 chromosomes.
A sperm cell also has 23 chromosomes. When human
sex cells join together, the new cell that forms has
46 chromosomes.

## Why Is Meiosis Important?

Meiosis is necessary for all organisms that carry out
sexual reproduction. It is important because it keeps
the chromosome number the same from one generation
to the next. Just one extra chromosome in a cell can be
harmful for an individual. ☑

When two sex cells join during fertilization, all of the
sperm's chromosomes combine with all of the egg's chromosomes. The new cell has twice the number of chromosomes as each of the sex cells.

If the sex cells were diploid, the number of chromosomes would double in every generation. For example,
if each human sex cell had 46 chromosomes, each cell in
the offspring would have 92 chromosomes. How many
chromosomes would there be in each cell of the next
generation?

*Critical Thinking*
**6. Predict** What would
happen if sex cells were not
haploid?

_____
_____
_____
_____
_____
_____

☑ **READING CHECK**
**7. Define** What is the
function of meiosis?

_____
_____
_____
_____
_____

# Steps of Meiosis

## First cell division

**1** The chromosomes are copied before meiosis begins. The identical copies, or chromatids, are joined together.

**2** The nuclear membrane disappears. Pairs of homologous chromosomes line up at the equator of the cell.

## TAKE A LOOK
**8. Identify** How many times does the cell nucleus divide during meiosis?

_____

_____

**3** The chromosomes separate from their homologous partners. Then they move to the opposite ends of the cell.

**4** The nuclear membranes re-form, and the cell divides. The paired chromatids are still joined.

## Second cell division

**5** Each cell contains one member of the homologous chromosome pair. The chromosomes are not copied again between the two cell divisions.

**6** The nuclear membrane disappears. The chromosomes line up along the equator of each cell.

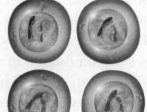

## TAKE A LOOK
**9. Identify** At the end of meiosis, how many sex cells have been produced from one cell?

_____

_____

**7** The chromatids pull apart and move to opposite ends of the cell. The nuclear membranes re-form, and the cells divide.

**8** Four new haploid cells have formed from the original diploid cell. Each new cell has half as many chromosomes as the original cell.

**SECTION 3** Meiosis *continued*

# How Does Meiosis Explain Mendel's Results?

The steps in meiosis explain why Mendel got his results. The figure below shows what happens to chromosomes during meiosis and fertilization in pea plants. The cross shown is between two true-breeding plants. One produces round seeds, and the other produces wrinkled seeds.

## Meiosis and Dominance

**Male Parent** In the plant cell nucleus below, each homologous chromosome has an allele for seed shape. Each allele carries the same instructions: to make wrinkled seeds.

**Female Parent** In the plant cell nucleus below, each homologous chromosome has an allele for seed shape. Each allele carries the same instructions: to make round seeds.

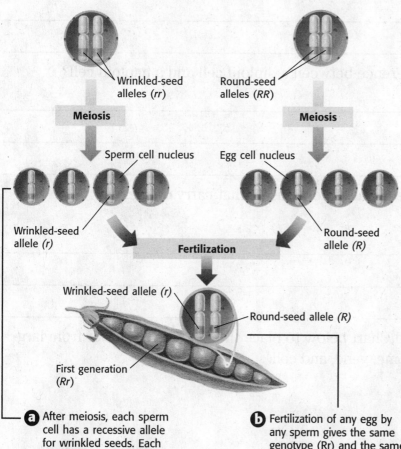

Wrinkled-seed alleles (*rr*)

Round-seed alleles (*RR*)

Meiosis

Meiosis

Sperm cell nucleus

Egg cell nucleus

Wrinkled-seed allele (*r*)

Round-seed allele (*R*)

**Fertilization**

Wrinkled-seed allele (*r*)

Round-seed allele (*R*)

First generation (*Rr*)

ⓐ After meiosis, each sperm cell has a recessive allele for wrinkled seeds. Each egg cell has a dominant allele for round seeds.

ⓑ Fertilization of any egg by any sperm gives the same genotype (Rr) and the same phenotype (round). This result is exactly what Mendel found in his studies.

**TAKE A LOOK**
**10. Explain** How many genotypes are possible for the offspring? Explain your answer.

_____

_____

_____

_____

_____

_____

# Section 3 Review

7.2.b, 7.2.e

## SECTION VOCABULARY

| | |
|---|---|
| **diploid** a cell that contains two haploid sets of chromosomes<br><br>  <u>Wordwise</u> The root *dipl* means "twice" or "double."<br><br>**haploid** describes a cell, nucleus, or organism that has only one set of unpaired chromosomes | **homologous chromosomes** chromosomes that have the same sequence of genes and the same structure<br><br>**meiosis** a process in cell division during which the number of chromosomes decreases to half the original number by two divisions of the nucleus, which results in the production of sex cells (gametes or spores) |

**1. Identify** Is a sex cell a diploid cell or a haploid cell?

_____

_____

_____

**2. Compare** What is the difference between a diploid cell and a haploid cell?

_____

_____

_____

**3. Explain** Why is meiosis necessary in organisms that carry out sexual reproduction?

_____

_____

**4. Organize** Use the Pyramid Chart below to place the following in order from largest to smallest: chromosome, gene, and cell.

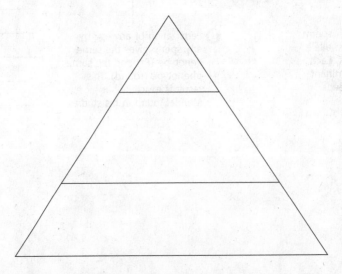

## SECTION 1 What Does DNA Look Like?

**California Science Standards**

7.2.e

---

**BEFORE YOU READ**

After you read this section, you should be able to answer these questions:

• What units make up DNA?

• What does DNA look like?

• How does DNA copy itself?

---

## What Is DNA?

Genes determine the inherited traits of organisms. Genes are located on chromosomes inside cells. *Chromosomes* are made of protein and DNA, or *deoxyribonucleic acid*. **DNA** is the genetic material of living things.

## What Is DNA Made Of?

DNA is made up of many repeating units called **nucleotides**. A nucleotide contains a sugar, a phosphate, and a base. The sugar and the phosphate are the same for every nucleotide. However, each nucleotide has one of four different bases.

The four bases found in DNA nucleotides are *adenine*, *thymine*, *guanine*, and *cytosine*. Scientists often refer to a base by its first letter: A for adenine, T for thymine, G for guanine, and C for cytosine. Each base has a different shape.

**The Four Nucleotides of DNA**

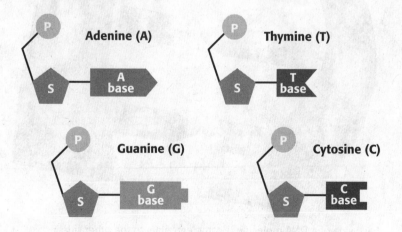

Adenine (A)

Thymine (T)

Guanine (G)

Cytosine (C)

---

**STUDY TIP**

**Define** When you come across a word you don't know, circle it. When you figure out what it means, write the word and its definition in your notebook.

**TAKE A LOOK**

**1. Identify** What are two things that are the same in all nucleotides?

_____

_____

_____

---

SECTION 1 What Does DNA Look Like? *continued*

## What Does DNA Look Like?

As you can see in the figure below, the DNA molecule looks like a twisted ladder. This spiral shape is called a *double helix*. The two sides of the ladder are made of the sugar and phosphate parts of nucleotides. The sugars and phosphates alternate along each side of the ladder. The rungs of the DNA ladder are made of pairs of bases. ☑

The bases in DNA can fit together only in certain ways. Adenine on one side of a DNA rung always pairs with thymine on the other side. Guanine always pairs with cytosine. This means that adenine is *complementary* to thymine, and guanine is complementary to cytosine. Because the pairs of bases in DNA are complementary, the two sides of the DNA molecule are also complementary.

✓ **READING CHECK**

**2. Identify** What are the sides of the DNA "ladder" made of?

_____

_____

*Critical Thinking*

**3. Apply Concepts** Imagine that you are a scientist studying DNA. You measure the number of cytosines and thymines in a small strand of DNA. There are 45 cytosines and 55 thymines. How many guanines are there in the strand? How many adenines are there?

_____

_____

**TAKE A LOOK**

**4. Identify** How can DNA bases pair up?

_____

_____

_____

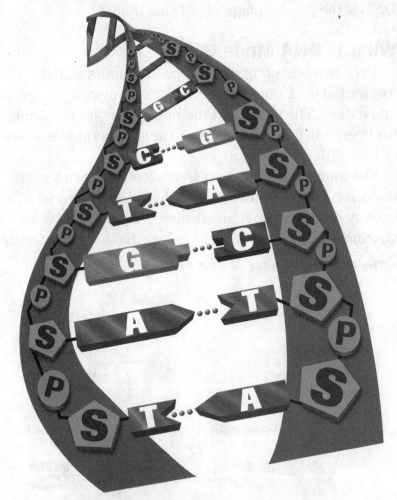

Each side of a DNA molecule is complementary to the other side.

**SECTION 1** What Does DNA Look Like? *continued*

## How Does DNA Copy Itself?

Before a cell divides, it makes a copy of its genetic information. The pairing of bases allows the cell to *replicate*, or make copies of, DNA. Remember that bases are complementary and can fit together only in certain ways. Therefore, the order of bases on one side of the DNA controls the order of bases on the other side. For example, the base order CGAC can fit only with the complementary base order GCTG. ☑

When DNA replicates, the double helix splits in the middle, and the pairs of bases separate. The unpaired bases attract new complementary bases. This action builds a new complementary strand of nucleotides on each side of the split. Finally, two DNA molecules are formed. Half of each one, that is, one strand, comes from the original molecule. The other strand is built from new nucleotides.

✔ READING CHECK
**5. Explain** What happens to genetic information before a cell divides?
_____
_____

The DNA molecule splits down the middle. Two identical DNA molecules form from the strands of the original molecule.

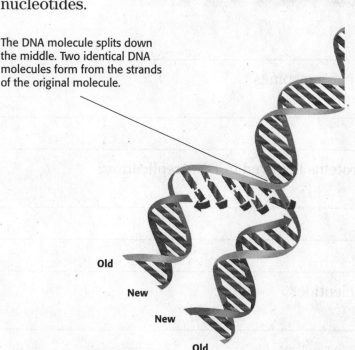

Old

New

New

Old

**TAKE A LOOK**
**6. Compare** What is the difference between an "old" and a "new" strand of DNA?
_____
_____
_____

DNA is copied every time a cell divides. Each new cell gets a complete copy of all of the cell's DNA. Proteins in the cell unwind, copy, and rewind the DNA. Other proteins help with the job of carrying out the instructions found in DNA. Therefore, DNA is usually found with several kinds of proteins.

# Section 1 Review

7.2.e

## SECTION VOCABULARY

| | |
|---|---|
| **DNA** deoxyribonucleic acid, a molecule that is present in all living cells and that contains the information that determines the traits that a living thing inherits and needs to live | **nucleotide** in a nucleic-acid chain, a subunit that consists of a sugar, a phosphate, and a nitrogenous base |

**1. Compare** How are the four kinds of DNA nucleotides different from each other?

_____

_____

**2. Apply Concepts** The diagram shows part of a DNA molecule. Using the order of bases in the top strand, write the letters of the bases that belong on the bottom strand.

_____

**3. Describe** How is DNA related to chromosomes?

_____

_____

**4. Identify Relationships** How are proteins involved in DNA replication?

_____

_____

_____

**5. List** What are three parts of a nucleotide?

_____

_____

_____

**6. Explain** What happens when DNA replicates?

_____

_____

_____

_____

CHAPTER 7 | Genes and DNA

SECTION
**2** **How DNA Works**

**BEFORE YOU READ**

After you read this section, you should be able to answer these questions:

• What does DNA look like in different cells?
• How does DNA help make proteins?
• What happens if a gene changes?

**California Science Standards**

7.1.a, 7.2.e

## What Does DNA in Cells Look Like?

The human body contains trillions of cells. Most cells are very small and can be seen only with a microscope. A typical skin cell, for example, has a diameter of about 0.0025 cm. However, almost every cell contains about 2 m of DNA. How can 2 m of DNA fit into the nucleus of such a small cell?

Large amounts of DNA can fit inside a cell because the DNA is tightly bundled by proteins. The proteins found with DNA help support the structure and function of DNA. Together, the DNA and the proteins it winds around make up a chromosome.

**STUDY TIP**

**Clarify Concepts** As you read the text, make a list of ideas that are confusing. Discuss these with a small group. Ask your teacher to explain things that your group is unsure about.

**CALIFORNIA STANDARDS CHECK**

**7.2.e** Students know DNA (deoxyribonucleic acid) is the genetic material of living organisms and is located in the chromosomes of each cell.

**1. Identify** What are two things that are found in a chromosome?

_____

_____

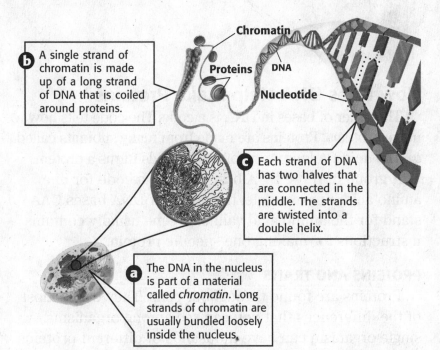

**b** A single strand of chromatin is made up of a long strand of DNA that is coiled around proteins.

**Chromatin**

**Proteins** **DNA**

**Nucleotide**

**c** Each strand of DNA has two halves that are connected in the middle. The strands are twisted into a double helix.

**a** The DNA in the nucleus is part of a material called *chromatin*. Long strands of chromatin are usually bundled loosely inside the nucleus.

**TAKE A LOOK**
**2. Describe** What is chromatin made of?

_____

_____

## DNA IN DIVIDING CELLS

When a cell divides, its genetic material is spread equally into each of the two new cells. How can each of the new cells receive a full set of genetic material? It is possible because DNA replicates before a cell divides.

Remember that when DNA replicates, the strand of DNA splits down the middle. New strands are made when nucleotide bases bind to the exposed strands. Each of the new strands is identical to the original DNA strand. This is because the DNA bases can join only in certain ways. A always pairs with T, and C always pairs with G.

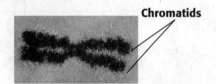

When a cell is ready to divide, it has already copied its DNA. The copies stay attached as two chromatids. The two identical chromatids form a chromosome.

**Chromatin**

**Chromatids**

## How Does DNA Help Make Proteins?

The order of bases in DNA is a code. The code tells how to make proteins. Proteins are made from many subunits called *amino acids*. A long string of amino acids forms a protein.

A group of three DNA bases acts as a code for one amino acid. For example, the group of DNA bases CAA stand for the amino acid valine. A gene usually contains instructions for making one specific protein.

### PROTEINS AND TRAITS

Proteins are found throughout cells. They cause most of the differences that you can see among organisms. A single organism can have thousands of different proteins.

Proteins act as chemical messengers for many of the activities in cells. They help determine traits, such as the color of your eyes and how tall you will grow.

*Critical Thinking*

**3. Predict Consequences** Imagine that DNA did not replicate before cell division. What would happen to the amount of DNA in each of the new cells formed during cell division?

_____

_____

_____

_____

**TAKE A LOOK**

**4. Identify** How many chromatids make up a chromosome?

_____

_____

*Math Focus*

**5. Calculate** How many DNA bases are needed to code for five amino acids?

_____

_____

## HELP FROM RNA

**RNA**, or *ribonucleic acid*, is a chemical that helps DNA make proteins. RNA is similar to DNA. It can act as a temporary copy of part of a DNA strand. One difference between DNA and RNA is that RNA contains the base *uracil* instead of thymine. Uracil is often referred to as U. ☑

## How Are Proteins Made in Cells?

The first step in making a protein is to copy one side of part of the DNA. This mirrorlike copy is made of RNA. It is called *messenger RNA* (mRNA). It moves out of the nucleus and into the cytoplasm of the cell.

**6. Identify** What is one difference between RNA and DNA?

_____

_____

_____

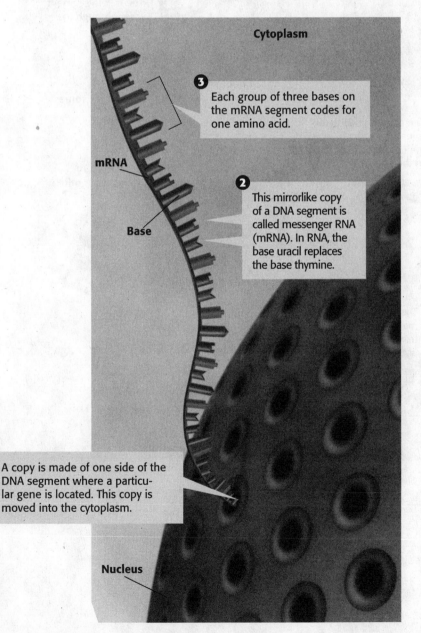

Cytoplasm

**3** Each group of three bases on the mRNA segment codes for one amino acid.

mRNA

Base

**2** This mirrorlike copy of a DNA segment is called messenger RNA (mRNA). In RNA, the base uracil replaces the base thymine.

**1** A copy is made of one side of the DNA segment where a particular gene is located. This copy is moved into the cytoplasm.

Nucleus

**TAKE A LOOK**

**7. Compare** How does the shape of RNA differ from the shape of DNA?

_____

_____

_____

**SECTION 2** How DNA Works *continued*

## RIBOSOMES

In the cytoplasm, the messenger RNA enters a protein assembly line. The "factory" that runs this assembly line is a ribosome. A **ribosome** is a cell organelle composed of RNA and protein. The mRNA moves through a ribosome as a protein is made.

*Critical Thinking*

**8. Explain** Proteins are made in the cytoplasm, but DNA never leaves the nucleus of a cell. How does DNA control how proteins are made?

_____

_____

_____

_____

_____

_____

_____

**TAKE A LOOK**
**9. Identify** What does tRNA do?

_____

_____

_____

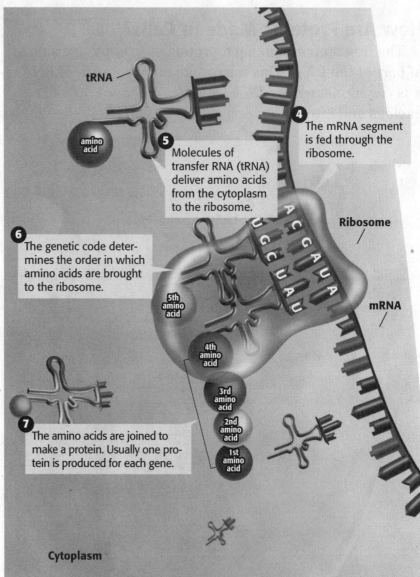

tRNA

amino acid

**5** Molecules of transfer RNA (tRNA) deliver amino acids from the cytoplasm to the ribosome.

**4** The mRNA segment is fed through the ribosome.

Ribosome

**6** The genetic code determines the order in which amino acids are brought to the ribosome.

mRNA

5th amino acid

4th amino acid

3rd amino acid

2nd amino acid

1st amino acid

**7** The amino acids are joined to make a protein. Usually one protein is produced for each gene.

Cytoplasm

# What Happens If Genes Change?

Read this sentence: "Put the book on the desk." Does it make sense? What about this sentence: "Rut the zook in the tesk."? Changing only a few letters in a sentence can change what the sentence means. It can even keep the sentence from making any sense at all! In a similar way, even small changes in a DNA sequence can affect the protein that the DNA codes for. A change in the nucleotide-base sequence of DNA is called a **mutation**.

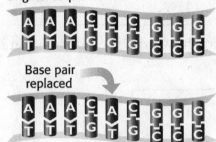

Original sequence

Base pair replaced

**TAKE A LOOK**
**10. Compare** What happens to the bottom strand of DNA when there is a change in a base on the top strand?

_____

_____

Some mutations happen because of mistakes when DNA is copied. Other mutations happen when something in the environment damages DNA. Things that can cause mutations are called *mutagens*. Examples of mutagens include X-rays and ultraviolet radiation. Ultraviolet radiation is one type of energy in sunlight. It can cause suntans and sunburns.

Mutations can cause changes in traits. Some mutations produce new traits that can help an organism survive. For example, a mutation might allow an organism to survive with less water. If there is a drought, the organism will be more likely to survive.

Many mutations produce traits that make an organism less likely to survive. For example, a mutation might make an animal a brighter color. This might make the animal easier for predators to find.

Some mutations are neither helpful nor harmful. These mutations may not affect the protein that a gene codes for. If a mutation does not cause a change in a protein, then the mutation will not help or hurt the organism.

Cells make proteins that can find and fix mutations. However, not all mutations can be fixed. If a mutation happens in egg or sperm cells, the changed gene can be passed from one generation to the next.

**Say It**

**Brainstorm** Whether a mutation is helpful or harmful to an organism often depends on the organism's environment. In a group, discuss how the same mutation could be helpful in one environment but harmful in another.

# Section 2 Review

7.1.a, 7.2.e

## SECTION VOCABULARY

| | |
|---|---|
| **mutation** a change in the nucleotide-base sequence of a gene or DNA molecule <br><br> <u>Wordwise</u> The root *mut* means "to change." Another example is *mutant*. | **ribosome** a cell organelle composed of RNA and protein; the site of protein synthesis <br><br> **RNA** ribonucleic acid, a molecule that is present in all living cells and that plays a role in protein production |

**1. Identify** What structures in cells contain DNA and proteins?

_____

**2. Calculate** How many amino acids can a sequence of 24 DNA bases code for?

_____

**3. Explain** Fill in the Flow Chart below to show how the information in the DNA code becomes a protein.

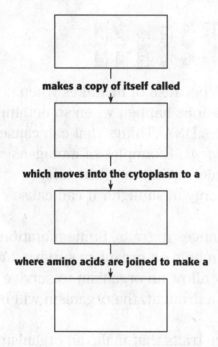

makes a copy of itself called

which moves into the cytoplasm to a

where amino acids are joined to make a

**4. Describe** How can a mutation in a DNA base sequence cause a change in a protein?

_____

_____

_____

**5. Draw Conclusions** How can a mutation in a DNA base sequence cause a change in a trait?

_____

_____

_____

**CHAPTER 8** Studying Earth's Past
**SECTION 1**

# The Study of Earth's History

After you read this section, you should be able to answer these questions:

• How fast does Earth change?

• How do paleontologists use fossils?

**California Science Standards**
7.4.a, 7.4.b, 7.4.e

## How Fast Does Earth Change?

Where do rocks come from? How do mountains form? How does Earth change? Have you ever wondered about these things? Through history, many people have studied how Earth changes. Many different ideas have been put forward to explain how Earth changes with time.

Until about 200 years ago, most people believed that Earth changes because of sudden events, such as floods. The belief that Earth changes only because of sudden events is called **catastrophism**. However, scientists soon began to realize that catastrophism could not explain all of their observations about the things that happen on Earth.

### SLOW CHANGES

During the late 1700s, scientists began to observe that most changes on Earth happen very slowly. They reasoned that the slow processes that shape Earth now have been the same through all of Earth's history. Over a very long time, the small changes have added up to form the features we see on Earth today. The theory that the Earth changes only because of small changes over long periods of time is called **uniformitarianism**.

| Catastrophism | |
|---|---|
| Uniformitarianism | |

By the mid-1800s, most scientists accepted uniformitarianism. However, they also saw that sudden events can change Earth's surface. For example, large floods can cause a lot of erosion in a short period of time. These observations helped scientists to realize that not all changes on Earth happen slowly.

**STUDY TIP**
**Graphic Organizer** As you read this section, make a table comparing catastrophism, uniformitarianism, and modern ideas about how Earth changes.

*Critical Thinking*
**1. Identify Evidence** What very slow processes might scientists have observed to make them understand that Earth changes slowly? Give two examples.

_____

_____

**TAKE A LOOK**
**2. Identify** Fill in the blank spaces in the table to show how catastrophism is different from uniformitarianism.

## SLOW CHANGES AND SUDDEN EVENTS

Today, scientists understand that neither catastrophism nor uniformitarianism is completely correct. Most geologic change is slow, but sudden changes happen sometimes.

Sudden changes can have short-term or long-term effects. The wind from a hurricane affects only a small part of Earth for a short time. However, the impact of a comet on Earth may put clouds of dust into the atmosphere. These clouds may decrease the temperature everywhere on Earth for many years. ☑

## How Do Scientists Study Earth's Past?

Scientists can use fossils to learn about what Earth was like in the past. A *fossil* is any evidence that life once existed in a place. Some fossils are made from the remains, such as shells, of dead organisms. Other fossils are simply signs, such as footprints, that an organism once existed. The study of fossils and ancient life is called **paleontology**. Scientists who study paleontology are called *paleontologists*.

Fossils provide evidence that life on Earth has changed with time. Different organisms have appeared and disappeared over Earth's history. For example, fossils show that dinosaurs once lived on Earth, even though none are alive today.

Fossils of dinosaurs have been found in many places on Earth. However, no dinosaurs are alive today. The fossils show that the kinds of life on Earth have changed over time.

Fossils also provide evidence that Earth has changed over time. For example, there are fossils of sea life from millions of years ago in deserts and on the tops of mountains. The fossils show that some areas that are now deserts or mountains were once parts of an ocean.

**READING CHECK**

**3. Explain** According to scientists today, how fast do changes on Earth happen?

_____

_____

_____

_____

**CALIFORNIA STANDARDS CHECK**

**7.4.e** Students know fossils provide <u>evidence</u> of how life and <u>environmental</u> conditions have changed.

**Word Help: <u>evidence</u>** information showing whether an idea or belief is true or valid

**Word Help: <u>environment</u>** the surrounding natural conditions that affect an organism

**4. Explain** What are two things that paleontologists can learn from fossils?

_____

_____

_____

_____

# Section 1 Review

7.4.a, 7.4.b, 7.4.e

## SECTION VOCABULARY

| | |
|---|---|
| **catastrophism** a principle that states that geologic change occurs suddenly<br><br>**Wordwise** The prefix *cata-* means "against" or "very." The root *stroph* means "to turn." The suffix *–ism* means "a belief in." | **paleontology** the scientific study of fossils<br><br>**Wordwise** The root *paleon* means "old." The suffix *–ology* means "the science of."<br><br>**uniformitarianism** a principle that geologic processes that occurred in the past can be explained by current geologic processes |

**1. Identify** How can sudden events affect Earth?

_____

_____

**2. Explain** What caused scientists in the 1700s to reason that Earth changes slowly with time?

_____

_____

_____

**3. Define** What is a fossil?

_____

_____

**4. Describe** One kind of fossil forms from the body parts of organisms. What is another kind of fossil that can form?

_____

_____

**5. Apply Concepts** Imagine that you find a layer of rock containing many fossil clams. The layer of rock is in southern California, 50 km from the ocean. The fossils are about 5 million years old. Clams usually live in shallow ocean water. Based on the fossils, what can you guess about the environment in southern California 5 million years ago? Explain your answer.

_____

_____

_____

_____

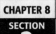

**CHAPTER 8** Studying Earth's Past

**SECTION 2** **Relative Dating**

**California Science Standards**

7.3.c, 7.4.c

> **BEFORE YOU READ**
>
> After you read this section, you should be able to answer these questions:
> • How do sedimentary rocks form?
> • What is relative dating?
> • How can geologists learn how bodies of rock formed?

## What Is the Rock Cycle?

The history of Earth, from its formation to the present, is often called the *geologic record*. It is a record of the changes on Earth through time. The geologic record is made of rocks. Since different kinds of rocks form in different environments, geologists can use rocks to learn what Earth's environment was like in the past.

Geologists divide rocks into three main groups based on how they form. *Igneous rocks* form when melted rock cools and hardens. *Metamorphic rocks* form when rocks change because of temperature or pressure. **Sedimentary rocks** form from pieces of other rocks. Igneous and metamorphic rocks can form deep underground, but sedimentary rocks always form at or near Earth's surface. Therefore, geologists most often use sedimentary rocks to learn how Earth's surface has changed with time. ☑

Rocks can change from one kind to another. For example, sedimentary rocks can melt and then cool to form igneous rocks. Igneous rocks can be put under pressure and change into metamorphic rocks. The *rock cycle* is made up of all of the different ways that rocks can change from one form to another.

**STUDY TIP**

**Compare** In your notebook, make a chart explaining different ways that rock layers can be changed after they form.

**READING CHECK**

1. **Identify** Where do sedimentary rocks form?

_____

_____

**TAKE A LOOK**

2. **List** What are the three main kinds of rock?

_____

_____

_____

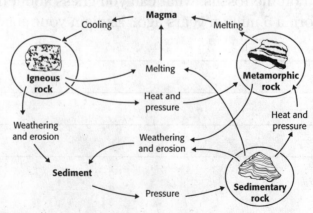

# How Do Sedimentary Rocks Form?

Weathering, erosion, and deposition are important steps in forming sedimentary rocks. *Weathering* happens when a rock is broken into smaller pieces. Physical weathering happens when rocks crack and break. Chemical weathering happens when rocks react with air or water.

Weathering turns rock into sediment. *Sediment* is pieces of rock that are moved over Earth's surface. *Erosion* happens when sediment moves from place to place.

Water, wind, ice, and gravity can move sediment over long or short distances. However, the sediment eventually falls back to Earth's surface. *Deposition* happens when sediment is laid down on Earth's surface. When sediment is laid down, it is usually loose. Therefore, gravity causes the sediment to be laid down in fairly flat layers. ☑

✓ **READING CHECK**

**3. Explain** Why is sediment usually laid down in flat layers?

_____

_____

_____

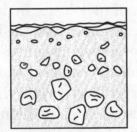
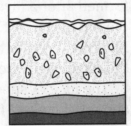

Weathering happens when rocks break down into small pieces called sediment.

Erosion happens when sediment is moved from place to place. Water and other forces can move sediment across Earth's surface.

Deposition happens when sediment is laid down on Earth's surface. Sediment is usually deposited in flat layers.

## ROCK FROM SEDIMENT

After loose sediment is deposited, it may be *lithified*, or hardened, into sedimentary rock. The particles of sediment are pressed together until they stick to one another.

In some cases, dead organisms can be buried in sediment before it hardens. The remains of dead organisms can form fossils in sedimentary rocks. Fossils can help scientists learn what kinds of organisms lived where the sediment was deposited. The rock that forms with a fossil can give clues about the environment that the organism lived in. ☑

During any one period of time, many kinds of rock are forming in different parts of Earth. This has been true through all of Earth's history. Therefore, no one area contains the geologic record for all of Earth.

✓ **READING CHECK**

**4. Describe** What can scientists learn from fossils?

_____

_____

_____

# How Can Geologists Use Sedimentary Rocks to Learn About Earth's Past?

Imagine that you get a newspaper every day. At the end of the day, you stack the day's paper on top of the paper from yesterday. In time, you build up a large stack of newspapers. Where are the oldest newspapers in the pile? Where are the newest ones? The oldest papers are at the bottom of the pile, and the newest ones are at the top.

Layers of sedimentary rock are similar to your stack of newspapers. In most cases, the oldest layers of sedimentary rock are found below the youngest layers. The idea that younger rocks lie above older rocks is called **superposition**.

The idea of superposition can help geologists to learn the order in which different rock layers formed. For example, a layer of rock that is near the top of a cliff formed after a layer of rock lower in the cliff. The layer at the top of the cliff is younger than the layers lower down. Figuring out whether a rock layer is older or younger than the rock layers around it is called **relative dating**.

The idea of superposition can also help geologists learn about the ages of fossils. Each fossil in a rock layer formed from an organism that lived when the sediment was being deposited. Therefore, fossils in a younger rock layer are younger than fossils in an older rock layer.

 **Say It**

**Share Experiences** Have you ever been to a place where you could see many rock layers stacked up? In a group, talk about what you observed.

---

**CALIFORNIA STANDARDS CHECK**

**7.4.c** Students know that the rock cycle includes the formation of new sediment and rocks and that rocks are often found in layers, with the oldest generally on the bottom.

**Word Help: cycle**
a repeating series of events

**Word Help: layer**
a separate or distinct portion of matter that has thickness

**5. Explain** What is relative dating?

_____
_____
_____
_____
_____
_____

**TAKE A LOOK**
**6. Identify** Fill in the blank line in the figure.

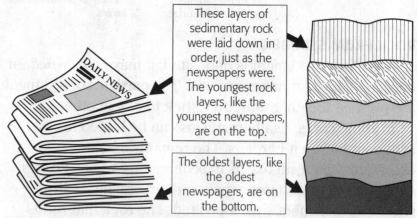

These layers of sedimentary rock were laid down in order, just as the newspapers were. The youngest rock layers, like the youngest newspapers, are on the top.

The oldest layers, like the oldest newspapers, are on the bottom.

The idea of _____ says that rock layers at the bottom of a body of rock are older than layers at the top. Geologists can use this idea to determine the relative age of different rock layers.

Superposition is a very important idea. However, it can be used only if rock layers have not been *disturbed*, or changed, since they formed.

---

# How Can Rock Layers Be Disturbed?

Gravity causes sediment to be deposited in flat, horizontal layers. Flat, horizontal layers of sediment should form flat, horizontal layers of rock. If rock layers are not horizontal, then some force must have disturbed them after they were formed. ☑

## CHANGED ROCK LAYERS

Folding and tilting are two ways that rock layers can be disturbed. *Folding* happens when rock layers are bent because of pressure. *Tilting* happens when forces from inside Earth move rock layers so that they are slanted.

Folding happens when rock layers bend and buckle under pressure.

Tilting happens when forces from inside Earth cause rock layers to become slanted.

Faults and intrusions can cut across many rock layers. A *fault* is a break or crack in Earth's crust. Large pieces of rock can move or slide along a fault. An *intrusion* is a mass of igneous rock that forms when melted rock moves into cracks in rock layers and then cools. ☑

A fault is a break in Earth's crust. Rock can slide along a fault and disturb rock layers.

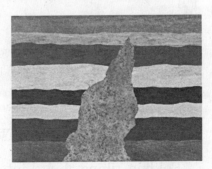

Intrusions form when melted rock moves through cracks in rock layers. The melted rock cools and hardens to form igneous rock.

**READING CHECK**

**7. Describe** What is one thing that tells a geologist that rock layers have been disturbed?

_____

_____

**TAKE A LOOK**

**8. Compare** How is folding different from tilting?

_____

_____

_____

_____

_____

_____

**READING CHECK**

**9. Identify** What kind of rock is an intrusion made of?

_____

_____

**TAKE A LOOK**

**10. Define** What is a fault?

_____

_____

## MISSING ROCK LAYERS

Think back to your stack of newspapers. Imagine that you want to read something in the paper from Valentine's Day, February 14. However, when you look, the paper from February 14 is not there. The papers go from February 13 to February 15. What happened? Maybe you didn't put that day's newspaper on the stack. Maybe someone took that paper out of the stack.

The same ideas that apply to a missing newspaper apply to a missing rock layer. An **unconformity** is a break in, or a missing part of, the geologic record. Unconformities can form when sediment is not deposited in an area for a long time. If sediment is not deposited, no new layer of rock can form. This is like your forgetting to put a newspaper onto the stack.

Unconformities can also form when erosion removes a layer of rock after it formed. This is like someone taking a paper out of the stack.

**11. Infer** Imagine that you are a geologist and you find an unconformity between two rock layers. What can you guess about the environment at the time the unconformity was forming?

_____

_____

_____

_____

1. Sediment is eroded from hills or mountains. It moves downhill. The sediment is deposited in layers in a low area.

Nondeposition

2. If erosion stops, no more sediment moves downhill. Deposition stops. No sediment layers form for a long time.

3. When erosion begins again, more sediment moves downhill. It is deposited in the low area. An unconformity has formed where no sediment was deposited for a long time.

Unconformity

Erosion

Unconformity

Uplift

2. The area is uplifted and exposed to erosion by wind and water.

3. Deposition resumes.

**TAKE A LOOK**

**12. Identify** Look at the first picture. Label the oldest and youngest layers of rock in the picture. Assume that the layers have not been disturbed.

Folding, tilting, faults, intrusions, and unconformities all disturb rock layers. If rock layers are disturbed, geologists may not be able to use the idea of superposition to learn their relative ages. However, geologists can use other methods to learn their relative ages.

# How Can Geologists Learn How Bodies of Rock Formed?

Geologists study rock bodies to help put together the parts of the geologic record. They often find groups of rock layers that have been affected by several events. In order to figure out how the body of rock formed, they must figure out the order of the events that happened. Figuring out when different events happened is like putting together a puzzle. ☑

Look at the picture below. It shows three layers of sedimentary rock. The rock layers have been disturbed by an igneous rock intrusion. Which is older, the sedimentary rock or the igneous rock? The sedimentary rock is older than the igneous rock. You know this because the igneous rock cuts across the sedimentary rock.

Sedimentary rock

This igneous rock intrusion is _____ than the sedimentary rocks around it. The igneous rock cuts through the sedimentary rock layers.

Igneous rock intrusion

## LAW OF CROSSCUTTING RELATIONSHIPS

A feature, such as an intrusion, that cuts across rock layers is younger than the rock layers it cuts across. This statement is known as the **law of crosscutting relationships**. Geologists can use the law of crosscutting relationships to learn how a rock body formed. ☑

How can you use the law of crosscutting relationships to figure out how a body of rock formed? The figures on the top of the next page show a complicated body of rock. Use the figures to learn how to use the law of crosscutting relationships.

---

**✓ READING CHECK**

**13. Identify** What is one reason that geologists study rock bodies?

_____

_____

_____

**TAKE A LOOK**
**14. Describe** Fill in the blank line in the figure.

**✓ READING CHECK**

**15. Rephrase** Rewrite the law of crosscutting relationships in your own words.

_____

_____

_____

_____

_____

_____

**SECTION 2** Relative Dating *continued*

This body of rock has many different features in it. You can use the law of crosscutting relationships to figure out how it formed.

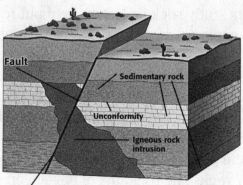

## TAKE A LOOK
**16. Explain** How do you know that the fault is the youngest feature in the rock body?

_____

_____

_____

1. This fault cuts through all of the other parts of the rock body. It must be the youngest feature.

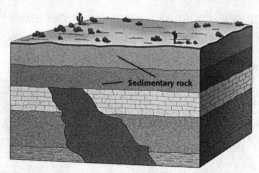

## TAKE A LOOK
**17. Identify** Label the unconformity in the figure.

2. This is what the rock body must have looked like before the fault formed. This unconformity and the layers of rock above it are the next-youngest features.

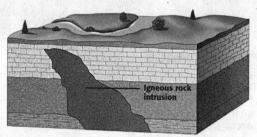

3. This is what the rock body must have looked like before the unconformity and sedimentary rock layers formed. The igneous rock intrusion cuts through the rock layers around it. Therefore, the intrusion is the next-youngest feature.

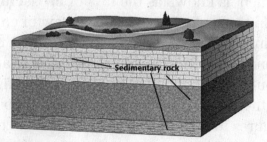

4. Before the intrusion formed, this rock body was made of three layers of sedimentary rock.

# Section 2 Review

7.3.c, 7.4.c

## SECTION VOCABULARY

| | |
|---|---|
| **law of crosscutting relationships** the principle that a fault or body of rock is younger than any other body of rock that it cuts through | **superposition** a principle that states that younger rocks lie above older rocks if the layers have not been disturbed |
| **relative dating** any method of determining whether an event or object is older or younger than other events or objects | **unconformity** a break in the geologic record created when rock layers are eroded or when sediment is not deposited for a long period of time |
| **sedimentary rock** a rock that forms from compressed or cemented layers of sediment | |

**1. Identify** Give two ways that an unconformity can form.

_____

_____

**2. Apply Concepts** The figure below shows a body of rock. The body of rock contains many different features. Figure out the order that the different features formed in. Then, write the letters for the features in the order that they formed.

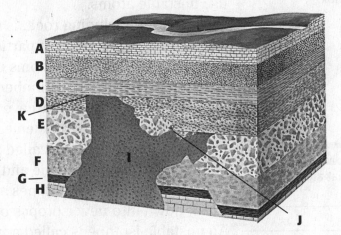

_____

**3. Explain** How do sedimentary rocks form?

_____

_____

_____

**4. Describe** What does the idea of superposition say about rock layers that have not been disturbed?

_____

_____

**CHAPTER 8** Studying Earth's Past

**SECTION 3** Absolute Dating

**California Science Standards**

7.3.c, 7.4.d

---

### BEFORE YOU READ

After you read this section, you should be able to answer these questions:

• How can geologists learn the exact age of a rock?
• How old is Earth?

---

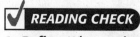

**Learn New Words** As you read, underline words that you don't understand. When you learn what they mean, write the words and their definitions in your notebook.

## What Is Radioactive Decay?

Geologists can use the methods of relative dating to learn whether a rock is older or younger than another rock. However, they often also need to know exactly how old a rock is. Finding the exact age of an object is called **absolute dating**. One way to learn the age of a rock is to use unstable atoms.

All matter, including rock, is made of atoms. All atoms are made of three kinds of particles: protons, neutrons, and electrons. All of the atoms of an element, such as uranium, have the same number of protons. However, some atoms of an element have different numbers of neutrons. Atoms of an element that have different numbers of neutrons are called *isotopes*. ☑

Many isotopes are stable and are always in the same form. However, other isotopes are unstable and can break down into new isotopes of different elements. An unstable isotope is called a *radioactive isotope*. **Radioactive decay** happens when a radioactive isotope breaks down into a new isotope.

---

✓ **READING CHECK**

**1. Define** What are isotopes?

_____

_____

_____

---

**TAKE A LOOK**

**2. Compare** How is a radioactive isotope different from a stable isotope?

_____

_____

_____

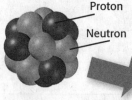

This isotope is unstable, or radioactive.

Proton

Neutron

Electron

After radioactive decay, an isotope of a new element is left. The new isotope is stable.

Radioactive isotopes can decay in different ways. During one kind of radioactive decay, a neutron becomes a proton and an electron. The electron moves to a different part of the atom.

---

**SECTION 3** Absolute Dating *continued*

## RADIOMETRIC DATING

A radioactive isotope is also called a *parent isotope*. When a parent isotope breaks down, the new isotope that is formed is called a *daughter isotope*. Because of radioactive decay, the amounts of parent and daughter isotope in a rock are always changing. However, they change at a constant, known rate. Therefore, scientists can learn the age of a rock by studying the amounts of parent and daughter isotopes in it.

**Radiometric dating** is the process of determining the absolute age of a sample based on the ratio of parent isotope to daughter isotope. In order to use a radioactive isotope to find the age of a rock, you need to know the half-life of the isotope.

The **half-life** of a radioactive isotope is the amount of time it takes for half of a sample of the isotope to decay. For example, imagine that a sample of a parent isotope has a half-life of 10,000 years. The parent isotope has a mass of 12 mg. After 10,000 years, only one-half, or 6 mg, of the parent isotope will be left.

## Critical Thinking
**3. Infer** What happens to the amount of parent isotope in a rock with time? What happens to the amount of daughter isotope?

_____

_____

_____

_____

| **0 years** Parent isotope = 16 mg This sample contains 16 mg of a parent isotope. The isotope has a half-life of 10,000 years. | **10,000 years** Parent isotope = (1/2) x (16 mg) = _____ After one half-life, 1/2 of the original mass of parent isotope is left. | **20,000 years** Parent isotope = (1/2) x (1/2) x (16 mg) = _____ After two half-lives, (1/2) x (1/2), or 1/4 of the original mass of parent isotope is left. | **30,000 years** Parent isotope = (1/2) x (1/2) x (1/2) x (16 mg) = _____ After three half-lives, (1/2) x (1/2) x (1/2), or 1/8 of the original mass of parent isotope is left. |

## Math Focus
**4. Calculate** Fill in the blank lines in the figure with the mass of parent isotope that is left at each step.

The half-lives of different isotopes can be very different. Some parent isotopes have half-lives of more than 4 billion years. Others have half-lives of only about 6,000 years. Very old rocks can be dated only if isotopes with long half-lives are used. Very young rocks can be dated only if isotopes with short half-lives are used.

How do scientists know which isotope to use to find the age of a rock? They use information about the relative age of the rock to guess about how old the rock is. Then, they find its age, using an isotope that is useful for dating rocks of that age.

## IMPORTANT ISOTOPES IN RADIOMETRIC DATING

Potassium-40 is an isotope that is often used in radiometric dating. It has a half-life of 1.3 billion years. It decays to produce the daughter isotope argon-40. Scientists usually use potassium to date rocks that are older than about 1 million years.

Uranium-238 is also used for radiometric dating. It has a half-life of 4.5 billion years. It decays to produce lead-206. Uranium-238 is used to date rocks that are older than about 10 million years.

**TAKE A LOOK**

**5. Identify** Fill in the spaces in the chart to show the features of potassium-40 and uranium-238.

| Parent isotope | Daughter isotope | Half-life |
|---|---|---|
| Potassium-40 | | |
| Uranium-238 | | |

**CALIFORNIA STANDARDS CHECK**

**7.4.d** Students know that evidence from geologic layers and radioactive dating indicates Earth is approximately 4.6 billion years old and that life on this planet has existed for more than 3 billion years.

**Word Help: evidence**
information showing whether an idea or belief is true or valid

**Word Help: layer**
a separate or distinct portion of matter that has thickness

**Word Help: indicate**
to be or give a sign of; to show

**Word Help: approximately**
almost; about

**6. Explain** How did geologists determine the age of the solar system?

_____

_____

_____

_____

_____

## How Old Is Earth?

Suppose you wanted to find the age of Earth. You might try to find the oldest rocks that you could. Would these rocks tell you the age of Earth? Probably not, because all of the rocks that were around when Earth formed have been recycled by plate tectonics and erosion.

Radiometric dating can give accurate ages only for rocks that have not been melted or weathered. Therefore, none of the rocks on Earth can be used to find the age of Earth. However, scientists can use rocks from other parts of the solar system to learn how old it is.

For example, the moon and some meteorites contain rock that formed as our solar system was forming. *Meteorites* are small pieces of rock that have traveled through space and fallen to Earth's surface. Meteorites can be collected on Earth. Astronauts have collected rocks from the moon. Scientists have performed radiometric dating on these rocks. The absolute ages of the rocks show that the solar system, including Earth, is between 4.5 billion and 4.6 billion years old.

# Section 3 Review

7.3.c, 7.4.d

## SECTION VOCABULARY

| | |
|---|---|
| **absolute dating** any method of measuring the age of an event or object in years<br><br>**half-life** the time required for half of a sample of a radioactive isotope to break down by radioactive decay to form a daughter isotope | **radioactive decay** the process in which a radioactive isotope tends to break down into a stable isotope of the same element or another element<br><br>**radiometric dating** a method of determining the absolute age of an object by comparing the relative percentages of a radioactive (parent) isotope and a stable (daughter) isotope |

**1. Describe** How is radioactive decay related to radiometric dating?

_____

_____

**2. Calculate** A parent isotope has a half-life of 1 million years. If a rock contained 20 mg of the parent isotope when it formed, how much parent isotope would be left in the rock after 2 million years? Show your work.

_____

_____

**3. List** What are two radioactive isotopes that are useful for dating old rocks?

_____

_____

**4. Identify** About how old are the Earth and the solar system?

_____

**5. Apply Concepts** A geologist uses relative dating methods to guess that a rock is between 1 million and 5 million years old. What is one radioactive isotope the geologist can use to learn the exact age of the rock? Explain your answer.

_____

_____

**6. Explain** Why can't geologists use rocks from Earth to learn how long ago Earth formed?

_____

_____

_____

SECTION
**1** **Looking at Fossils**

**California Science Standards**

7.3.c, 7.4.c, 7.4.e

BEFORE YOU READ

**After you read this section, you should be able to answer these questions:**

• What are fossils?

• How are fossils formed?

• What can fossils tell us about the history of life on earth?

## What Are Fossils?

Can you name any dinosaurs? Do you know what they looked like or how they moved? Scientists have been able to tell us many things about organisms, such as dinosaurs, that lived millions of years ago. How do scientists learn about these organisms if they have never seen them? They study fossils. A **fossil** is the trace or remains of an organism that lived long ago. Fossils can form in five different ways. ☑

### FOSSILS IN ROCKS

Usually when an organism dies, it begins to decay or it is eaten by other organisms. Sometimes, organisms are quickly buried by sediment when they die. Sediment can preserve the organism. Hard parts, such as shells, teeth, and bones, are preserved more often than soft parts, such as organs and skin. The parts of the organism that remain can become fossils when sediment hardens to form sedimentary rock. ☑

### FOSSILS IN AMBER

Sometimes organisms such as insects are caught in sticky tree sap. If the sap hardens around the insect, a fossil is created. Hardened tree sap is called *amber*. Some of the best insect fossils are found in amber. Frogs and lizards have also been found in amber.

---

**STUDY TIP**

**Organize** Make a spider map to show the different ways fossils can form.

---

✓ **READING CHECK**

**1. Define** What is a fossil?

_____

_____

_____

_____

---

✓ **READING CHECK**

**2. List** Give three examples of hard parts of an organism that could become fossils.

_____

_____

_____

---

This insect is preserved in amber. It is more than 38 million years old.

## FROZEN FOSSILS

Ice and cold temperatures slow down decay and can allow fossils to form. Woolly mammoths, which are relatives of modern elephants, became extinct about 10,000 years ago. Scientists have found frozen remains of mammoths preserved in blocks of ice. By studying these fossils, scientists hope to learn more about the mammoths and their environment.

## PETRIFICATION

Organisms can also become fossils by petrification. In *petrification*, minerals replace an organism's tissues. During one form of petrification, minerals fill the tiny spaces in an organism's hard tissues, such as bone. Sometimes, the organism's tissues are completely replaced by minerals. In petrified wood, for example, all of a tree's wood is replaced by minerals. The wood becomes a rock. ☑

## FOSSILS IN ASPHALT

In some places asphalt can bubble at the Earth's surface and form sticky pools. The La Brea asphalt deposits in Los Angeles, California, are at least 38,000 years old. These pools have trapped and preserved many different organisms. These include saber-toothed cats and dire wolves that lived from 10,000 to 40,000 years ago. From these fossils, scientists have learned about the ancient environment of southern California.

# What Other Kinds of Fossils Have Been Found?

Organisms can leave behind clues about their lives. These clues are also fossils. These fossils were made by an organism, but they do not include parts of the organism's body.

## TRACE FOSSILS

Evidence of an organism and its activities can be fossilized. This is called a **trace fossil**. Tracks are an example of a trace fossil. They form when footprints are filled with sediment and preserved in rock. Tracks can show how big an animal was and how fast it was moving. For example, parallel paths of dinosaur tracks have led scientists to hypothesize that some dinosaurs moved in herds. ☑

 **Say It**

**Discuss** Have you ever seen any fossils? What kind of organisms were they? Where did you see them? How were they made? Describe these fossils to your classmates.

✓ **READING CHECK**

**3. Define** What is petrification?

_____

_____

_____

_____

✓ **READING CHECK**

**4. Define** What is a trace fossil?

_____

_____

_____

_____

**SECTION 1** Looking at Fossils *continued*

These dinosaur tracks are found in Arizona. They show that the dinosaur was running when it made the tracks.

## TAKE A LOOK
**5. Identify** What kind of fossils are dinosaur tracks?

_____

_____

Burrows are another kind of trace fossil. *Burrows* are shelters made by animals such as clams that bury themselves in sediment. A burrow is preserved when it is filled with sediment and buried quickly. A coprolite is also a trace fossil. *Coprolites* are preserved animal dung.

### MOLDS AND CASTS

Molds and casts are two more kinds of fossils. The print, or impression, left in sediment or in rock where a plant or animal was buried is a *mold*. The figure below shows two types of molds from the same organism. One is an internal mold of the inside of the shell. The other is an external mold of the outside of the shell.

A cast is an object that forms when sediment fills a mold and becomes rock. Like a mold, a cast can show what the inside or outside of an organism looked like. ☑

**READING CHECK**

**6. Compare** What is the difference between a cast and a mold?

_____

_____

_____

_____

_____

The fossil on the left is the internal mold of an ammonite. It formed when the sediment filled the ammonite's shell. On the right is the external mold of the ammonite. The shell later dissolved.

# What Can Fossils Tell Us?

Think about your favorite outdoor place. Observe the plants and animals around you, including the birds, insects, and grasses. Now, imagine that you are a scientist at the same site 65 million years from now. What types of fossils would you dig up? Would you find fossils for every bird, insect, and grass that existed? Based on the fossils you found, how would you reconstruct this place? Fossils can show scientists three main things:

1. the kind of organisms that lived in the past
2. how the environment has changed
3. how organisms have changed

## THE INFORMATION IN THE FOSSIL RECORD

Scientists know some of the history of life on Earth from fossils. Some parts of this history are more complete than others. Scientists know more about organisms that had hard body parts than about organisms that had only soft body parts.

Some organisms lived in environments where fossils can form more easily. Scientists also know more about these organisms than those that lived in other environments. The fossil record is incomplete because most organisms never became fossils, and many fossils have not been discovered yet.

## A HISTORY OF ENVIRONMENTAL CHANGES

Fossils can show evidence of climate change. For example, today Antarctica is covered with ice and snow. However, scientists have found fossil evidence of forests and freshwater organisms in Antarctica. These fossils show that the climate must have been much warmer in the past.

Copyright © by Holt, Rinehart and Winston. All rights reserved.

---

**CALIFORNIA STANDARDS CHECK**

**7.4.e** Students know fossils provide <u>evidence</u> of how life and environmental conditions have changed.

**Word Help: evidence** information showing whether an idea or belief is true or valid

**7. List** Name three things fossils can show scientists.

_____

_____

_____

_____

_____

**TAKE A LOOK**
**8. Explain** What is one reason this organism could be fossilized?

_____

_____

## A HISTORY OF CHANGING ORGANISMS

To understand how life on Earth has changed, scientists compare fossils. Scientists also look for similarities between fossils and living organisms. However, only a small fraction of the organisms that have existed in Earth's history have been fossilized. As a result, the fossil record is incomplete. This means scientists do not have a continuous record of changes in life on Earth. ☑

## How Do Scientists Know How Old Fossils Are?

To understand the history of life on Earth, scientists have put fossils in order based on their ages. How do scientists know how old a fossil is? In some cases, scientists can use *absolute dating methods*, such as radiometric dating, to determine the age of fossils. More commonly, scientists use relative dating methods.

With *relative dating methods*, scientists don't know the exact age of a fossil. However, they do which fossils are older than others. One of these relative dating methods is called *superposition*. Fossils found in older layers of rock come from more ancient life forms. Fossils found in younger layers of rock are from more recent organisms.

## USING FOSSILS TO DATE ROCKS

Fossils of certain types of organisms can be found all over the world. These fossils are found only in rock layers of a certain age. They are called index fossils. **Index fossils** are fossils of organisms that lived during a relatively short geologic time span. To be an index fossil, a fossil organism must be found throughout the world. It must be easy to identify and many fossils of that organism must exist.

*Phacops* is an example of an index fossil. This organism lived about 400 million years ago. When scientists find *Phacops* in a rock layer, they know the rock layer is about 400 million years old.

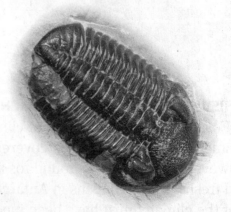

---

✓ **READING CHECK**

**9. Explain** How can scientists find out how life has changed?

_____

_____

_____

_____

*Critical Thinking*

**10. Explain** Would you expect to find fossils of an organism that lived relatively recently in old layers of rock or in younger layers? Explain your answer.

_____

_____

_____

_____

_____

_____

# Section 1 Review

7.3.c, 7.4.c, 7.4.e

## SECTION VOCABULARY

| | |
|---|---|
| **fossil** the trace or remains of an organism that lived long ago, most commonly preserved in sedimentary rock | **trace fossil** a fossilized mark that formed in sedimentary rock by the movement of an animal on or within soft sediment |
| **index fossil** a fossil that is used to establish the age of a rock layer because the fossil is distinct, abundant, and widespread and the species that formed that fossil existed for only a short span of geologic time | |

**1. List** Give three examples of trace fossils.

_____

**2. Explain** Why is the fossil record incomplete?

_____

_____

_____

**3. Explain** Why can some fossils form in cold temperatures?

_____

_____

**4. Infer** Which kind of organism is more likely to be found as a fossil in amber—a frog or a rabbit? Explain your answer.

_____

_____

_____

**5. Apply Concepts** What could you conclude if you found a fossil of a tropical plant in a cold climate?

_____

_____

**6. List** What three conditions must a fossil meet in order to be an index fossil?

_____

_____

_____

CHAPTER 9 | The History of Life on Earth

SECTION
2 | **Earth's Changing Continents**

**California Science Standards**

7.4.a, 7.4.e, 7.4.f

**BEFORE YOU READ**

After you read this section, you should be able to answer these questions:

• What is plate tectonics?

• How do tectonic plates move?

• What is continental drift?

## What Does Plate Tectonics Explain About the Earth?

The ground we stand on may feel still, but the surface of the Earth is moving. Sometimes, we can feel this movement as earthquakes. The Earth's surface has moved so much that the continents have actually changed locations.

The Earth has a thin, cool outer layer called the *lithosphere*. This layer is broken into several small sections called *tectonic plates*. These plates rest on a layer of rock called the *mantle*. The mantle is solid, but it moves very slowly. As the mantle moves, it drags the tectonic plates on top of it. ☑

### Earth's Tectonic Plates

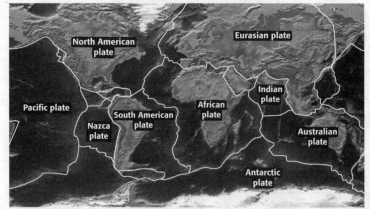

Earth has about 12 large plates and many smaller ones. The theory of how Earth's tectonic plates move and change shape is called **plate tectonics**. Tectonic plates can move in three ways: toward each other, away from each other, or past each other. Where plates move apart, new lithosphere forms. When plates move toward each other they may collide, in some cases, to form mountains. In other cases, one plate slides under the other plate and into the mantle.

**STUDY TIP**

**Outline** As you read, make an outline of this section. Use the header questions to help you make your outline.

**✓ READING CHECK**

**1. Complete** The lithosphere is broken into small sections called

_____

_____.

**TAKE A LOOK**

**2. Identify** Which plate do you live on?

_____

_____

## What Happens to Continents as Plates Move?

As tectonic plates move, the continents move along with them. **Continental drift** describes how continents have moved around Earth's surface throughout its history. As a continent moves, it carries with it rocks and fossils. Today, the rocks and fossils can give evidence of how the continent moved.

### GEOLOGIC EVIDENCE FOR CONTINENTAL DRIFT

Rocks in India, southern Africa, and Brazil contain deep scratches and scars that were formed by glaciers. But how could glaciers exist in places with such warm climates? The climates of these areas must have been much colder at one time. Scientists now know that these areas were part of a single land mass, or continent. It was located near the South Pole about 280 million years ago.

### FOSSIL EVIDENCE FOR CONTINENTAL DRIFT

Fossils can also give evidence for continental drift. Fossils of a reptile called *Mesosaurus* are found in South America and southern Africa. The continents are separated by 3,000 miles of ocean. Scientists don't think *Mesosaurus* could have swum across this ocean. This suggests that the two continents were once joined.

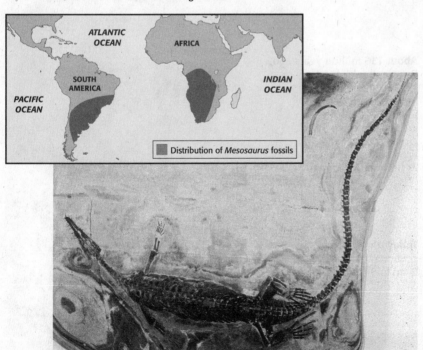

Fossils of *Mesosaurus* were found in both South America and southwestern Africa.

### Math Focus

**3. Calculate** Tectonic plates move slowly, but may be moving for millions of years. If a plate moves 4 cm per year, how many kilometers would it move in 1 million years?

_____

### TAKE A LOOK

**4. Explain** How do the shaded areas on the map give evidence for continental drift?

_____

_____

_____

_____

_____

_____

# How Have the Continents Changed?

By putting together all the evidence, scientists can draw maps that show how Earth's geography has changed over time. The figure below shows how the continents have shifted through Earth's history

When the large land mass called *Pangaea* split apart, the plants and animals living on each continent were separated. This process explains why different organisms live on different continents. It also explains why fossils of the same organisms are found on different continents.

Continental drift also led to changes in climate. It caused ocean currents and winds to flow differently. These changes affected the flow of heat around the Earth.

## The Breakup of Pangaea

*Critical Thinking*

**5. Predict** Do you think the continents will look the same way in 50 million years as they do today? Explain your answer.

_____

_____

_____

_____

_____

_____

**About 245 million years ago,** the continents were one giant land mass called Pangaea.

**About 136 million years ago,** Pangaea broke apart. The North Atlantic and Indian oceans began to form. Plants and animals were separated. Ocean currents and wind patterns changed as new oceans formed.

## TAKE A LOOK

**6. Explain** Why did it take so long for the continents to move to where they are today?

_____

_____

_____

**Today,** the continents continue to move about 2 cm to 5 cm per year.

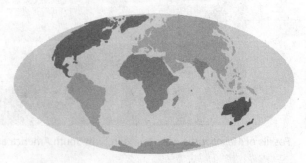

# What Is the Panama Land Bridge?

About 3 million years ago, North and South America became joined by a strip of land called the Panama Land Bridge. This land bridge led to changes in both life and climate.

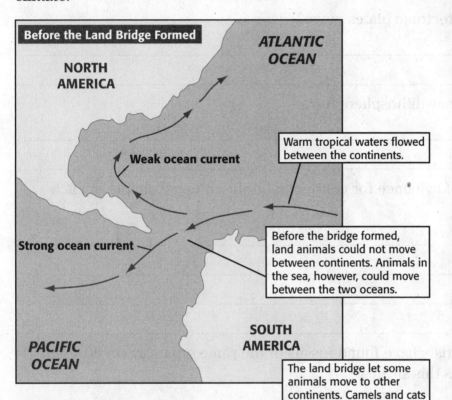

**Before the Land Bridge Formed**

ATLANTIC OCEAN

NORTH AMERICA

Weak ocean current

Warm tropical waters flowed between the continents.

Strong ocean current

Before the bridge formed, land animals could not move between continents. Animals in the sea, however, could move between the two oceans.

SOUTH AMERICA

PACIFIC OCEAN

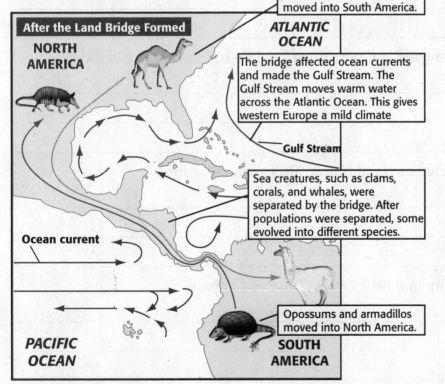

The land bridge let some animals move to other continents. Camels and cats moved into South America.

**After the Land Bridge Formed**

ATLANTIC OCEAN

NORTH AMERICA

The bridge affected ocean currents and made the Gulf Stream. The Gulf Stream moves warm water across the Atlantic Ocean. This gives western Europe a mild climate

Gulf Stream

Sea creatures, such as clams, corals, and whales, were separated by the bridge. After populations were separated, some evolved into different species.

Ocean current

Opossums and armadillos moved into North America.

PACIFIC OCEAN

SOUTH AMERICA

---

**CALIFORNIA STANDARDS CHECK**

**7.4.f** Students know how movements of continental and oceanic plates through time, with associated changes in climate and geographic conditions, have <u>affected</u> the past and present <u>distribution</u> of organisms.

**Word Help: <u>affect</u>**
to change; to have an effect on; to influence

**Word Help: <u>distribution</u>**
the relative arrangement of objects or organisms in time or space

**7. Explain** How did life on the North and South American continents change after the land bridge formed?

_____

_____

_____

_____

_____

# TAKE A LOOK

**8. Explain** How does the Gulf Stream affect the climate of western Europe?

_____

_____

_____

_____

# Section 2 Review

7.4.a, 7.4.e, 7.4.f

## SECTION VOCABULARY

| | |
|---|---|
| **continental drift** the hypothesis that states that the continents once formed a single land mass, broke up, and drifted to their present locations | **plate tectonics** the theory that explains how large pieces of the Earth's outermost layer, called tectonic plates, move and change shape |

**1. Explain** What makes tectonic plates move?

_____

_____

**2. Identify** Where does new lithosphere form?

_____

_____

**3. List** Give two types of evidence for continental drift with an example of each type.

_____

_____

_____

_____

**4. Apply Concepts** Scientists have found fossils of the same organism on different continents. What does this suggest?

_____

_____

**5. Describe** What was Pangaea and how does it relate to the continents today?

_____

_____

_____

**6. Explain** How did the Panama land bridge affect sea creatures?

_____

_____

**7. Explain** How did continental drift cause climates to change?

_____

_____

_____

**CHAPTER 9** The History of Life on Earth
**SECTION 3** Time Marches On

## BEFORE YOU READ

After you read this section, you should be able to answer these questions:

• How do geologists measure time?

• How has life changed over millions of years?

• What can cause a mass extinction?

## How Can Geologic Time Be Measured?

Geologists have developed a time scale for the 4.6 billion years of Earth's existence. The **geologic time scale** divides these billions of years into distinct intervals of time. Each interval is distinct because it shows a particular change in life or the surface of the Earth itself.

The largest divisions in geologic time are called *eons*. Eons are divided into *eras*, the second-largest divisions of geologic time. Eras are divided into *periods*. Periods are divided into *epochs*. In the figure below, the most recent divisions of time are at the top and the oldest divisions of time are at the bottom.

**STUDY TIP**

**Organize** As you read, make a chart showing the eras of geologic times. Include major changes in life that happened during each era.

| Geologic Time Scale | | | | |
|---|---|---|---|---|
| Eon | Era | Period | Epoch | Millions of years ago |
| PHANEROZOIC | Cenozoic | Quaternary | Holocene | 0.01 |
| | | | Pleistocene | 1.8 |
| | | Tertiary | Pliocene | 5.3 |
| | | | Miocene | 23.0 |
| | | | Oligocene | 33.9 |
| | | | Eocene | 55.8 |
| | | | Paleocene | 65.5 |
| | Mesozoic | Cretaceous | | 146 |
| | | Jurassic | | 200 |
| | | Triassic | | 251 |
| | Paleozoic | Permian | | 299 |
| | | Carboniferous | | 359 |
| | | Devonian | | 416 |
| | | Silurian | | 444 |
| | | Ordovician | | 488 |
| | | Cambrian | | 542 |
| PROTEROZOIC | | These three eons together are known as *Precambrian time* because they came before the Cambrian Period. | | |
| ARCHEAN | | | | |
| HADEAN | | | | 4,600 |

## Math Focus
**1. Calculate** The Paleozoic Era lasted for about how many years?

_____

_____

## TAKE A LOOK
**2. Identify** The last dinosaur became extinct at the end of the Cretaceous period. In which era did this happen?

_____

## How Is Geologic Time Divided?

The boundaries between geologic time periods correspond to major changes in Earth's history. Most boundaries are defined by major developments in living things or major extinctions of living things. **Extinction** is the death of every member of a species. Extinctions can happen because of competition among species. They can also happen when the environment changes. ☑

At some points in Earth's history, mass extinctions have occured. A *mass extinction* is the extinction of many species around the same time. Gradual events, such as climate change and changes in ocean currents, can cause mass extinctions. Catastrophic events such as the impact of an asteroid can also cause mass extinctions.

Bones of dinosaurs that lived about 150 million years ago have been found at Dinosaur National Monument in Utah. About 150 million years is only 3% of the total time life has been on Earth!

## What Happened in Precambrian Time?

Precambrian time stretches from the formation of Earth 4.6 billion years ago to about 542 million years ago. The early Earth was very different from today's Earth. The atmosphere did not have oxygen as it does today. Life on Earth began during this time. The first organisms appeared in Earth's oceans more than 3.6 billion years ago. These organisms were called prokaryotes. *Prokaryotes* are single-celled organisms without a nucleus. ☑

### LIFE AND OXYGEN

*Cyanobacteria*, a type of prokaryote, were some of the first organisms on Earth. Cynanobacteria use sunlight to make their food by photosynthesis. During photosynthesis, cyanobacteria release oxygen. As these organisms photosynthesized millions of years ago, oxygen began to build up in the atmosphere.

✔ **READING CHECK**

**3. Define** What is extinction?

_____

_____

_____

✔ **READING CHECK**

**4. Identify** When did life first appear on Earth?

_____

_____

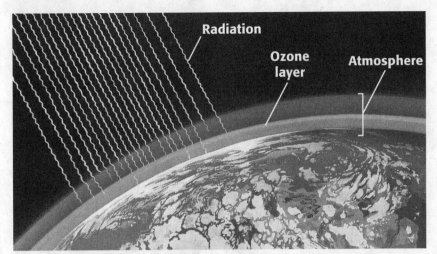

Oxygen in the atmosphere formed a layer of ozone. Ozone absorbs harmful radiation from the sun.

**TAKE A LOOK**
**5. Identify** How does the ozone layer function in the atmosphere?

_____

_____

_____

As oxygen built up in the atmosphere, some of it formed ozone. *Ozone* in the atmosphere absorbs harmful radiation from the sun. Without ozone, the sun's radiation would have been deadly to organisms on land. Life during this time could only exist in the oceans and underground. As the ozone layer formed, less radiation reached Earth's surface. This allowed organisms to survive on land.

**MULTICELLULAR ORGANISMS**

After about 1 billion years, more complex organisms began to emerge. These organisms were known as *eukaryotes* and contained a nucleus and other specialized structures in their cells. Eukaryotic cells may have evolved into more complex organisms.

# What Happened in the Paleozoic Era?

The *Paleozoic Era* began about 542 million years ago and ended 251 million years ago. Scientists used to think that the earliest forms of life existed in the Paleozoic Era. They now believe earlier forms of life existed in the Precambrian.

**THE CAMBRIAN EXPLOSION**

Many new and complex life forms appeared during the *Cambrian Period*, the first period of the Paleozoic Era. This period is often referred to as "the Cambrian explosion," but it was not an actual explosion. For the first time on Earth, there were many types of organisms that had hard parts, such as shells and exoskeletons.

**CALIFORNIA STANDARDS CHECK**

**7.4.G** Students know how to explain <u>significant</u> developments and extinctions of plant and animal life on the geologic time scale.

**Word Help: significant** important

**6. Describe** What were the first organisms to appear on Earth?

_____

_____

_____

_____

**SECTION 3** Time Marches On *continued*

## Life in the Paleozoic Era

### Critical Thinking

**7. Infer** Why is it important to scientists that many organisms during the Cambrian period had hard parts?

_____

_____

_____

_____

_____

_____

All major plant groups, except for flowering plants, appeared during this era. Animals used the plants for food and shelter.

Near the end of the Paleozoic, reptiles and insects appeared.

During the middle of the Paleozoic, plants, fungi, and animals moved onto land.

### TAKE A LOOK

**8. List** List three groups of organisms that appeared during the Paleozoic.

_____

_____

_____

Fishes appeared during this era. Other sea creatures, such as sponges, corals, squids, and trilobites, also lived during the Paleozoic.

Some types of organisms that exist today, such as ferns and salamanders, also lived during this era. However, during the Paleozoic these organisms were giants.

### THE PERMIAN EXTINCTION

The largest mass extinction took place about 251 million years ago. This event at the end of the Permian period is called the *Permian extinction*. Scientists do not know for sure what caused this mass extinction. Some hypotheses include loss of coastal habitat when Pangaea formed, climate change, and volcanoes. Around 90% of marine species and 78% of land species became extinct. Groups such as reptiles and amphibians survived. ☑

**READING CHECK**

**9. Identify** What event happened at the end of the Paleozoic Era?

_____

_____

# What Happened in the Mesozoic Era?

The *Mesozoic Era* began about 251 million years ago. Scientists believe that the reptiles that survived the Permian Extinction evolved into many different species in the Mesozoic Era. The Mesozoic Era is commonly called the *Age of Reptiles*.

**Life in the Mesozoic Era**

Dinosaurs that could use feathers for flight appeared during this era. Scientists think that some dinosaurs were the ancestors of birds.

Conifers were the most important plants in the early Mesozoic.

Dinosaurs dominated Earth for about 150 million years. Some dinosaurs had large spines on their bodies for defense. Others traveled in herds.

Flowering plants appeared in the latter part of the era.

The first mammals appeared during the Mesozoic.

## THE CRETACEOUS-TERTIARY EXTINCTION

About 65 million years ago, all of the dinosaurs and half of the animal and plant species became extinct. This event is called the *Cretaceous-Tertiary (or K-T) extinction*. Scientists know this mass extinction took place because many fossils disappeared from the fossil record at this time. ☑

Scientists have made several hypotheses to explain this mass extinction. According to one, an asteroid hit Earth. The impact caused giant dust clouds and fires that blocked out sunlight. With little sunlight, many plants died. Animals that ate the plants, and their predators, also died.

## What Happened in the Cenozoic Era?

The *Cenozoic Era* began about 65 million years ago and continues today. Scientists have more information about the Cenozoic than any other era. Cenozoic rocks formed on top of rocks from earlier eras. Because of this, Cenozoic fossils are often closer to Earth's surface. This makes them easier to find.

*Critical Thinking*

**13. Explain** Many movies and cartoons show cavemen and dinosaurs together. Explain why this view is not correct.

_____

_____

_____

_____

_____

_____

**TAKE A LOOK**

**14. Identify** What group of animals seems to be dominant in the Cenozoic Era?

_____

### Life in the Cenozoic Era

Early in the Cenozoic, mammals were small and lived in forests. Larger mammals, such as the mammoth, appeared later in the era.

Some of the larger mammals had teeth that were adapted for eating specific foods. Some also developed larger brains.

Some larger mammals had long legs.

Humans appeared very late in the Cenozoic Era.

### THE CENOZOIC ERA IN RECENT TIMES

The landscape around us today developed during the Cenozoic. Climate has continued to change during this era. There have been ice ages, during which the climate was very cold. To survive, many organisms migrated toward the equator. Others adapted to the cold or became extinct. In the future, geologists might draw the line for a new era when life on Earth undergoes another major change.

# Section 3 Review

**7.4.d, 7.4.e, 7.4.g**

## SECTION VOCABULARY

| **extinction** the death of every member of a species | **geologic time scale** the standard method used to divide the Earth's long natural history into manageable parts |
|---|---|

**1. List** What are the four divisions of geological time?

_____

_____

**2. List** List three events that can cause a mass extinction.

_____

_____

**3. Compare** Use a Venn Diagram to compare the types of organisms found in the Paleozoic Era and the Cenozoic Era.

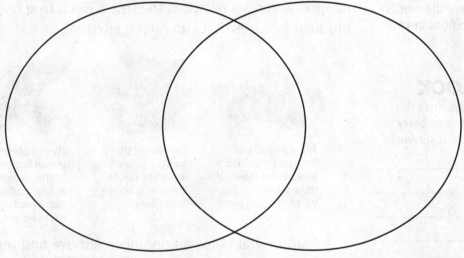

**4. Explain** How were cyanobacteria important to the development of life on Earth?

_____

_____

_____

**5. Explain** How do scientists know that the K-T extinction took place?

_____

_____

_____

**CHAPTER 10** The Evolution of Living Things

**SECTION 1** Change Over Time

California Science Standards

7.3.c, 7.3.d

---

**BEFORE YOU READ**

**After you read this section, you should be able to answer these questions:**

• How are organisms different from one another?

• How do scientists know that species change over time?

• How can you tell if species are related?

---

**STUDY TIP**

**Learn New Words** As you read this section, circle the words you don't understand. When you figure out what they mean, write the words and their definitions in your notebook.

**TAKE A LOOK**

**1. Explain** How does the coloring of the strawberry poison frog help it survive?

_____

_____

_____

_____

*Critical Thinking*

**2. Infer** Give an example of a behavior that could help an organism survive.

_____

_____

_____

## What Are Adaptations?

The pictures below show three different kinds of frogs. These frogs all have some things in common. For example, they all have long back legs to help them move. However, as you can see in the pictures, there are also many differences between the frogs. Each frog has some physical features that can help it survive.

The red-eyed tree frog has green skin. It hides in the leaves of trees during the day. It comes out at night.

The skin of the smokey jungle frog looks like leaves. It can hide on the forest floor.

The strawberry poison frog has brightly-colored skin. Its bright coloring warns predators that it is poisonous.

A feature that helps an organism survive and reproduce in its environment is called an **adaptation**. Some adaptations, such as striped skin or a long neck, are physical features. Other adaptations are behaviors that help an organism find food, protect itself, or reproduce.

Living things with the same features may be members of the same species. A **species** is a group of organisms that can mate with one another to produce fertile offspring. *Fertile* offspring are offspring that can reproduce. For example, all smokey jungle frogs are members of one species. Therefore, smokey jungle frogs can mate with each other to produce offspring. The offspring can also reproduce.

A group of individuals of the same species living in the same place is a *population*. For example, all of the smokey jungle frogs living in a certain jungle are a population.

## CHANGE OVER TIME

Scientists estimate that there has been life on Earth for over 3 billion years. Earth has changed a great deal during its history. Living things have changed in this time too. Since life first appeared on Earth, many species have died out and many new species have appeared.

Scientists observe that species change over time. They also observe that the inherited characteristics in populations change over time. Scientists think that as populations change, new species form. New species descend from older species. The process in which populations change over time is called **evolution**. ☑

# What Is the Evidence That Organisms Have Changed?

Much of the evidence that organisms have changed over time is buried in sedimentary rock. *Sedimentary rock* forms when pieces of sand, dust, or soil are deposited in flat layers. Sedimentary rocks may contain fossils. These fossils provide evidence that organisms have changed over Earth's history.

## FOSSILS

**Fossils** are the remains or imprints of once-living organisms. Some fossils formed from whole organisms or from parts of organisms. Some fossils are signs, such as footprints, that an organism once existed. ☑

Fossils can form when layers of sediment cover a dead organism. Minerals in the sediment may seep into the organism and replace its body with stone. Fossils can also form when an organism dies and leaves an imprint of itself in sediment. Over time, the sediment can become rock and the imprint can be preserved as a fossil.

**READING CHECK**

**3. Define** What is evolution?

_____

_____

_____

**READING CHECK**

**4. Identify** What are two kinds of fossils?

_____

_____

_____

Some fossils, like this trilobite, form from the bodies of organisms. The trilobite was an ancient marine animal.

Some fossils, like these ferns, form when an organism leaves an imprint in sediment. Over time, the sediment becomes rock and the imprint is preserved as a fossil.

## TAKE A LOOK

**5. Compare** Which of the fossils looks most like an organism that lives today? Give the modern organism that the fossil looks like.

_____

_____

_____

**SECTION 1** Change Over Time *continued*

**7.3.c** Students know how independent lines of <u>evidence</u> from geology, fossils, and comparative anatomy provide the bases for the theory of evolution.

**Word Help: evidence**
information showing whether an idea or belief is true or valid

**6. Explain** How do fossils give evidence that organisms have changed over time?

_____

_____

_____

_____

### THE FOSSIL RECORD

Comparing fossils provides evidence that organisms have changed over time. Rocks from different times in Earth's history contain fossils of different organisms. Fossils in newer layers of rock tend to be similar to present-day organisms. Fossils from older layers are less similar to present-day organisms. By studying fossils, scientists have made a timeline of life known as the **fossil record.**

## How Do Scientists Compare Organisms?

Scientists observe that all living things have some features in common. They also observe that all living things inherit features in a similar way. Therefore, scientists think that all living species are descended from a common ancestor. Scientists compare features of fossils and of living organisms to determine whether ancient species are related to modern species.

### COMPARING STRUCTURES

When scientists study the anatomy, or structures, of different organisms, they find that some organisms share traits. These organisms may share a common ancestor. For example, the figure below shows that humans, cats, dolphins, and bats have similar structures in their front limbs. These similarities suggest that humans, cats, dolphins, and bats have a common ancestor.

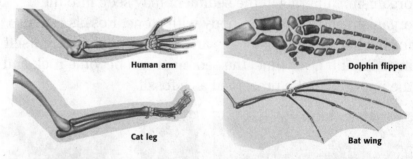

Human arm    Dolphin flipper

Cat leg    Bat wing

**Comparing Structures** The front limb bones of humans, cats, dolphins, and bats show some similarities. This suggests that all of these species share a common ancestor.

## TAKE A LOOK

**7. Color** Color the bones in each front limb to show which bones are similar. Use a different color for each bone.

Scientists can study the structures in modern organisms and compare them to structures in fossils. In this way, scientists can gather evidence that living organisms are related to organisms that lived long ago.

**SECTION 1** Change Over Time *continued*

## COMPARING CHEMICAL DATA

The genetic information in an organism's DNA determines the organism's traits. RNA and proteins also affect the traits of an organism. Scientists compare these chemicals in organisms. The more alike these chemicals are between any two species, the more recently the two species shared a common ancestor.

Comparing DNA, RNA, and proteins can be very useful in determining whether species are related. However, this method can only be used on organisms that are alive today.

## What Is the Evidence That Organisms Are Related?

Examining an organism carefully can give scientists clues about its ancestors. For example, whales look like some fish. However, unlike fish, whales breathe air, give birth to live young, and produce milk. These traits show that whales are mammals. Therefore, scientists think that whales evolved from ancient mammals. By examining fossils from ancient mammals, scientists have been able to determine how modern whales may have evolved. ☑

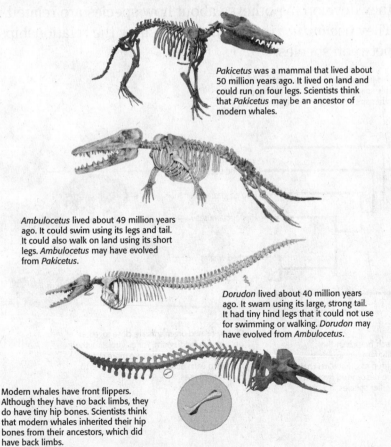

*Pakicetus* was a mammal that lived about 50 million years ago. It lived on land and could run on four legs. Scientists think that *Pakicetus* may be an ancestor of modern whales.

*Ambulocetus* lived about 49 million years ago. It could swim using its legs and tail. It could also walk on land using its short legs. *Ambulocetus* may have evolved from *Pakicetus*.

*Dorudon* lived about 40 million years ago. It swam using its large, strong tail. It had tiny hind legs that it could not use for swimming or walking. *Dorudon* may have evolved from *Ambulocetus*.

Modern whales have front flippers. Although they have no back limbs, they do have tiny hip bones. Scientists think that modern whales inherited their hip bones from their ancestors, which did have back limbs.

*Critical Thinking*

**8. Infer** Why can DNA, RNA, and proteins be used to compare only living organisms?

_____
_____
_____

☑ **READING CHECK**

**9. Describe** Why do scientists think that whales evolved from ancient mammals and not ancient fish?

_____
_____
_____

## TAKE A LOOK
**10. Compare** Give two ways that modern whales are different from *Pakicetus*, and two ways that they are similar.

_____
_____
_____
_____
_____

## EVIDENCE FROM FOSSILS

Fossils provide several pieces of evidence that some ancient mammals are related to each other and to modern whales. First, fossils of each species share some traits with fossils of an earlier species. Second, fossils of some species show new traits that are also found in fossils of later species. Third, each species had traits that allowed it to survive in a particular time and place in Earth's history. ☑

## EVIDENCE FROM MODERN WHALES

Some features of modern whales also suggest that they are related to ancient mammals. For example, modern whales do not have hind limbs. However, they do have tiny hip bones. Scientists think that modern whales inherited these hip bones from the whales' four-legged ancestors. Scientists often use this kind of evidence to determine the relationships between organisms.

## How Do Scientists Show the Relationships Between Organisms?

As scientists analyze fossils and living organisms, they develop hypotheses about how species are related. They use *branching diagrams* to show the relationships between species.

☑ **READING CHECK**

**11. Identify** Give one piece of evidence that indicates ancient mammals are related to each other and to modern whales.

_____

_____

_____

_____

**TAKE A LOOK**

**12. Use a Model** According to the diagram, which animals are most closely related to whales?

_____

_____

_____

**13. Use a Model** According to the diagram, which animals are least closely related to whales?

_____

_____

_____

This line represents an ancient species. This species is the common ancestor of the other species on the diagram.

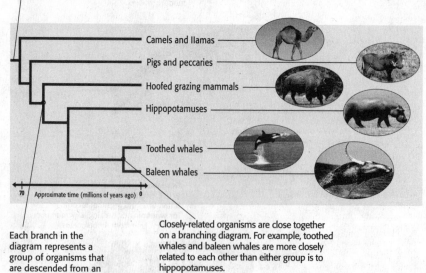

- Camels and llamas
- Pigs and peccaries
- Hoofed grazing mammals
- Hippopotamuses
- Toothed whales
- Baleen whales

70 ← Approximate time (millions of years ago) → 0

Each branch in the diagram represents a group of organisms that are descended from an earlier species.

Closely-related organisms are close together on a branching diagram. For example, toothed whales and baleen whales are more closely related to each other than either group is to hippopotamuses.

# Section 1 Review

7.3.c, 7.3.d

## SECTION VOCABULARY

| | |
|---|---|
| **adaptation** a characteristic that improves an individual's ability to survive and reproduce in a particular environment | **fossil record** a historical sequence of life indicated by fossils found in layers of Earth's crust |
| **evolution** the process in which inherited characteristics within a population change over generations such that new species sometimes arise | **species** a group of organisms that are closely related and can mate to produce fertile offspring |
| **fossil** the trace or remains of an organism that lived long ago, most commonly preserved in sedimentary rock | |

**1. Identify** What evidence suggests that humans and bats have a common ancestor?

_____

_____

_____

**2. Make a Model** Humans are most closely related to chimpanzees. Humans are least closely related to orangutans. Fill in the blank spaces on the branching diagram to show how humans, orangutans, chimpanzees, and gorillas are related.

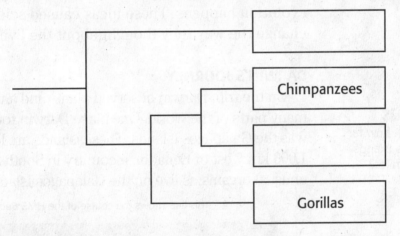

Chimpanzees

Gorillas

**3. Infer** A scientist studies the DNA of three different species. The DNA from species A is more similar to DNA from species B than DNA from species C. Which species are probably the most closely related? Explain your answer.

_____

_____

_____

# How Does Evolution Happen?

**California Science Standards**

7.3.b

**BEFORE YOU READ**

After you read this section, you should be able to answer these questions:

• Who was Charles Darwin?

• What ideas affected Darwin's thinking?

• What is natural selection?

## Who Was Charles Darwin?

In 1831, Charles Darwin graduated from college. Although he eventually earned a degree in religion, Darwin was most interested in the study of plants and animals.

Darwin's interest in nature led him to sign on for a five-year voyage around the world. He was a naturalist on the HMS *Beagle*, a British ship. A *naturalist* is someone who studies nature. During the trip, Darwin made observations that helped him form a theory about how evolution happens. These ideas caused scientists to change the way they thought about the living world.

### DARWIN'S JOURNEY

On the trip, Darwin observed plants and animals from many parts of the world. One place Darwin found interesting was the Galápagos Islands. These islands are located about 1,000 km west of Ecuador, a country in South America. Many unusual organisms live on the Galápagos Islands.

---

**STUDY TIP**

**Summarize** After you read this section, make a chart showing the four steps of natural selection. In the chart, explain what happens at each step.

---

# Math Focus

**1. Convert** About how far are the Galápagos Islands from Ecuador in miles?

1 km = 0.62 mi

---

# TAKE A LOOK

**2. Describe** Which continent are the Galápagos Islands closest to?

---

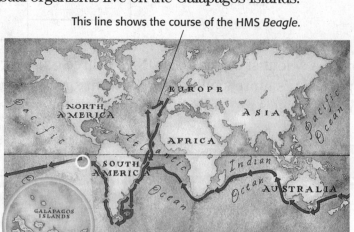

This line shows the course of the HMS *Beagle*.

Darwin studied plants and animals on the Galápagos Islands.

**SECTION 2** How Does Evolution Happen? *continued*

## DARWIN'S FINCHES

Darwin observed that the animals and plants on the Galápagos Islands were similar to those in Ecuador. However, they were not identical. For example, Darwin closely observed birds called finches. The finches on the Galápagos Islands were slightly different from the finches in Ecuador. In addition, the finches on each island in the Galápagos differed from the finches on the other islands. ☑

Darwin hypothesized that the island finches were descendents of South American finches. He thought the first finches on the islands were blown there from South America by a storm. He suggested that over many generations, the finch populations evolved adaptations that helped them survive in the different island environments. For example, the beaks of different finch species are adapted to the kind of food the species eat.

**3. Describe** What did Darwin observe about the finches on the Galápagos Islands?

_____

_____

_____

_____

The large ground finch has a wide, strong beak. It can easily crack open large, hard seeds. Its beak works like a nutcracker.

The cactus finch has a tough beak. It uses its beak to eat cactus parts and insects. Its beak works like a pair of needle-nose pliers.

*Critical Thinking*

**4. Infer** What can you guess about the environment in which the cactus finch lives based on the information in the figure? Explain your answer.

_____

_____

_____

_____

_____

The warbler finch has a small, narrow beak. It can catch small insects with its beak. Its beak works like a pair of tweezers.

# How Did Darwin Develop the Theory of Evolution by Natural Selection?

After Darwin returned to England, he spent many years thinking about his experiences on the trip. In 1859, Darwin published a famous book called *On the Origin of Species by Means of Natural Selection.* In his book, Darwin proposed the theory that evolution happens by natural selection.

**Natural selection** happens when organisms that are well adapted to their environment survive, but less well-adapted organisms do not. When the better-adapted organisms reproduce, they pass their useful traits on to their offspring. Over time, more members of the population have these traits. Darwin combined ideas about breeding, population, and Earth's history to come up with a theory to explain his observations. ☑

## IDEAS ABOUT BREEDING

In Darwin's time, farmers and breeders had produced many kinds of farm animals and plants. They learned that if they bred plants or animals that had a desirable trait, some of the offspring may have the trait. A **trait** is a form of an inherited characteristic. The practice in which humans select plants or animals for breeding based on desired traits is called **selective breeding**.

Selective breeding showed Darwin that the traits of organisms can change and that certain traits can spread through populations. For example, most pets, such as the dogs below, have been bred for a variety of desired traits. Over the past 12,000 years, people have selectively bred dogs to produce more than 150 breeds. ☑

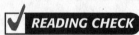

**READING CHECK**

**5. Define** What is natural selection?

_____

_____

_____

_____

_____

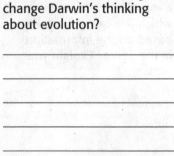

**READING CHECK**

**6. Explain** How did ideas about selective breeding change Darwin's thinking about evolution?

_____

_____

_____

_____

_____

People have selectively bred dogs for different traits. Today, there are over 150 dog breeds.

**SECTION 2** How Does Evolution Happen? *continued*

## IDEAS ABOUT POPULATION

During Darwin's time, a scientist named Thomas Malthus was studying human populations. He observed that there were more babies being born than there were people dying. He thought that the human population could grow more rapidly than food supplies could grow. This would result in a worldwide food shortage. Malthus also pointed out that the size of human populations is limited by problems, such as starvation and disease. ☑

Darwin realized that Malthus's ideas can apply to all species, not just humans. He knew that any species can produce many offspring. He also knew starvation, disease, competition, and predation limited the populations of all species. Only a limited number of individuals live long enough to reproduce.

Darwin reasoned that the survivors had traits that helped them survive in their environment. He also thought that the survivors would pass on some of their traits to their offspring.

## IDEAS ABOUT EARTH'S HISTORY

New information about Earth's history also affected Darwin's ideas about evolution. During Darwin's time, most geologists thought that Earth was very young. But important books, such as *Principles of Geology* by Charles Lyell, were changing ideas about the Earth. Lyell's book gave evidence that Earth is much older than anyone once thought. ☑

Darwin believed that evolution happens slowly. Darwin reasoned that if Earth was very old, there would be enough time for organisms to change slowly.

| Idea | How it contributed to Darwin's theory |
|------|----------------------------------------|
| Selective breeding | |
| | helped Darwin realize that not all of an organism's offspring will survive to reproduce |
| | helped Darwin realize that slow changes can produce large differences over a long period of time |

✔ **READING CHECK**

**7. Identify** According to Thomas Malthus, what are two things that can limit the size of human populations?

_____

_____

✔ **READING CHECK**

**8. Explain** How did Charles Lyell's book change how scientists thought about Earth's history?

_____

_____

## TAKE A LOOK

**9. Describe** Fill in the blank spaces in the table.

## Say It

**Give Examples** The figure shows one example of how the four steps of natural selection can work. In a group, talk about three or more other examples of how natural selection can affect populations.

## HOW NATURAL SELECTION WORKS

Natural selection has four steps: *overproduction, inherited variation, struggle to survive,* and *successful reproduction.*

❶ **Overproduction**  A tarantula's egg sac can hold 500 to 1,000 eggs. Some of the eggs will survive and develop into adult spiders. Some will not.

❷ **Inherited Variation**  Every individual has its own combination of traits. Each tarantula is similar, but not identical, to its parents

## TAKE A LOOK

**10. Identify** Why are some tarantulas more likely to survive than others?

_____

_____

❸ **Struggle to Survive**  Some tarantulas may have traits that make it more likely that they will survive. For example, a tarantula may be better able to fight off predators, such as this wasp.

❹ **Successful Reproduction**  The tarantulas that are best adapted to their environment are likely to survive and reproduce. Their offspring may inherit the traits that help them to survive.

## GENETICS AND EVOLUTION

Darwin knew that organisms inherit traits, but not how they inherit traits. He also knew that there is great variation among organisms, but not how that variation happens. Today, scientists know that genes determine the traits of an organism. These genes are exchanged and passed on from parent to offspring.

# Section 2 Review

7.3.b

## SECTION VOCABULARY

| | |
|---|---|
| **natural selection** the process by which individuals that are better adapted to their environment survive and reproduce more successfully than less well adapted individuals do; a theory to explain the mechanism of evolution | **selective breeding** the human practice of breeding animals or plants that have certain desired traits <br><br> **trait** a genetically determined characteristic |

1. **Explain** How did the ideas in Charles Lyell's book affect Darwin's thinking about evolution?

   _____

   _____

   _____

2. **Identify** In what way are the different finch species of the Galápagos Islands adapted to the different environments on the islands?

   _____

   _____

3. **Compare** How is natural selection different from selective breeding?

   _____

   _____

   _____

   _____

4. **Describe** How did Darwin apply Malthus's ideas about human populations to the theory of evolution by natural selection?

   _____

   _____

   _____

   _____

5. **List** What are the four steps of natural selection?

   _____

   _____

   _____

   _____

**CHAPTER 10** The Evolution of Living Things

**SECTION 3** **Natural Selection in Action**

 **California Science Standards**

7.3.a, 7.3.e, 7.4.f

---

**BEFORE YOU READ**

**After you read this section, you should be able to answer these questions:**

• Why do populations change?

• How are new species formed?

• Why do some species become extinct?

---

## Why Do Populations Change?

The theory of evolution by natural selection explains how a change in the environment can change a population. Natural selection happens when members of a population have a variety of traits. Factors in the environment determine which traits are favorable and which are unfavorable.

Members of a species have different traits because their genes are different. The *genetic variation* of a population is a measure of the genetic differences between members of the population.

The members of a population with high genetic variation have many different alleles. Remember that an *allele* is a version of a gene. Because there are many different alleles in the population, there will be a large variety of traits in the population. If the environment changes, some of the individuals may have traits that will help them to survive in the new environment. ☑

The members of a population with low genetic variation do not have very many different alleles. Therefore, they have many of the same traits. If the environment changes, it is less likely that some individuals will have traits that help them survive. Therefore, populations with low genetic variation are not as able to adapt to changes in their environment.

 **STUDY TIP**

**Summarize** As you read, underline the important ideas in each paragraph. When you finish reading, write a short summary of the section using the ideas that you underlined.

---

**✓ READING CHECK**

**1. Explain** Why do individuals in a population with high genetic variation have a large variety of traits?

_____

_____

_____

_____

Cheetahs are an endangered species. Their populations have low genetic variation. Therefore, they are less likely to be able to survive a change in their environment.

---

**SECTION 3** Natural Selection in Action *continued*

## ENVIRONMENTAL FACTORS

The greater the number of traits in a population, the more likely that some individuals will survive and reproduce. Which traits are favorable and which are unfavorable? The answer depends on environmental factors. *Environmental factors* are the conditions in an environment that affect the organisms that live there.

Different environments have different environmental factors. These factors include nonliving things, such as climate. For example, organisms that live in a desert need to be able to survive without much water. Organisms that live in the ocean need to be able to survive in salty water. Environmental factors can also be living things, such as the types of food and predators in an area.

Different traits are useful in different environments. Imagine two rabbits living in a forest. The forest floor is covered with dark-colored material. A dark-colored rabbit can blend in with this material. It can easily hide from its predators. A white rabbit cannot blend as well with the forest floor. It is less able to hide from its predators. Therefore, it will probably not survive as well as the dark-colored rabbit.

Now, imagine the same two rabbits living in a snowy area. In this environment, the white rabbit can blend in with the snow. The dark-colored rabbit cannot. Therefore, in this environment, the white rabbit is more likely to survive than the dark-colored rabbit.

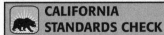

**CALIFORNIA STANDARDS CHECK**

**7.3.a** Students know both genetic <u>variation</u> and <u>environmental factors</u> are causes of evolution and <u>diversity</u> of organisms.

**Word Help: variation**
a difference in the usual form or function

**Word Help: environment**
the surrounding natural conditions that affect an organism

**Word Help: factor**
a condition or event that brings about or contributes to a result

**Word Help: diversity**
variety

**2. Identify** What determines whether a trait is favorable or unfavorable?

_____
_____

This rabbit can blend in with the forest floor. Therefore, it can hide from its predators easily. In this environment, its coloring can help it to survive.

This rabbit cannot blend in with the forest floor. It cannot hide from its predators. In this environment, it is less likely to survive.

In this environment, the dark-colored rabbit is easy to see. It is less likely to survive.

This rabbit can blend in with the snow. It can hide from its predators easily. In this environment, its coloring can help it to survive.

*Critical Thinking*

**3. Make Predictions** What are two traits that may help an animal survive in a cold environment?

_____
_____

**4. Define** Write the definition of speciation in your own words.

_____

_____

_____

## TAKE A LOOK

**5. Explain** How can a lake cause a population to become separated?

_____

_____

_____

_____

**6. Explain** Why may separated populations develop different traits?

_____

_____

_____

_____

## How Do New Species Form?

The formation of a new species as a result of evolution is called **speciation**. Three events often lead to speciation: separation, adaptation, and reproductive isolation. ☑

### SEPARATION

Speciation may happen when a group of individuals becomes separated from the rest of a population. The process of separation can happen in many ways. A newly formed canyon, mountain range, or lake can divide a population. Movements of Earth's tectonic plates can also split populations and cause new species to evolve.

Many natural features can cause populations to become separated. Canyons, mountains, and lakes are some examples of these features.

### ADAPTATION

After two groups have been separated, each group continues to be affected by natural selection. Different environmental factors may affect each population. Therefore, different traits can be favored in each population. Over many generations, different traits may spread through each population. ☑

### REPRODUCTIVE ISOLATION

Natural selection can cause two separated populations to become very different from each other. With time, the members of the two populations may be unable to mate successfully. The two populations may then be considered different species. The figures on the next page show how species of Galápagos finches may have evolved through separation, adaptation, and reproductive isolation.

**SECTION 3** Natural Selection in Action *continued*

**① Separation** Some finches left the South American mainland and reached one of the Galápagos Islands.

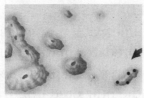

**② Adaptation** The finches on the island reproduced. Over time, they adapted to the environment on the island.

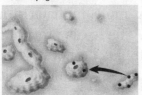

**③ Separation** Some finches flew to a second island.

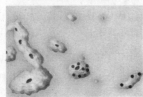

**④ Adaptation** These finches reproduced on the second island. Over time, they adapted to the second island's environment.

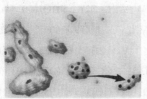

**⑤ Reproductive Isolation** After many generations, the finches on the second island were unable to successfully mate with the finches on the first island. The populations of finches on the two islands had become different species.

**⑥ Speciation** This process may have happened many times as finches flew to the different islands in the Galápagos.

## What Causes Species to Become Extinct?

Organisms have traits that help them survive in their environment. What happens if the environment changes? Sometimes organisms can survive and reproduce after the environment changes. Sometimes the species cannot adapt fast enough to survive in the new environment.

If a species does not have the adaptations needed to survive, it may become extinct. A species is **extinct** when all the individuals of the species have died out completely. Species may become extinct for many reasons. ☑

### INCREASED COMPETITION

Organisms need resources such as food, water, shelter, space, and sunlight. Different species compete for these resources. If the amount of resources decreases or the number of organisms increases, there is more competition for the remaining resources. If the members of a species cannot gather the resources they need, the species may become extinct.

**TAKE A LOOK**
**7. Identify** Where did all of the finches on the Galápagos Islands originally come from?

_____
_____

**✓ READING CHECK**

**8. Describe** What does it mean for a species to become extinct?

_____
_____
_____

**SECTION 3** Natural Selection in Action *continued*

## NEW PREDATORS

Sometimes, a new species of predator enters an area. The new predator may hunt members of other species that live in the area. The prey species may not have adaptations to avoid the new predator. If the predator kills too many members of the prey species, the prey can become extinct.

A new species may travel to an area from nearby or humans may bring it in. For example, humans brought the European red fox to Australia. The foxes prey on many animals, such as numbats. Numbats do not have adaptations to escape foxes. Their numbers are decreasing. They may become extinct because of the foxes.

## LOSS OF HABITAT

Most species get the food, water, and shelter they need from the habitat in which they live. However, habitats can be destroyed by human activities. For example, the figure below shows a forest that people have harvested for wood. Many populations once depended on the trees for food and shelter. Now, the trees cannot support these populations. Natural disasters, such as floods, storms, and fires, can also destroy habitats.

People cut down these trees for their wood. Many species once depended on the trees for food and shelter.

When a population loses its habitat, it may move to a new area. The population may not have adaptations that allow it to live in other environments. When this happens, species may become extinct.

---

**CALIFORNIA STANDARDS CHECK**

**7.3.e** Students know that extinction of a species <u>occurs</u> when the <u>environment</u> changes and the adaptive characteristics of a species are <u>insufficient</u> for its <u>survival</u>.

**Word Help: occur**
to happen

**Word Help: environment**
the surrounding natural conditions that affect an organism

**Word Help: insufficient**
not enough

**Word Help: survive**
to continue to live or exist

**9. Identify** Give three things that can cause a species to become extinct.

_____

_____

_____

**TAKE A LOOK**
**10. Explain** How can a loss of habitat cause a species to go extinct?

_____

_____

_____

_____

# Section 3 Review

7.3.a, 7.3.e, 7.4.f

## SECTION VOCABULARY

| **extinct** describes a species that has died out completely | **speciation** the formation of new species as a result of evolution |
|---|---|

**1. Define** What is genetic variation?

_____

_____

**2. Describe** What kinds of environmental factors may affect organisms that live on a rocky beach? Give three examples.

_____

_____

_____

**3. List** What are three events that can lead to speciation?

_____

_____

_____

**4. Identify** Give three examples of things that can cause groups of individuals to become separated.

_____

_____

_____

**5. Explain** How can the introduction of a new predator cause a species to go extinct?

_____

_____

_____

**6. Identify Relationships** How is genetic variation related to a species' chances of becoming extinct? Explain your answer.

_____

_____

_____

# SECTION 1 Sorting It All Out

**California Science Standards**

7.3.d

### BEFORE YOU READ

**After you read this section, you should be able to answer these questions:**

• What is classification?

• How do scientists name organisms?

• How do scientists classify organisms?

• How does a branching diagram show how organisms are related?

## Why Do We Classify Things?

Imagine that you live in a tropical rain forest and must get your own food, shelter, and clothing from the forest. What do you need to know to survive in the forest? You need to know which plants are safe to eat and which are not. You need to know which animals you can eat and which ones might eat you. In other words, you need to study the organisms around you and put them into useful groups, or classify them.

Biologists use a *classification system* to group the millions of different organisms on Earth. **Classification** is putting things into groups based on characteristics the things share. Classification helps scientists answer several important questions:

• What are the defining characteristics of each species?

• When did the characteristics of an organism evolve?

• What are the relationships between different species?

## How Do Scientists Classify Organisms?

What are some ways we can classify organisms? Perhaps we could group them by where they live or how they are useful to humans. Throughout history, people have classified organisms in many different ways.

In the 1700s, a Swedish scientist named Carolus Linnaeus created his own system. This system was based on the structure or characteristics of organisms. With his new system, Linnaeus founded modern taxonomy. **Taxonomy** is the science of describing, classifying, and naming organisms. Classifying organisms by their characteristics is called *systematics.* ☑

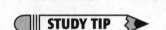

**STUDY TIP**

**Organize** As you read, make a diagram to show the eight-level system of organization.

**Say It**

**Discuss** With a partner, describe some items at home that you have put into groups. Explain why you grouped them and what characteristics you used.

✓ **READING CHECK**

**1. Explain** How did Linnaeus classify organisms?

_____

_____

_____

**SECTION 1** Sorting It All Out *continued*

## SHARED DERIVED CHARACTERISTICS

Taxonomists group organisms by their *shared derived characteristics*. Derived characteristics evolved in an ancestor of one group but not another. For example, both lions and house cats have retractable claws. This derived characteristic must have evolved in an ancestor of lions and house cats. Because these animals share these characteristics, they must be more closely related than those animals that do not.

## How Can Scientists Show How Organisms Are Related?

Shared derived characteristics can be shown in a *branching diagram*. Each characteristic on the branching diagram is shared by only the animals above it. The characteristics found higher on the diagram evolved more recently than the characteristics below them.

In this diagram, all of the animals have hair and mammary glands. However, only the brown bear, lion, and house cat give birth to live young. More recent organisms are at the ends of branches high on the diagram. For example, according to the diagram, the house cat evolved more recently than the platypus. ☑

☑ **READING CHECK**

**3. Identify** On a branching diagram, where would you see the characteristics that evolved most recently?

_____

_____

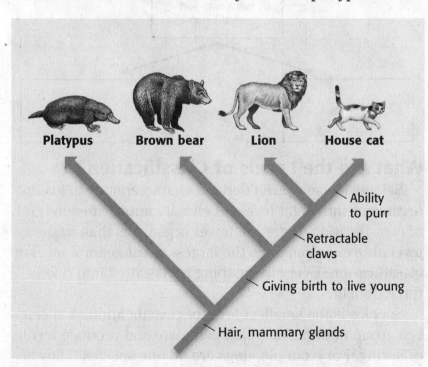

**Platypus    Brown bear    Lion    House cat**

Ability to purr

Retractable claws

Giving birth to live young

Hair, mammary glands

This branching diagram shows the similarities and differences between four kinds of mammals. The bottom of the diagram begins in the past, and the tips of the branches end in the present.

## How Do Scientists Name Organisms?

We usually call organisms by common names. For example, "cat," "dog," and "human" are all common names. Most of the time, these names are useful. However, people who speak a language other than English have different names for a cat and dog. Sometimes, organisms are even called by different names in English. For example, a cougar, mountain lion, and a puma are three names for the same animal! ☑

Scientists need to be sure they are all talking about the same organism. They give organisms *scientific names*. Scientific names are the same in all languages. An organism has only one scientific name.

Scientific names are based on the system created by Linnaeus. He gave each kind of organism a two-part name. The first part of the name is the *genus*, and the second part is the *species*. All genus names begin with a capital letter. All species names begin with a lowercase letter. Both words in a scientific name are underlined or italicized. For example, the scientific name for the Asian elephant is *Elephas maximus*. ☑

**READING CHECK**

**4. List** What are two problems with common names?

_____

_____

_____

_____

**READING CHECK**

**5. Identify** What are the two parts of a scientific name?

_____

_____

_____

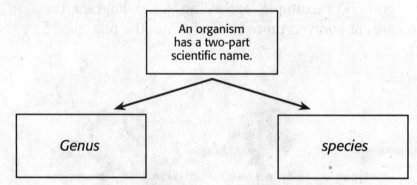

## What Are the Levels of Classification?

Scientists use shared derived characteristics to group organisms into eight levels of classification. At each level of classification, there are fewer organisms than in the level above. A domain is the largest, most general level of classification. Every living thing is classified into one of three domains.

Species is the smallest level of classification. A species is a group of organisms that can mate and produce fertile offspring. For example, dogs are all one species. They can mate with each other and have fertile offspring.

**SECTION 1** Sorting It All Out *continued*

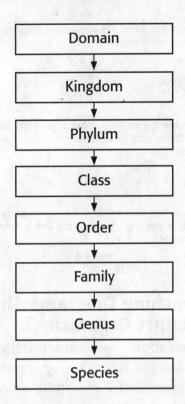

This diagram shows the levels of classification of the house cat, in domain Eukarya.

Kingdom Animalia: All animals are in the kingdom Animalia.

Phylum Chordata: All animals in the phylum Chordata have a hollow nerve cord. Most have a backbone.

Class Mammalia: Animals in the class Mammalia have a backbone. They also nurse their young.

Order Carnivora: Animals in the order Carnivora have a backbone and nurse their young. They also have special teeth for tearing meat.

## TAKE A LOOK
**6. Identify** Which level contains organisms that are more closely related: a phylum or a class?

_____

_____

Family Felidae: Animals in the family Felidae are cats. They have a backbone, nurse their young, have special teeth for tearing meat, and have retractable claws.

## TAKE A LOOK
**7. Describe** How does the number of organisms change from the level of kingdom to the level of species?

_____

_____

_____

Genus *Felis:* Animals in the genus *Felis* share traits with other animals in the same family. However, these cats cannot roar; they can only purr.

Species *Felis catus*: The species *Felis catus* is the common house cat. The house cat shares traits with all of the organisms in the levels above the species level, but it also has unique traits.

# What Do Branching Diagrams Show About Living and Extinct Organisms?

Scientists learn about the characteristics of extinct organisms from fossils. Extinct organisms can be placed in a branching diagram along with living organisms. These diagrams show when the extinct organisms evolved and when they became extinct. The more characteristics an extinct organism shared with a living one, the more closely these organisms are related.

## TAKE A LOOK
**8. Identify** Which genus that lived in the Miocene era evolved into the modern horse?

_____

_____

## Critical Thinking
**9. Infer** Branches for some species never reach the top of the diagram. What do you think is the reason?

_____

_____

_____

_____

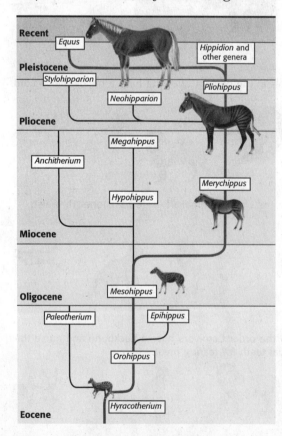

This branching diagram shows the modern horse and the genera it is related to. The diagram also shows how the genera evolved from organisms that are now extinct.

# Section 1 Review

7.3.d

## SECTION VOCABULARY

| | |
|---|---|
| **classification** the division of organisms into groups, or classes, based on specific characteristics | **taxonomy** the science of describing, naming, and classifying organisms<br><br>**Wordwise** The root *tax* means "to arrange" or "to put in order." The suffix *–nomy* means "the science of." |

**1. List** List the eight levels of classification from the largest to the smallest.

_____

_____

**2. Identify** According to the branching diagram below, which characteristic do ferns have that mosses do not?

_____

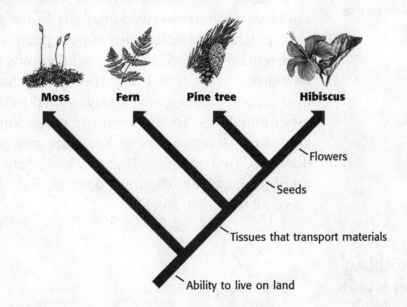

Moss     Fern     Pine tree     Hibiscus

Flowers

Seeds

Tissues that transport materials

Ability to live on land

**3. Organize** Construct a diagram similar to the one above. Use the following organisms: frog, snake, kangaroo, and rabbit. Include a change that happened before the first organism and changes that happened between the other organisms.

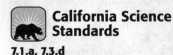

CHAPTER 11 | Classification

### SECTION 2

# Domains and Kingdoms

**California Science Standards**
7.1.a, 7.3.d

**BEFORE YOU READ**

After you read this section, you should be able to answer these questions:

• Which domains are made up of prokaryotic organisms?

• Which kingdoms are classified in the domain Eukarya?

## How Do Scientists Classify Organisms?

For hundreds of years, all organisms were classified as either plants or animals. However, as more organisms were discovered, scientists found some organisms that did not fit well into these two kingdoms. Some animals, for example, had characteristics of both plants and animals.

Scientists started adding new kingdoms to include new discoveries. Eventually, they found that organisms in some kingdoms were closely related to those in other kingdoms. Today, scientists group kingdoms into *domains*. All organisms on Earth are grouped into three domains. Two domains, Bacteria and Archaea, are made up of prokaryotes. The third domain, Eukarya, is made up of all the eukaryotes.

---

**STUDY TIP**

**List** As you read this section, make a list of the domains and kingdoms scientists use to classify organisms.

*Critical Thinking*

**1. Apply Concepts** In which domain would multicellular organisms be classified? Explain your answer.

_____

_____

_____

_____

---

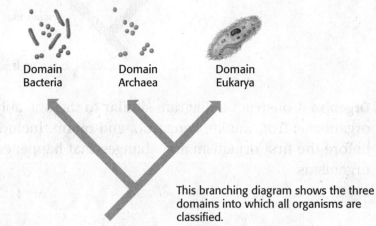

This branching diagram shows the three domains into which all organisms are classified.

At each level of classification, organisms within a group are more like each other than organisms in other groups. For example, organisms in each domain are more like each other than they are like organisms in the other domains. Scientists are still working to describe the kingdoms in each of the three domains.

**SECTION 2** Domains and Kingdoms *continued*

# How Are Prokaryotes Classified?

A prokaryote is a single-celled organism that does not have a nucleus. Prokaryotes are the oldest group of organisms on Earth. They make up two domains: Archaea and Bacteria.

## DOMAIN ARCHAEA

Domain **Archaea** is made up of prokaryotes. The cell walls and cell membranes of archaea are made of different substances than those of other prokaryotes. Many archaea can live in extreme environments where other organisms could not survive. ☑

## DOMAIN BACTERIA

All bacteria belong to domain **Bacteria**. Bacteria can be found in the air, in soil, in water, and even on and inside the human body!

We often think of bacteria as bad, but not all bacteria are harmful. One kind of bacterium changes milk into yogurt. *Escherichia coli* is a bacterium that lives in human intestines. It helps break down undigested food and produces vitamin K. Some bacteria do cause diseases, such as pneumonia. However, other bacteria make chemicals that can help us fight bacteria that cause disease. ☑

The Grand Prismatic Spring in Yellowstone National Park contains water that is about 90°C (190°F). Most organisms would die in such a hot environment.

Interactive Reader and Study Guide     **169**     Classification

---

☑ **READING CHECK**

**2. Compare** How are members of Archaea different from other prokaryotes?

_____

_____

_____

_____

☑ **READING CHECK**

**3. Explain** Are all bacteria harmful? Explain your answer.

_____

_____

_____

_____

**TAKE A LOOK**

**4. Identify** What kind of prokaryotes do you think could live in this spring? Explain your answer.

_____

_____

_____

**Word Help: <u>construct</u>**
to build; to make from parts

**5. Identify** Based on the branching diagram, which two kingdoms in Eukarya evolved most recently? How do you know?

_____

_____

_____

_____

_____

_____

# How Are Eukaryotes Classified?

Organisms whose cells have membrane-bound organelles and a nucleus are called *eukaryotes*. All eukaryotes belong to domain **Eukarya**. Domain Eukarya includes the following kingdoms: Protista, Plantae, Fungi, and Animalia.

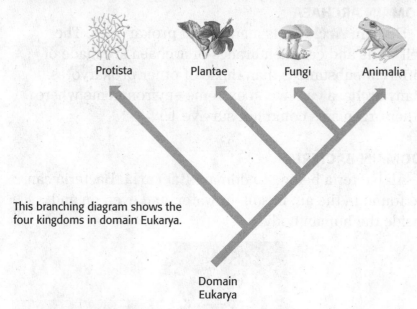

Protista    Plantae    Fungi    Animalia

Domain Eukarya

This branching diagram shows the four kingdoms in domain Eukarya.

**KINGDOM PROTISTA**

Members of kingdom **Protista** are either single-celled or simple multicellular organisms. They are commonly called *protists*. Scientists think that the first protists evolved from ancient bacteria about 2 billion years ago. Much later, ancient protists gave rise to plants, fungi, and animals.

Kingdom Protista contains many different kinds of organisms. Some, such as *Paramecium*, resemble animals. They are called *protozoa*. Plantlike protists are called *algae*. Some algae, such as phytoplankton, are single cells. Others, such as kelp, are multicellular. Multicellular slime molds also belong to kingdom Protista.

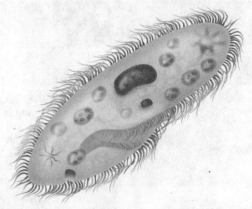

## KINGDOM FUNGI

Molds and mushrooms are members of kingdom **Fungi**. Some fungi (singular, *fungus*) are unicellular. That is, they are single-celled organisms. Yeast is unicellular. Most other fungi are multicellular. Unlike plants, fungi do not perform photosynthesis. However, they also do not eat food, as animals do. Instead, fungi break down materials in the environment with digestive juices and absorb them. ☑

**✓ READING CHECK**

**6. Describe** How do fungi get food?

_____

_____

_____

*Amanita* is a poisonous fungus. You should never eat wild fungi.

## KINGDOM PLANTAE

Although plants differ in size and appearance, most people can easily identify the members of kingdom Plantae. Kingdom **Plantae** contains organisms that are eukaryotic, have cell walls, and make food by photosynthesis. Most plants need sunlight to carry out photosynthesis. Therefore, plants must live in places where light can reach.

The food that plants make is important for the plants and also for other organisms. Many animals, fungi, protists, and bacteria get nutrients from plants. When they digest the plant material, they get the energy stored by the plant. Plants also provide homes for other organisms.

## Math Focus

**7. Calculate** If the average student's arms can extend about 1.3 m, how many students would have to join hands to form a human chain around a giant sequoia?

_____

The giant sequoia is one of the largest members of kingdom Plantae. A giant sequoia can measure 30 m around the base and grow more than 91 m tall!

## KINGDOM ANIMALIA

Kingdom **Animalia** contains complex, multicellular organisms. Organisms in kingdom Animalia are commonly called *animals*. The following are some characteristics of animals:

- Their cells do not have cell walls.
- They are able to move from place to place.
- They have sense organs that help them react quickly to their environment.

## TAKE A LOOK

**8. Identify** Which animal characteristic can be seen in this bald eagle?

_____

_____

## STRANGE ORGANISMS

Some organisms are not easy to classify. For example, some plants can eat other organisms to get nutrition as animals do. Some protists use photosynthesis as plants do but also move around as animals do.

**Red Cup Sponge**

## Critical Thinking

**9. Apply Concepts** To get nutrients, a Venus' flytrap uses photosynthesis and traps and digests insects. Its cells have cell walls. Into which kingdom would you place this organism? Explain your answer.

_____

_____

_____

_____

_____

What kind of organism is this red cup sponge? It does not have sense organs and cannot move for most of its life. Because of this, scientists once classified sponges as plants. However, sponges cannot make their own food as plants do. They must eat other organisms to get nutrients. Today, scientists classify sponges as animals. Sponges are usually considered the simplest animals.

# Section 2 Review

7.1.a, 7.3.d

## SECTION VOCABULARY

**Animalia** a kingdom made up of complex, multicellular organisms that lack cell walls, can usually move around, and quickly respond to their environment

**Archaea** in a modern taxonomic system, a domain made up of prokaryotes that differ from other prokaryotes in the makeup of their cell walls and in their genetics; this domain aligns with the traditional kingdom Archaebacteria

**Bacteria** in a modern taxonomic system, a domain made up of prokaryotes that differ from other prokaryotes in the makeup of their cell walls and in their genetics

**Eukarya** in a modern taxonomic system, a domain made up of all eukaryotes; this domain aligns with the traditional kingdoms Protista, Fungi, Plantae, and Animalia

**Fungi** a kingdom made up of nongreen, eukaryotic organisms that have no means of movement, reproduce by using spores, and get food by breaking down substances in their surroundings and absorbing the nutrients

**Plantae** a kingdom made up of complex, multicellular organisms that are usually green, have cell walls made of cellulose, cannot move around, and use the sun's energy to make sugar by photosynthesis

**Protista** a kingdom of mostly one-celled eukaryotic organisms that are different from plants, animals, bacteria, and fungi

**1. Explain** Why is a two-kingdom classification system no longer used by scientists?

_____

_____

_____

_____

**2. Compare** Create a Venn Diagram to compare members of Kingdom Plantae and Kingdom Fungi.

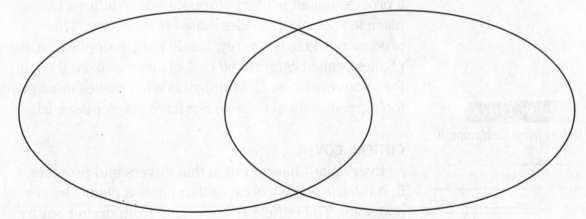

**3. Compare** What is one major difference between domain Eukarya and domains Bacteria and Archaea?

_____

_____

**CHAPTER 12** Introduction to Plants
**SECTION 1** # What Is a Plant?

**California Science Standards**

7.1.b, 7.1.d, 7.5.a

**BEFORE YOU READ**

After you read this section, you should be able to answer these questions:

• What characteristics do all plants share?

• What are two differences between plant cells and animal cells?

• How are vascular plants different from nonvascular plants?

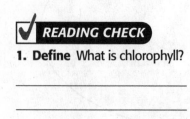
**STUDY TIP**

**Organize** As you read, make a diagram to show the major groups of plants. Be sure to include the characteristics of each group.

## What Is a Plant?

A plant is an organism that uses sunlight to make food. Trees, grasses, ferns, cactuses, and dandelions are all types of plants. Plants can look very different, but they all share four characteristics.

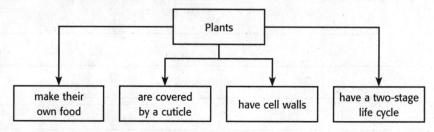

### MAKING THEIR OWN FOOD

Plants make food from carbon dioxide and water in a process called *photosynthesis*. Photosynthesis takes place in special organelles called *chloroplasts*. The process needs light energy. Inside the chloroplasts, a green pigment called *chlorophyll* collects energy from the sun for photosynthesis. Chlorophyll is what makes most plants look green. Animal cells do not have chloroplasts. ☑

**READING CHECK**

1. **Define** What is chlorophyll?

_____

_____

_____

_____

### CUTICLE COVER

Every plant has a cuticle that covers and protects it. A *cuticle* is a waxy layer that coats a plant's leaves and stem. The cuticle keeps plants from drying out by keeping water inside the plant.

SECTION 1 **What Is a Plant?** *continued*

## CELL WALLS

How do plants stay upright? They do not have skeletons, as many animals do. Instead, each plant cell is surrounded by a stiff cell wall. The cell wall is outside the cell membrane. Cell walls support and protect the plant cell. Animal cells do not have cell walls.

**Structures in a Plant Cell**

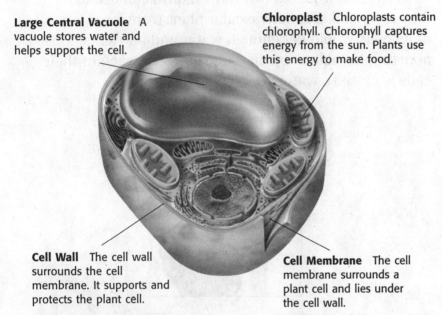

**Large Central Vacuole** A vacuole stores water and helps support the cell.

**Chloroplast** Chloroplasts contain chlorophyll. Chlorophyll captures energy from the sun. Plants use this energy to make food.

**Cell Wall** The cell wall surrounds the cell membrane. It supports and protects the plant cell.

**Cell Membrane** The cell membrane surrounds a plant cell and lies under the cell wall.

## TWO-STAGE LIFE CYCLE

Many organisms, including plants, produce offspring when a sperm joins with an egg. This is called *sexual reproduction*. In animals, sexual reproduction happens in every generation. However, plants do not produce sperm and eggs in every generation.

Plants have a two-stage life cycle. This means that they need two generations to produce eggs and sperm. In the *sporophyte* stage, a plant makes spores. A *spore* is a cell that can divide and grow into a new plant. This new plant is called a *gametophyte*. In the gametophyte stage, the plants produce sperm and eggs. The sperm and eggs then join to produce a new sporophyte. ☑

# What Are the Main Groups of Plants?

There are two main groups of plants: vascular and non-vascular. A **vascular plant** has specialized vascular tissues. *Vascular tissues* move water and nutrients from one part of a plant to another. A **nonvascular plant** does not have vascular tissues to move water and nutrients.

**READING CHECK**

**3. List** What are the two stages of the plant life cycle?

_____
_____

**SECTION 1** What Is a Plant? *continued*

## NONVASCULAR PLANTS

Instead of special tissues to move water and nutrients, nonvascular plants depend on diffusion to move these materials. In *diffusion*, water and nutrients move through a cell membrane and into a cell. Diffusion works best over short distances. Each cell must get water and nutrients from the environment or a cell that is close by.

Nonvascular plants can rely on diffusion because they are small. If a nonvascular plant were large, not all of its cells would get enough water and nutrients. Most nonvascular plants live in damp areas, so each of their cells is close to water. ☑

**Nonvascular Plants**

Mosses, liverworts, and hornworts

## VASCULAR PLANTS

Many of the plants we are most familiar with are vascular plants. They include ferns, pine trees, cactuses, and tulips. Vascular plants are divided into two groups: seedless plants and seed plants. Seed plants are divided into two more groups based on whether or not the plant has flowers. Nonflowering seed plants, such as pine trees, are called **gymnosperms**. Flowering seed plants, such as magnolias, are called **angiosperms**.

| Vascular Plants | | |
|---|---|---|
| Seedless plants | Seed plants | |
| Ferns, horsetails, and club mosses | Nonflowering | Flowering |
| | Gymnosperms | Angiosperms |

---

**✓ READING CHECK**

**4. Identify** How do water and nutrients move through a nonvascular plant?

_____

_____

_____

*Critical Thinking*

**5. Apply Concepts** Do you think a sunflower is a gymnosperm or an angiosperm? Explain your answer.

_____

_____

_____

# Section 1 Review

7.1.b, 7.1.d, 7.5.a

## SECTION VOCABULARY

| | |
|---|---|
| **angiosperm** a flowering plant that produces seeds within a fruit<br>   **Wordwise** The root *angi* means "vessel."<br>**gymnosperm** a woody, vascular seed plant whose seeds are not enclosed by an ovary or fruit<br>   **Wordwise** The root *gymn* means "naked." The root *sperm* means "seed." | **nonvascular plant** a plant that lacks specialized conducting tissues and true roots, stems, and leaves<br>**vascular plant** a plant that has specialized tissues that conduct materials from one part of the plant to another |

**1. Explain** What are the two main differences between a plant cell and an animal cell?

_____

_____

_____

_____

**2. Organize** Fill in each box in the figure below with one of the main characteristics of plants.

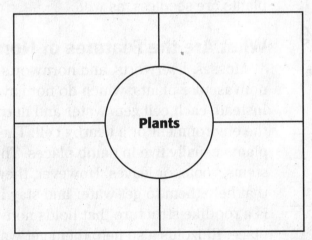

**3. Predict** What would happen to a plant if its chloroplasts stopped working? Explain your answer.

_____

_____

_____

**4. Compare** What is the main difference between vascular and nonvascular plants?

_____

_____

_____

CHAPTER 12 Introduction to Plants

**SECTION 2 Seedless Plants**

**California Science Standards**

7.2.a, 7.5.a

**After you read this section, you should be able to answer these questions:**

• What are the differences between seedless vascular plants and nonvascular plants?

• How do seedless vascular plants reproduce?

• How do nonvascular plants reproduce?

---

**STUDY TIP**

**Organize** As you read this section, make a chart that compares vascular plants and nonvascular plants.

*Critical Thinking*

**1. Apply Concepts** Why wouldn't you expect to see nonvascular plants in the desert?

_____

_____

_____

_____

**✓ READING CHECK**

**2. List** What are two functions of the rhizoid?

_____

_____

_____

**TAKE A LOOK**

**3. Identify** Are the male and female gametophytes separate plants or part of the same plant?

---

## What Are Seedless Plants?

When you think of plants, you probably think of plants like flowers that make seeds, but many plants don't.

Remember that plants are divided into two main groups: nonvascular plants and vascular plants. All nonvascular plants are seedless, and some vascular plants are seedless, as well.

## What Are the Features of Nonvascular Plants?

Mosses, liverworts, and hornworts are types of nonvascular plants, which do not have vascular tissue. Instead, each cell gets water and nutrients directly from the environment or a nearby cell. Therefore, nonvascular plants usually live in damp places. They do not have true stems, roots, or leaves. However, they do have features that help them to get water and stay in place. A **rhizoid** is a rootlike structure that holds nonvascular plants in place. Rhizoids also help them get water and nutrients. ☑

| Nonvascular plants |
|---|
| • have no vascular tissue |
| • have no true roots, stems, leaves, or seeds |
| • are usually small |
| • live in damp places |

### Moss Life Cycle

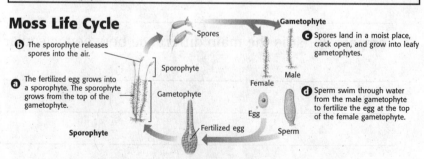

**ⓑ** The sporophyte releases spores into the air.

Spores

**Gametophyte**

**ⓒ** Spores land in a moist place, crack open, and grow into leafy gametophytes.

Sporophyte

**ⓐ** The fertilized egg grows into a sporophyte. The sporophyte grows from the top of the gametophyte.

Gametophyte

Male

Female

**ⓓ** Sperm swim through water from the male gametophyte to fertilize the egg at the top of the female gametophyte.

Egg

Sperm

Sporophyte

Fertilized egg

**SECTION 2** Seedless Plants *continued*

## REPRODUCTION IN NONVASCULAR PLANTS

Like all plants, nonvascular plants have a two-stage life cycle. They have a sporophyte generation, which produces spores, and a gametophyte generation, which produces eggs and sperm. Nonvascular plants can also reproduce asexually, that is, without eggs and sperm.

## IMPORTANCE OF NONVASCULAR PLANTS

Nonvascular plants are usually the first plants to live in a new environment, such as newly exposed rock. When these plants die, they break down and help form a thin layer of soil. Then, plants that need soil in order to grow can move into these areas.

Some nonvascular plants are important as food or nesting material for animals. A nonvascular plant called peat moss is important to humans. When it turns to peat, it can be burned as a fuel.

## What Are the Features of Seedless Vascular Plants?

Vascular plants have specialized tissues that deliver water and nutrients to all their cells. Therefore, seedless vascular plants are often larger than nonvascular plants. They do not have to live in places that are damp. ☑

Many seedless vascular plants, such as ferns, have a structure called a rhizome. The **rhizome** is an underground stem that produces new leaves and roots.

*Critical Thinking*

**4. Apply Concepts** What do you think is the reason that nonvascular plants can be the first plants to grow in a new environment?

_____

_____

_____

_____

✓ **READING CHECK**

**5. Explain** How do the cells of a seedless vascular plant get water?

_____

_____

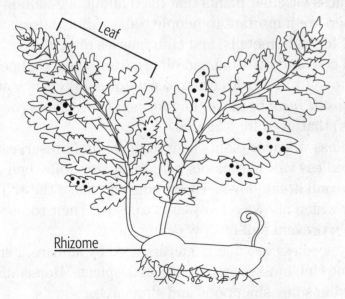

Leaf

Rhizome

## REPRODUCTION IN SEEDLESS VASCULAR PLANTS

Seedless vascular plants and nonvascular plants have very similar life cycles. First, the sperm from a male gametophyte joins with the egg from a female gametophyte. The sporophyte that grows from the egg and sperm produces spores. Then, these spores grow into new gametophytes.

Seedless vascular plants can also reproduce asexually. This can happen when new plants branch off from older plants. It can happen also when pieces of one plant fall off and begin to grow as new plants. ☑

**Fern Life Cycle**

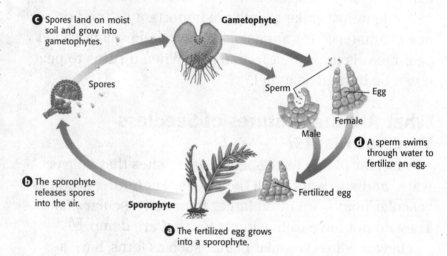

**C** Spores land on moist soil and grow into gametophytes.

**Gametophyte**

Spores

Sperm

Egg

Female

Male

**d** A sperm swims through water to fertilize an egg.

**b** The sporophyte releases spores into the air.

**Sporophyte**

Fertilized egg

**a** The fertilized egg grows into a sporophyte.

## IMPORTANCE OF SEEDLESS VASCULAR PLANTS

Seedless vascular plants that lived about 300 million years ago are important to people today. After these ancient ferns, horsetails, and club mosses died, they formed coal and oil. Coal and oil are fossil fuels that people remove from Earth's crust to use for energy. They are called *fossil fuels* because they formed from plants (or animals) that lived long ago. ☑

Seedless vascular plants help to make and preserve soil. Seedless vascular plants help form new soil when they die and break down. Their roots can make the soil deeper, which allows other plants to grow. Their roots also help prevent soil from washing away.

Many seedless vascular plants are used by humans. Ferns and some club mosses are popular houseplants. Horsetails are used in some shampoos and skincare products.

---

**✓ READING CHECK**

**6. Describe** What are two ways in which seedless nonvascular plants reproduce asexually?

_____

_____

_____

_____

_____

## TAKE A LOOK

**7. Apply Concepts** Does this figure show sexual or asexual reproduction? Explain your answer.

_____

_____

_____

_____

_____

**✓ READING CHECK**

**8. Explain** Where does coal come from?

_____

_____

_____

_____

_____

# Section 2 Review

7.2.a, 7.5.a

## SECTION VOCABULARY

| **rhizoid** a rootlike structure in nonvascular plants that holds the plants in place and helps plants get water and nutrients | **rhizome** a horizontal, underground stem that produces new leaves, shoots, and roots |
|---|---|

**1. Compare** What are two differences between a rhizoid and a rhizome?

_____

_____

_____

**2. Explain** In which generation does sexual reproduction occur? Explain your answer.

_____

_____

**3. Compare** Use a Venn Diagram to compare vascular and nonvascular plants.

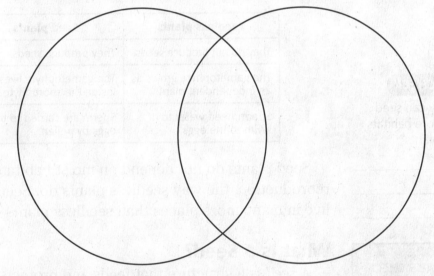

**4. Apply Concepts** Nonvascular plants are usually very small. How does their structure limit their size?

_____

_____

**5. List** Name six kinds of seedless plants.

_____

_____

CHAPTER 12 | Introduction to Plants

SECTION
**3** **Seed Plants**

**California Science Standards**

7.2.a, 7.5.f

**BEFORE YOU READ**

After you read this section, you should be able to answer these questions:

• How are seed plants different from seedless plants?

• What are the parts of a seed?

• How do gymnosperms and angiosperms reproduce?

## What Are Seed Plants?

Many of the plants you are most familiar with are seed plants. Seed plants include trees, such as oaks and pine trees, as well as flowers, such as roses and dandelions. Seed plants are one of the two main groups of vascular plants.

Like all plants, seed plants have a two-stage life cycle. However, seed plants differ from seedless plants, as shown below.

| Seedless plants | Seed plants |
|---|---|
| They do not produce seeds. | They produce seeds. |
| The gametophyte grows as an independent plant. | The gametophyte lives inside the sporophyte. |
| Sperm need water to swim to the eggs. | Sperm are carried to the eggs by pollen. |

Seed plants do not depend on moist habitats for reproduction, the way seedless plants do. Seed plants can live in many more places than seedless plants can. ☑

## What Is a Seed?

A *seed* is a structure that feeds and protects a young plant. It forms after fertilization, when a sperm and an egg join. A seed has the following three main parts:

• a young plant, or sporophyte

• *cotyledons*, early leaves that provide food for the young plant

• a seed coat that covers and protects the young plant

**STUDY TIP** ✏

**List** As you read this section, list the characteristics of gymnosperms and angiosperms.

✔ **READING CHECK**

**1. Explain** Why can seed plants live in more habitats than seedless plants?

_____

_____

_____

**CALIFORNIA STANDARDS CHECK**

**7.5.f** Students know the structures and processes by which flowering plants <u>generate</u> pollen, ovules, seeds, and fruit.

**Word Help: <u>generate</u>** to bring about; to produce

**2. Identify** What process must occur before a seed can develop?

_____

_____

_____

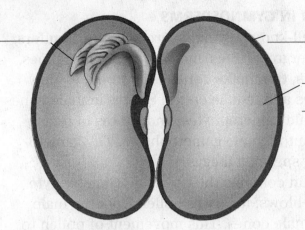

A seed contains stored food and a young plant, or sporophyte. A seed is surrounded and protected by a seed coat.

**TAKE A LOOK**
**3. Label** Label the parts of a seed with these terms: young plant, seed coat, cotyledon.

## ADVANTAGES OF HAVING SEEDS

Seeds give plants some advantages. For example, when the young plant inside a seed begins to grow, it uses the food stored in the seed. In contrast, the spores of seedless plants don't have stored food to help a new plant grow. Therefore, they will live only if they land in an area with enough resources.

Another advantage is that seeds can be spread by animals. The spores of seedless plants are usually spread by wind. Animals often spread seeds more efficiently than the wind spreads spores. Therefore, seeds that are spread by animals are more likely to find a good place to grow.

*Critical Thinking*
**4. Apply Concepts** It is helpful for seed plants to have a supply of food in the seed. What do you think is the reason?

_____

_____

_____

_____

## What Kinds of Plants Have Seeds?

Seed plants are divided into two main groups: gymnosperms and angiosperms. *Gymnosperms* are non-flowering plants, and *angiosperms* are flowering plants.

## GYMNOSPERMS

Gymnosperms are seed plants that do not have flowers or fruits. They include plants such as pine trees and redwood trees. Many gymnosperms are evergreen, which means that they keep their leaves all year. Gymnosperm seeds usually develop in a cone, like a pine cone. ☑

**Pine Cone**

**Seeds**

**READING CHECK**
**5. Identify** What structure do gymnosperm seeds usually develop in?

_____

_____

**SECTION 3** Seed Plants *continued*

## REPRODUCTION IN GYMNOSPERMS

The most well-known gymnosperms are the conifers. Conifers are evergreen trees and shrubs, such as pines, spruces, and firs, that make cones to reproduce. They have male cones and female cones. Spores in male cones develop into male gametophytes, and spores in female cones develop into female gametophytes. The gametophytes produce sperm and eggs.

A **pollen** grain contains the tiny male gametophyte. When the wind blows, it carries pollen from the male cones to the female cones. This movement of pollen to the female cones is called **pollination**. Pollination is part of sexual reproduction in plants. ☑

After pollination, sperm fertilize the eggs in the female cones. A fertilized egg develops into a new sporophyte inside a seed. Eventually, the seeds fall from the cone. If the conditions are right, the seeds will grow.

**READING CHECK**

**6. Explain** How is gymnosperm pollen carried from one plant to another?

_____

_____

_____

## TAKE A LOOK

**7. Explain** Does this picture show an example of sexual or asexual reproduction? Explain.

_____

_____

_____

_____

_____

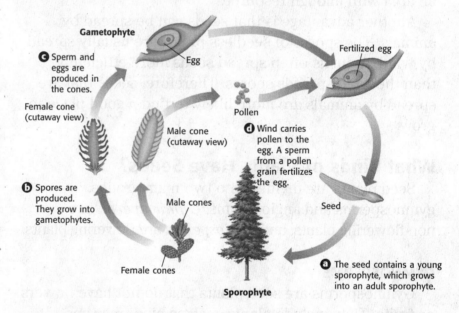

Gametophyte

**c** Sperm and eggs are produced in the cones.

Egg

Fertilized egg

Female cone (cutaway view)

Pollen

Male cone (cutaway view)

**d** Wind carries pollen to the egg. A sperm from a pollen grain fertilizes the egg.

**b** Spores are produced. They grow into gametophytes.

Male cones

Seed

Female cones

**a** The seed contains a young sporophyte, which grows into an adult sporophyte.

Sporophyte

## IMPORTANCE OF GYMNOSPERMS

Gymnosperms are used to make many products, such as medicines, building materials, and household products. Some conifers produce a drug used to fight cancer. Many trees are cut so that their wood can be used to build homes and furniture. Pine trees make a sticky substance called resin. Resin can be used to make soap, paint, and ink.

# What Are Angiosperms?

Angiosperms are seed plants that produce flowers and fruit. Maple trees, daisies, and blackberries are all examples of angiosperms. There are more angiosperms on Earth than any other kind of plant. They can be found in almost every land ecosystem, including grasslands, deserts, and forests.

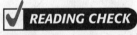

## Math Focus

**8. Calculate** There are 300,000 species of angiosperms on Earth and 840 species of gymnosperms. What percentage of seed plants are angiosperms?

## REPRODUCTION IN ANGIOSPERMS

In angiosperms, pollination takes place in flowers. Some angiosperms depend on the wind for pollination. Others rely on animals such as bees and birds to carry pollen from flower to flower.

Angiosperm seeds develop inside fruits. Some fruits and seeds, like those of a dandelion, are made to help the wind carry them. Other fruits, such as blackberries, attract animals that eat them. The animals drop the seeds in new places, where they can grow into plants. Some fruits, such as burrs, travel by sticking to animal fur. ☑

**READING CHECK**

**9. Identify** Where do angiosperm seeds develop?

## IMPORTANCE OF ANGIOSPERMS

Flowering plants provide food for animals. A mouse that eats seeds and berries uses flowering plants directly as food. An owl that eats a field mouse uses flowering plants indirectly as food. Flowering plants can also provide food for the animals that pollinate them.

People use flowering plants, too. Major food crops, such as corn, wheat, and rice, come from flowering plants. Many flowering trees, such as oak trees, can be used for building materials. Plants such as cotton and flax are used to make clothing and rope. Flowering plants are also used to make medicines, rubber, and perfume oils.

**Say It**

**Describe** Think of all the products you used today that came from angiosperms. Describe to the class five items you used in some way and what kind of angiosperm they came from.

# Section 3 Review

## SECTION VOCABULARY

| | |
|---|---|
| **pollen** the tiny granules that contain the male gametophyte of seed plants | **pollination** the transfer of pollen from the male reproductive structures to the female structures of seed plants |

1. **Compare** How are the gametophytes of seed plants different from the gametophytes of seedless plants?

_____

_____

_____

2. **Describe** What happens during pollination?

_____

_____

3. **Compare** Use a Venn Diagram to compare gymnosperms and angiosperms.

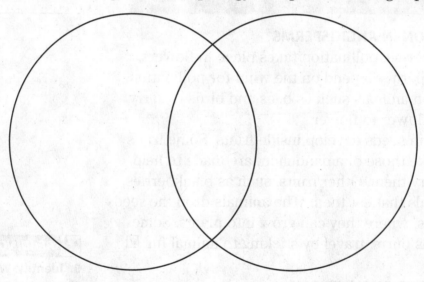

4. **Identify** What two structures are unique to angiosperms?

_____

5. **List** What are the three main parts of a seed? What does each part do?

_____

_____

_____

_____

# SECTION 4 Structures of Seed Plants

California Science Standards

7.5.a, 7.5.f

## BEFORE YOU READ

After you read this section, you should be able to answer these questions:

- What are the functions of roots and stems?
- What is the function of leaves?
- What is the function of a flower?

## What Are Seed Plants?

Remember that seed plants include trees, such as oaks and pine trees, as well as flowers, such as roses and dandelions. Seed plants are one of the two main groups of vascular plants.

## What Structures Are Found in a Seed Plant?

Just like the human body, a plant has different organs that do jobs for the organism. Seed plants have roots, shoots, and reproductive structures. A plant's roots and shoots help the plant to get water and nutrients. Roots are often found underground. Shoots include stems and leaves. They are usually found above ground. ☑

The roots of plants absorb and store water and nutrients.

### VASCULAR TISSUE

Like all vascular plants, seed plants have specialized tissues that move water and nutrients through the plant. There are two kinds of vascular tissue: xylem and phloem. **Xylem** moves water and minerals from the roots to the shoots. **Phloem** moves food molecules to all parts of the plant. The vascular tissues in the roots and shoots are connected.

---

**STUDY TIP**

**List** As you read this section, make a chart listing the structures of seed plants and their functions.

---

**READING CHECK**

**1. Identify** What are the three main parts of a seed plant?

_____

_____

_____

---

**CALIFORNIA STANDARDS CHECK**

**7.5.a** Students know plants and animals have levels of organization for structure and function, including cells, tissues, organs, organ systems, and the whole organism.

**Word Help: structure** the way in which a whole is put together

**2. Describe** What are the functions of xylem and phloem?

_____

_____

_____

_____

_____

## What Are Roots?

Roots are organs that have three main functions:

- to absorb water and nutrients from the soil
- to hold plants in the soil
- to store extra food made in the leaves

Roots have several structures that help them do these jobs. The *epidermis* is a layer of cells that covers the outside of the root, like skin. Some cells of the epidermis, called *root hairs*, stick out from the root. These hairs increase the root's surface area. A larger surface area helps the root absorb more water and minerals. A *root cap* is a group of cells found at the tip of a root. The root cap protects the root as it grows down through the soil.

## Critical Thinking

**3. Apply Concepts** What do you think happens to water and minerals right after they are absorbed by roots?

_____

_____

_____

**TAKE A LOOK**

**4. Identify** Where is the vascular tissue located in this root?

_____

_____

**5. Apply Concepts** How do you think food made in the leaves gets to the roots for storage?

_____

_____

_____

**Parts of a Root**

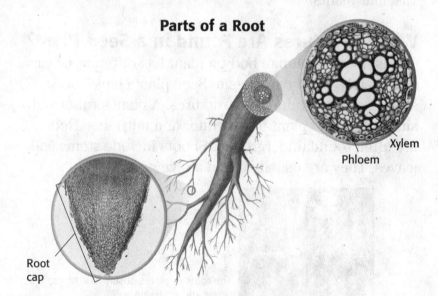

Root cap

Xylem

Phloem

### TYPES OF ROOT SYSTEMS

There are two kinds of root systems: taproot systems and fibrous root systems. A *taproot system* has one main root, or taproot, that grows downward. Many smaller roots branch from the taproot. Taproots can reach water deep underground. Carrots are plants that have taproot systems.

A *fibrous root system* has several roots that spread out from the base of a plant's stem. The roots are usually the same size. Fibrous roots usually get water from close to the soil surface. Many grasses have fibrous root systems.

**SECTION 4** Structures of Seed Plants *continued*

# What Are Stems?

A stem is an organ that connects a plant's roots to its leaves and reproductive structures. A stem does the following jobs: ☑

- Stems support the plant body. Leaves are arranged along stems so that each leaf can get sunlight.

- Stems hold up reproductive structures such as flowers. This helps bees and other pollinators find the flowers.

- Stems carry materials between the root system and the leaves and reproductive structures. Xylem carries water and minerals from the roots to the rest of the plant. Phloem carries the food made in the leaves to roots and other parts of the plant.

- Some stems store materials. For example, the stems of cactuses can store water.

## TYPES OF PLANT STEMS

There are two different types of stems: herbaceous and woody. *Herbaceous* stems are soft and flexible. Flowers, such as daisies and clover, have herbaceous stems. Many crops, such as tomatoes, corn, and beans, also have herbaceous stems.

Other plants have woody stems. *Woody* stems are stiff and are often covered by bark. Trees and shrubs have woody stems. The trunk of a tree is actually its stem!

✔ **READING CHECK**

**6. Define** What is a stem?

_____

_____

_____

_____

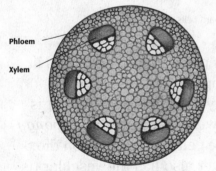

Herbaceous stems are thin and flexible.

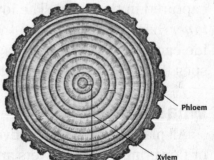

Woody stems are usually thick and stiff.

**TAKE A LOOK**

**7. Compare** How are these stems similar?

_____

_____

**8. Compare** How are these stems different?

_____

_____

## What Are Leaves?

Leaves are organs, too. Photosynthesis happens in leaves. Leaves absorb carbon dioxide from the air. Chloroplasts in leaf cells capture energy from sunlight. The leaves use the energy, carbon dioxide, and water to make food. ☑

All leaf structures are related to the leaf's main job, photosynthesis. A *cuticle* covers the surfaces of the leaf. It prevents the leaf from losing water. The *epidermis* is a single layer of cells beneath the cuticle. Tiny openings in the epidermis, called *stomata* (singular, *stoma*), let carbon dioxide enter the leaf. *Guard cells* open and close the stomata.

✓ **READING CHECK**

**9. Identify** What is the main function of a leaf?

_____

_____

**Structure of a Leaf**

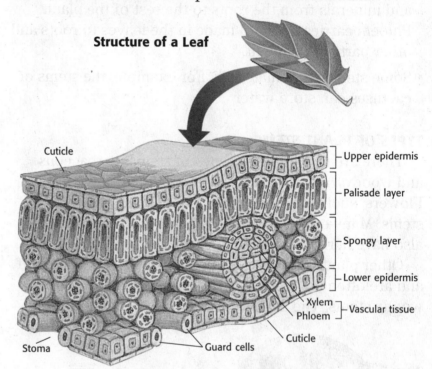

Cuticle — Upper epidermis
— Palisade layer
— Spongy layer
— Lower epidermis
Xylem
Phloem — Vascular tissue
Cuticle
Stoma — Guard cells

**TAKE A LOOK**

**10. Explain** Is this plant vascular or nonvascular? Explain your answer.

_____

_____

_____

Most photosynthesis takes place in the two layers in the middle of the leaf. The upper layer, called the *palisade layer*, contains many chloroplasts. Sunlight is captured in this layer. The lower layer, called the *spongy layer*, has spaces between the cells, where carbon dioxide can move. The spongy layer also has the vascular tissues that bring water to the leaves and move food away.

## What Are Flowers?

All plants have reproductive structures. In angiosperms, or flowering plants, flowers are the reproductive structures. Flowers produce eggs and sperm for sexual reproduction. ☑

✓ **READING CHECK**

**11. Identify** For what group of plants are flowers the reproductive structures?

_____

_____

**SECTION 4** Structures of Seed Plants *continued*

## PARTS OF A FLOWER

Flowers may have the following basic parts: sepals, petals, stamens, and one or more pistils. These parts are often arranged in rings, one inside the other. However, not all flowers have every part.

Different species of flowering plants can have different flower types. Flowers with all four parts are called *perfect flowers*. Flowers that have stamens but no pistils are male. Flowers that have pistils but no stamens are female.

**Parts of a Flower**

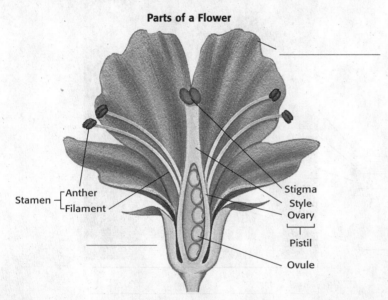

Stamen — ┌ Anther
         └ Filament

Stigma
Style
Ovary

Pistil

Ovule

## SEPALS

**Sepals** are leaves that make up the outer ring of flower parts. They are often green like leaves, but they may have other colors. Sepals protect and cover the flower while it is still a bud. When the flower begins to open, the sepals fold back, so the petals can be seen.

## PETALS

**Petals** are leaflike parts of a flower. They make up the next ring inside of the sepals. Petals are sometimes brightly colored, like the petals of poppy flowers or roses. This color helps attract insects and other animals. Many plants need these animals to help spread their pollen.

## STAMENS

A **stamen** is the male reproductive structure of a flower. Structures on the stamen called *anthers* produce pollen. Pollen contains the male gametophyte, which produces sperm. The anther rests on a thin stalk called a *filament*. ☑

### TAKE A LOOK

**12. Label** As you read, fill in the missing labels on the diagram.

**13. Identify** What two parts make up the stamen ?

_____

_____

**14. Identify** What three parts make up the pistil?

_____

_____

_____

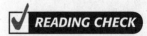

**READING CHECK**

**15. Identify** What is the male reproductive structure of a flower?

_____

## PISTILS

A **pistil** is the female reproductive structure. The tip of the pistil is called the *stigma*. The long, thin part of the pistil is called the *style*. The rounded base of the pistil is called the **ovary**. The ovary contains one or more ovules. Each **ovule** contains an egg. ☑

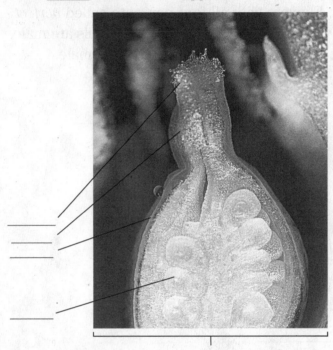

**16. Identify** What is the female reproductive structure of a flower?

_____

_____

## TAKE A LOOK

**17. Label** Label the female reproductive structures in this picture.

Pollen is brushed onto the style, and sperm from inside the pollen travel down the style to the ovary. A sperm can fertilize the egg of one ovule. After fertilization, an ovule develops into a seed. The ovary surrounding the ovule develops into a fruit.

## IMPORTANCE OF FLOWERS

Flowers are important to plants because they help plants reproduce. They are also important to animals, such as insects and bats, that use parts of flowers for food. Humans also use flowers. Some flowers, such as broccoli and cauliflower, can be eaten. Others, like chamomile, are used to make tea. Flowers are also used in perfumes, lotions, and shampoos.

**Say It**

**Discuss** What is your favorite flower? Have you ever seen any unusual flowers in nature? In groups of two or three, discuss your experiences with flowers.

# Section 4 Review

7.5.a, 7.5.f

## SECTION VOCABULARY

| | |
|---|---|
| **ovary** in flowering plants, the lower part of a pistil that produces eggs in ovules | **pistil** the female reproductive part of a flower that produces seeds and consists of an ovary, style, and stigma |
| **ovule** a structure in the ovary of a seed plant that contains an embryo sac and that develops into a seed after fertilization | **sepal** in a flower, one of the outermost rings of modified leaves that protect the flower bud |
| **petal** one of the usually brightly colored leaf-shaped parts that make up one of the rings of a flower | **stamen** the male reproductive structure of a flower that produces pollen and consists of an anther at the tip of a filament |
| **phloem** the tissue that conducts food in vascular plants | **xylem** the type of tissue in vascular plants that provides support and conducts water and nutrients from the roots |

**1. Label** Label the parts of this perfect flower.

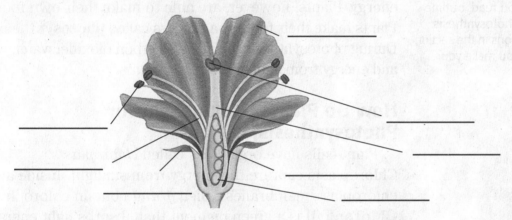

**2. Compare** How do taproot and fibrous root systems differ?

_____

_____

_____

**3. Describe** What are the three functions of a stem?

_____

_____

_____

**4. List** What are the four main organs of a flowering seed plant?

_____

_____

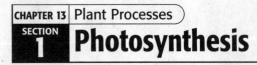

CHAPTER 13 | Plant Processes

### SECTION 1 | Photosynthesis

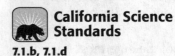
**California Science Standards**
7.1.b, 7.1.d

**BEFORE YOU READ**

After you read this section, you should be able to answer these questions:

• How do plants make food?

• How do plants get energy from food?

• How do plants exchange gases with the environment?

**STUDY TIP**

**Outline** As you read, outline the steps of photosynthesis. Use the questions in the section titles to help you make your outline.

## What Is Photosynthesis?

Many organisms, including humans, have to eat to get energy. Plants, however, are able to make their own food. Plants make their food by a process called **photosynthesis**. During photosynthesis, plants use carbon dioxide, water, and energy from sunlight to make sugars.

## How Do Plants Use Sunlight for Photosynthesis?

Plant cells have organelles called *chloroplasts*. Chloroplasts capture the energy from sunlight. Inside a chloroplast, membranes called *grana* contain chlorophyll. **Chlorophyll** is a green pigment that absorbs light energy. Many plants look green because chlorophyll reflects the green wavelengths of light. ☑

**READING CHECK**

**1. Define** What is chlorophyll?

_____

_____

_____

**Chloroplast**

**Plant cell**

Grana

Chloroplasts

**TAKE A LOOK**

**2. Identify** Where is chlorophyll found in a plant cell?

_____

_____

The grana in chloroplasts contain chlorophyll. Chlorophyll is a pigment that absorbs sunlight.

## How Do Plants Make Sugar?

During photosynthesis, plants take in water and carbon dioxide and absorb light energy. Plants use the light energy captured by chlorophyll to help form glucose molecules. *Glucose* is the sugar that plants use for food. In addition to producing sugar, plants give off oxygen during photosynthesis. ☑

The following chemical equation summarizes photosynthesis:

$$6CO_2 + 2H_2O \xrightarrow{\text{light energy}} C_6H_{12}O_6 + 6O_2$$

(carbon dioxide)  (water)  (glucose)  (oxygen)

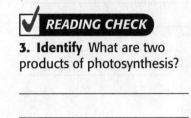

**READING CHECK**

**3. Identify** What are two products of photosynthesis?

_____

_____

Sugar is made in the leaves.

**TAKE A LOOK**

**4. Label** On the diagram, label the arrows to show what materials are entering and leaving the plant during photosynthesis.

**CALIFORNIA STANDARDS CHECK**

**7.1.d** Students know that mitochondria <u>liberate</u> energy for the work that cells do and that chloroplasts capture sunlight energy for photosynthesis.

**Word Help:** <u>liberate</u>
to release; to set free

**5. Identify** Which cell structures release the energy stored in sugar?

_____

_____

## How Do Plants Get Energy from Sugar?

Glucose molecules store energy. To use this energy, a plant cell needs its mitochondria to break down the glucose. This process of breaking down food molecules to get energy is called **cellular respiration**. During cellular respiration, cells use oxygen to break down food molecules. Like all cells, plant cells then use the energy from food to do work.

*Critical Thinking*

**6. Predict** What do you think would happen if a plant had no stomata?

_____

_____

_____

_____

## How Does a Plant Take In the Gases It Needs?

Plants take in carbon dioxide and give off oxygen. These gases move into and out of the leaf through openings called **stomata** (singular, *stoma*). Stomata allow gases to move through the plant's *cuticle*, the waxy layer that prevents water loss. Each stoma is surrounded by two guard cells. The guard cells act like double doors by opening and closing a stoma.

Water vapor also moves out of the leaf through stomata. The loss of water from leaves is called **transpiration**. Stomata open to allow carbon dioxide to enter a leaf but can close to prevent too much water loss.

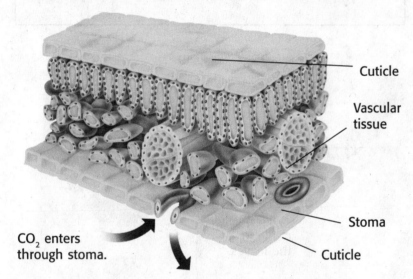

Cuticle

Vascular tissue

Stoma

Cuticle

$CO_2$ enters through stoma.

$H_2O$ and $O_2$ exit through stoma.

**TAKE A LOOK**

**7. Identify** Circle the guard cells in this picture. What is their function?

_____

_____

 **Say It**

**Describe** Think of all the ways in which photosynthesis is important to you. Describe to the class three ways you depend on photosynthesis.

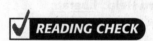 **READING CHECK**

**8. Complete** During photosynthesis, plants store light energy as

_____

_____

## Why Is Photosynthesis Important?

Plants and other photosynthetic organisms, such as bacteria and many protists, form the base of most food chains on Earth. During photosynthesis, plants store light energy as chemical energy. Animals get this energy when they eat plants. Other animals get energy from plants indirectly. They eat the animals that eat plants. Most organisms could not survive without photosynthetic organisms. ☑

Photosynthesis is also important because it produces oxygen. Recall that cellular respiration requires oxygen to break down food. Most organisms, including plants and animals, depend on cellular respiration to get energy from their food. Without the oxygen produced during photosynthesis, most organisms could not survive.

# Section 1 Review

7.1.b, 7.1.d

## SECTION VOCABULARY

| | |
|---|---|
| **cellular respiration** the process by which cells use oxygen to produce energy from food | **stoma** one of many openings in a leaf or a stem of a plant that enable gas exchange to occur (plural, stomata) |
| **chlorophyll** a green pigment that captures light energy for photosynthesis | **transpiration** the process by which plants release water vapor into the air through stomata; also the release of water vapor into the air by other organisms |
| **photosynthesis** the process by which plants, algae, and some bacteria use sunlight, carbon dioxide, and water to make food | |

**1. Explain** Why does chlorophyll look green?

_____

_____

**2. Identify** What is the role of mitochondria in plants? In what process do they take part?

_____

_____

**3. Compare** Complete the chart below to show the relationship between photosynthesis and cellular respiration.

| Photosynthesis | Cellular respiration |
|---|---|
| | Cells break down food to provide energy. |
| Oxygen is produced. | |

**4. Identify** What two structures in plant leaves help prevent the loss of water?

**5. Explain** Why are photosynthetic organisms, such as plants, so important to life on Earth?

_____

_____

_____

_____

CHAPTER 13 | Plant Processes

## SECTION 2 Reproduction of Flowering Plants

 **California Science Standards**
7.2.a, 7.5.f

**BEFORE YOU READ**

After you read this section, you should be able to answer these questions:

• What are pollination and fertilization?

• How do seeds and fruits form?

• How can flowering plants reproduce asexually?

## What Are Pollination and Fertilization?

Flowering plants are most obvious to us when they are in bloom. As flowers bloom, they surround us with bright colors and sweet fragrances. However, flowers are not just for us to enjoy. They are the structures for sexual reproduction in flowering plants. Pollination and fertilization take place in flowers.

**STUDY TIP**

**Summarize** As you read, write out or draw the steps of pollination and fertilization.

**TAKE A LOOK**

**1. Identify** Circle the part of the flower where pollination occurs.

**2. Identify** Draw an arrow to show where fertilization will take place.

Pollen grains land on the stigma and begin to grow pollen tubes.

Stigma
Anther
Pollen
Style
Ovary
Ovule

Pollen tube
Sperm
Ovary
Ovule containing egg

Sperm travel down pollen tubes and fertilize the eggs.

**CALIFORNIA STANDARDS CHECK**

**7.2.a** Students know the difference between the life cycles and reproduction methods of sexual and asexual organisms.

**3. Explain** Is fertilization a part of sexual reproduction or asexual reproduction? Explain.

_____

_____

_____

Sexual reproduction begins in flowers when wind or animals move pollen from one flower to another. *Pollination* occurs when pollen from an anther lands on a stigma. Each pollen grain grows a tube through the style to the ovary. The ovary has ovules, each of which contains an egg. *Fertilization* occurs when a sperm joins with the egg inside an ovule.

# What Happens After Fertilization?

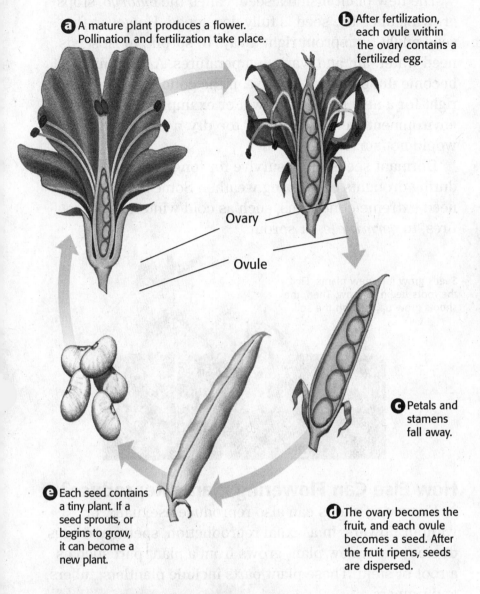

**a** A mature plant produces a flower. Pollination and fertilization take place.

**b** After fertilization, each ovule within the ovary contains a fertilized egg.

Ovary

Ovule

**c** Petals and stamens fall away.

**d** The ovary becomes the fruit, and each ovule becomes a seed. After the fruit ripens, seeds are dispersed.

**e** Each seed contains a tiny plant. If a seed sprouts, or begins to grow, it can become a new plant.

## TAKE A LOOK
**4. Identify** In step C, circle the structures that will become seeds.

## CALIFORNIA STANDARDS CHECK

**7.5.e** Students know the structures and <u>processes</u> by which flowering plants generate pollen, ovules, seeds, and fruit.

**Word Help: <u>processes</u>**
a set of steps, events, or changes

**5. Explain** Where do seeds and fruits come from?

_____

_____

_____

_____

_____

## THE FUNCTIONS OF FRUITS

When people think of fruit, they often think of apples or bananas. However, many things we call vegetables, such as tomatoes or green beans, are also fruits! A fruit is the ovary of the flower that has grown larger.

Fruits have two major functions. They protect seeds while the seeds develop. Fruits also help a plant spread its seeds to new environments. For example, an animal might eat a fruit and drop the seeds away from the parent plant. Fruits such as burrs spread when they get caught in an animal's fur. Other fruits are carried to new places by the wind, or even by water. ☑

## READING CHECK
**6. List** What are two functions of a fruit?

_____

_____

_____

**SECTION 2** Reproduction of Flowering Plants *continued*

## How Do Seeds Grow into New Plants?

The new plant inside a seed, called the *embryo*, stops growing once the seed is fully developed. However, the seed might not sprout right away. To sprout, most seeds need water, air, and warm temperatures. A seed might become **dormant**, or inactive, if the conditions are not right for a new plant to grow. For example, if the environment were too cold or too dry, a young plant would not survive. ☑

Dormant seeds often survive for long periods of time during droughts or freezing weather. Some seeds actually need extreme conditions, such as cold winters or forest fires, to *germinate*, or sprout.

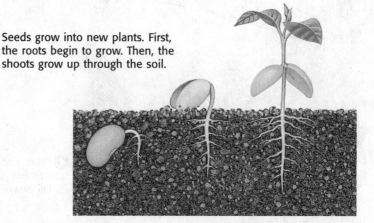

Seeds grow into new plants. First, the roots begin to grow. Then, the shoots grow up through the soil.

## How Else Can Flowering Plants Reproduce?

Flowering plants can also reproduce asexually, or without flowers. In asexual reproduction, sperm and eggs do not join. A new plant grows from a plant part such as a root or stem. These plant parts include plantlets, tubers, and runners.

*Kalanchoe* produces plantlets along the edges of its leaves. The plantlets will fall off and take root in the soil.

A potato is a tuber, or underground stem. The "eyes" of potatoes are buds that can grow into new plants.

The strawberry plant produces runners, or stems that grow along the ground. Buds along the runners take root and grow into new plants.

---

☑ **READING CHECK**

**7. Explain** Why would a seed become dormant?

_____

_____

_____

**TAKE A LOOK**

**8. Identify** Which part of a new plant grows first?

_____

_____

*Critical Thinking*

**9. Infer** When would asexual reproduction be important for the survival of a flowering plant?

_____

_____

_____

_____

_____

_____

Name ____________________ Class ____________ Date ____________

# Section 2 Review

7.2.a, 7.5.f

## SECTION VOCABULARY

| | |
|---|---|
| **dormant** describes the inactive state of a seed or other plant part when conditions are unfavorable to growth | |

**1. Compare** What is the difference between pollination and fertilization?

______________________________________________

______________________________________________

______________________________________________

**2. Summarize** Complete the Process Chart below to summarize how sexual reproduction produces new plants.

| |
|---|
| **A mature plant produces flowers.** |
| ↓ |
| |
| ↓ |
| |
| ↓ |
| |
| ↓ |
| **Seeds are spread. They sprout and grow into new plants.** |

**3. Identify** Name two environmental conditions that can cause a seed to become dormant.

______________________________________________

______________________________________________

**4. List** What are three structures a flowering plant can use to reproduce asexually?

______________________________________________

# SECTION 3 Plant Development and Responses

**California Science Standards**

7.1.f, 7.5.a

## BEFORE YOU READ

After you read this section, you should be able to answer these questions:

• What happens as plants develop?

• How do hormones affect plants?

• How do plants respond to the environment?

---

## What Happens As Plants Grow and Develop?

Plants and animals both grow and develop. However, plants develop differently than animals do. For example, as a baby bird develops, its cells *differentiate*, or become specialized to do a job. The bird's cells will differentiate only once. The cells of some plants, however, differentiate many times as the plant develops.

Imagine if you could grow another person from one organ, such as a heart. Humans cannot do this, of course, but some plants can grow a new plant this way. Some leaf cells can differentiate into cells that become roots and stems. This is a form of asexual reproduction.

**STUDY TIP**

**List** As you read, list the different stimuli a plant responds to and describe the plant's response.

The cells in this African violet leaf are differentiating. The differentiating cells will have new functions in the plant.

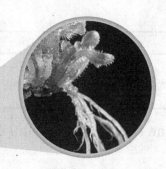

**TAKE A LOOK**

**1. Identify** What organs will be formed from these differentiated cells?

_____

_____

**READING CHECK**

**2. Define** What is a stimulus?

_____

_____

_____

_____

### WHEN PLANT CELLS DIFFERENTIATE

Plants grow and develop in response to stimuli. A **stimulus** (plural, *stimuli*) is anything that causes a reaction or change in an organism. Hot weather, for example, is a stimulus that your body may respond to by sweating. Many of a plant's responses to stimuli are caused by hormones. ☑

# What Is a Hormone?

What would happen if a plant could not respond to changes in its environment? The plant would probably die. A plant must respond to change so that it can still get the resources it needs to survive and reproduce.

A *hormone* is a chemical in a plant that causes cells to react in certain ways. Plants make hormones in response to the environment. For example, a change in the amount of available light causes a plant to make hormones called *auxins*. These hormones cause the plant's cells to grow differently so that they can get as much light as possible.

## HORMONE EFFECTS ON PLANT LIFE CYCLES

Hormones play important roles in each stage of a plant's life cycle. Hormones allow the plant to develop when conditions are favorable, such as in rainy, warm weather. For example, some hormones keep seeds dormant, or inactive. Other hormones end dormancy and cause the seed to grow. Another hormone causes roots and stems to grow.

## HORMONE USES IN AGRICULTURE

Plants make their own hormones. For example, *ethylene* is a hormone that causes fruits to ripen. However, humans often add hormones to plants to make fruits grow larger or to make fruits ripen sooner. Some fruits, such as bananas, are picked before they are ripe so that they can be shipped. Ethylene can be used to ripen these plants later.

*Critical Thinking*

**3. Apply Concepts** It is important for a plant to make a hormone that keeps its seeds dormant. What do you think is the reason?

_____

_____

_____

_____

**TAKE A LOOK**

**4. Explain** Which of these bunches of grapes do you think was treated with a hormone? Explain.

_____

_____

_____

_____

## How Do Plants Respond to the Environment?

What happens when you get cold? Do you shiver? Do your teeth chatter? These are your responses to an environmental stimulus such as cold air. Plants also respond to environmental stimuli, but not to the same ones we do and not in the same way. Plants respond to stimuli such as light and the pull of gravity.

Some plants respond to a stimulus, such as light, by growing in a particular direction. Growth in response to a stimulus is called a **tropism**. A tropism is either positive or negative. Plant growth toward a stimulus is a positive tropism. Plant growth away from a stimulus is a negative tropism. ☑

**READING CHECK**

**5. Define** What is a tropism?

_____

### PLANT GROWTH IN RESPONSE TO LIGHT

Recall that plants need sunlight in order to make food. What would happen to a plant that could get light from only one direction, such as through a window? To get as much light as possible, it would need to grow toward the light.

A plant will respond to low light levels by making auxins. These hormones build up on the shaded side of the shoot. They cause cells in the shade to grow longer than the cells facing the light. The plant stem bends because its cells are different sizes. This growth in response to light is called *phototropism*. Auxins also cause plants to grow in response to gravity.

**Math Focus**

**6. Calculate** Suppose a plant bends toward light at a rate of 0.3° per minute. In how many hours will the plant bend 90°?

_____

**TAKE A LOOK**

**7. Explain** Place an X on the picture to show where the light must be coming from. Explain your answer.

_____
_____
_____

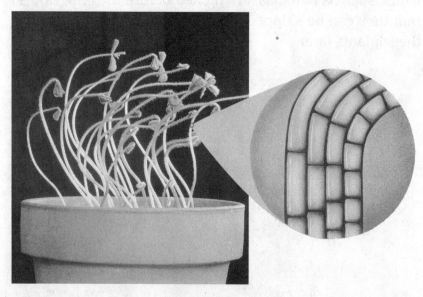

## PLANT GROWTH IN RESPONSE TO GRAVITY

Gravity can change the direction in which a plant's roots and shoots grow. Most shoot tips grow upward, away from the center of Earth. Most root tips grow downward, toward the center of Earth. If a plant is placed on its side or turned upside down, the roots and shoots will change direction. Shoots will turn to grow away from the Earth. Roots will turn to grow toward the Earth. This response is called *gravitropism.*

**Gravitropism**

To grow away from the pull of gravity, this plant has grown upward.

## TAKE A LOOK

**8. Apply Concepts** Look at the plant on the left. Draw an arrow on the flower pot to show the direction the roots are probably growing.

**9. Explain** Look at the plant on the right. What do you think made its stem bend?

_____

_____

_____

_____

## What Happens to Plants When Seasons Change?

Have you ever noticed that some plants will drop their leaves in the fall even before the weather turns cool? How do the plants know that fall is coming? We often notice the changing seasons because the temperature changes. Plants, however, respond to change in the length of the day.

## SHORT DAY AND LONG DAY PLANTS

Days are longer in summer and shorter in winter. The change in amount of daylight is a stimulus for many plants. Some plants that bloom in winter, such as poinsettias, need shorter periods of daylight to reproduce. They are called *short-day plants*. Others, such as clover, reproduce in spring or summer. They are called *long-day plants*.

## Math Focus

**10. Calculate** It must be dark for 70% of a 24-hour period before a certain plant will bloom. How many hours of daylight does this plant need to bloom?

_____

## EFFECT OF SEASONS ON LEAF COLOR

The leaves of some trees may change color as seasons change. As the days shorten in fall, the chlorophyll in leaves breaks down. This makes the orange and yellow pigments in the leaves easier to see. During the summer, chlorophyll hides other pigments.

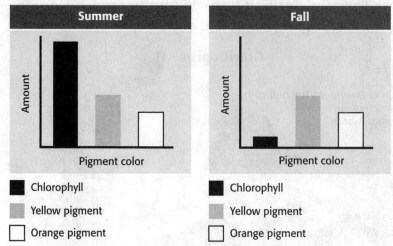

**Amount of Leaf Pigment Based on Season**

## TAKE A LOOK

**11. Identify** Which pigment's level decreases between summer and fall?

_____

_____

**12. Identify** Which pigments' levels stay the same between summer and fall?

_____

_____

## LOSS OF LEAVES

Every tree loses leaves throughout its life. Leaves are shed when they become old. For example, pine trees lose some of their leaves year-round. Because leaves are lost and replaced throughout the year, the tree always has some leaves. These trees are called *evergreen*. A leaf of an evergreen tree is covered with a thick cuticle. The cuticle protects the leaf from cold and dry weather.

*Deciduous* trees lose all of their leaves at about the same time each year. This generally happens as days shorten. The loss of leaves helps these plants survive cold or dry weather. In colder areas, deciduous trees usually lose their leaves before winter begins. In areas that have wet and dry seasons, deciduous trees lose their leaves before the dry season.

 **Say It**

**Describe** What is your favorite kind of tree? Use the Internet or reference books to find out if that tree is evergreen or deciduous. Describe to the class what the tree looks like and where it lives.

# Section 3 Review

7.1.f, 7.5.a

**SECTION VOCABULARY**

| **stimulus** anything that causes a reaction or change in an organism or any part of an organism | **tropism** growth of all or part of an organism in response to an external stimulus, such as light <br> <u>Wordwise</u> The root *trop* means "to turn." |
| --- | --- |

**1. Compare** How is cell differentiation different in plants and animals?

_____

_____

_____

**2. Compare** What is the difference between a negative tropism and a positive tropism?

_____

_____

_____

**3. Explain** What happens when a plant gets light from only one direction?

_____

_____

_____

_____

**4. Explain** Why do leaves look green during the summer even though they have orange and yellow pigments?

_____

_____

_____

**5. Explain** Many evergreen trees live in areas with long, cold winters. How can they keep their leaves all year?

_____

_____

_____

_____

CHAPTER 14 | Introduction to Animals
SECTION
**1 What Is an Animal?**

![bear] **California Science Standards**

7.1.f, 7.2.a, 7.5.a, 7.5.b, 7.5.c

**BEFORE YOU READ**

After you read this section, you should be able to answer these questions:

• What is an animal?

• What are the seven basic characteristics of animals?

**What Is an Animal?**

What do you think of when you think of an animal? You may think of a cat or dog, or even a giraffe or bear. Would you think of a sponge?

Animals come in many shapes and sizes, but they all share certain characteristics. An *animal* is an organism that is made up of many cells and must eat food to get energy. Animals cannot make their own food as plants do.

**What Are the Basic Characteristics of Animals?**

**1. ENERGY CONSUMPTION**

All organisms need energy to survive. Unlike plants, animals must get energy from other organisms. They are consumers. A **consumer** is an organism that feeds on other organisms or parts of other organisms. Some animals, such as lions, eat other animals. Some, such as pandas, eat plants. Other animals, such as black bears, can eat both plants and animals. ☑

>**STUDY TIP**
**List** As you read, make a list of the characteristics of animals.

✓ **READING CHECK**

**1. Define** What is a consumer?

_____

_____

_____

_____

 **Say It**

**Discuss** With a partner, choose 10 different kinds of animals, and describe what they eat. Make a list to share with your classmates.

**2. MOVEMENT**

Nearly all animals move during some part of their lives, often in order to find food or shelter. Muscle cells help animals move. Groups of muscle cells work together. They contract and relax to help the animal move.

## 3. MULTICELLULAR MAKEUP

Like all organisms, animals are made of cells. Unlike plant cells, animal cells do not have cell walls. Animal cells are surrounded only by cell membranes.

All animals are *multicellular*. That means they are made of many cells. All of an animal's cells work together to perform important functions, such as breathing, digesting food, and reproducing. ☑

## 4. LEVELS OF ORGANIZATION

Animals have different levels of organization in their bodies. This means their bodies are organized into structures made of smaller structures. Cells are the first, or smallest, level of organization in an animal. ☑

Cells specialize to do specific jobs. Groups of cells that are of the same kind and that work together form tissues. For example, muscle cells form muscle tissue. Tissues are the second level of organization in animals.

Tissues work together to form an organ. The heart, lungs, and kidneys are all organs. Organs are the third level of organization.

Organs work together to form an organ system. An organ system is the fourth level of organization. The organism may die if any part of an organ system stops working.

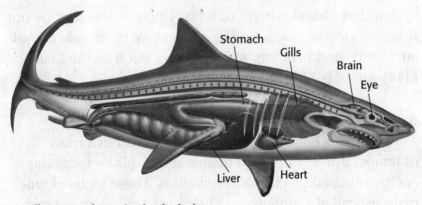

Like most other animals, sharks have organs for digestion, circulation, and sensing the environment.

**✓ READING CHECK**

**2. Define** What does multicellular mean?

_____

_____

**✓ READING CHECK**

**3. Identify** What is the first level of organization in animals?

_____

_____

**TAKE A LOOK**
**4. List** Name four organ systems you can see in this picture.

_____

_____

_____

_____

*Critical Thinking*

**5. Apply Concepts** What kind of symmetry do you have?

_____

**TAKE A LOOK**
**6. Demonstrate** Draw a line or lines on two of the pictures to show how you can divide each body into like parts.

## 5. BODY PLAN

A body plan is the general shape of an organism. One characteristic of a body plan is its symmetry. Animals can have three types of symmetry.

This tortoise has **bilateral symmetry**. The two sides of its body mirror each other. On each side of its body, the tortoise has one nostril, one eye, and two legs.

This sea star has **radial symmetry**. Its body is organized around the center, like spokes on a wheel.

This sponge is **asymmetrical**. You cannot draw a straight line to divide its body into two or more equal parts. You also cannot find a center point that its body is organized around.

Another characteristic of a body plan is whether or not it has a coelom. A **coelom** is a body cavity, or space, that surrounds and protects many organs, such as the heart. Many animals have coeloms. ☑

✓ **READING CHECK**

**7. Define** What is a coelom?

_____

_____

## 6. CONTROLLED BODY TEMPERATURE

All animals need to keep their bodies within a range of temperatures. Birds and mammals do this by using the energy released by chemical reactions. These kinds of animals are called *endotherms*. Their body temperatures stay almost the same, even when the temperature of the environment changes.

The body temperatures of other animals change with the temperature of the environment. These kinds of animals are called *ectotherms*. Some of these animals have behaviors that help control their body temperatures. For example, some lizards sit in the sun to warm up.

**SECTION 1** What Is an Animal? *continued*

## 7. REPRODUCTION AND DEVELOPMENT

Animals make more animals through reproduction. In **asexual reproduction**, there is only one parent. All the offspring have the same genes as the parent. Some animals, such as the hydra, reproduce asexually by budding. In *budding*, part of an organism develops into a new organism. The new organism then breaks off from the parent. In *fragmentation*, parts of an organism break off and then develop into new organisms. ☑

In **sexual reproduction**, offspring form when genetic information from two parents combines. The female parent produces sex cells called *eggs*. The male parent produces sex cells called *sperm*. The first cell of a new organism forms when an egg's nucleus and a sperm's nucleus join. This process is called *fertilization*.

A fertilized cell divides into many cells to form an *embryo*. An embryo is an organism at an early stage of development, such as the mouse embryo below. As an animal develops, its cells become specialized through differentiation. In **differentiation**, cells develop different structures to do specific jobs. ☑

✓ **READING CHECK**

**8. Identify** What are two ways some animals can reproduce asexually?

_____

_____

✓ **READING CHECK**

**9. Explain** What happens to the cells in an embryo as the embryo develops?

_____

_____

_____

_____

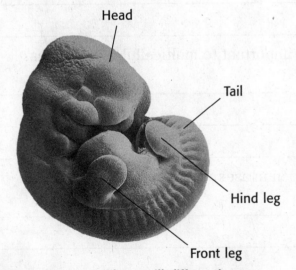

Head

Tail

Hind leg

Front leg

Cells in the mouse embryo will differentiate as the mouse develops. These cells will produce skin, muscles, nerves, and all the other parts of the mouse's body.

# Section 1 Review

7.1.f, 7.2.a, 7.5.a, 7.5.b, 7.5.c

## SECTION VOCABULARY

| | |
|---|---|
| **asexual reproduction** reproduction that does not involve the union of sex cells and in which one parent produces offspring that are genetically identical to the parent<br><br>   <u>Wordwise</u> The prefix *a-* means "not."<br><br>**coelom** a body cavity that contains the internal organs<br><br>**consumer** an organism that eats other organisms or organic matter | **differentiation** the process in which the structure and function of the parts of an organism change to enable specialization of those parts<br><br>**sexual reproduction** reproduction in which the sex cells from two parents unite to produce offspring that share traits from both parents |

**1. Predict** What would happen to an animal such as a shark if its heart failed?

_____

_____

**2. Compare** What is the difference between an endotherm and an ectotherm?

_____

_____

_____

**3. Explain** Why is differentiation important to multicellular organisms?

_____

_____

**4. Explain** Does fertilization happen in asexual reproduction?

_____

_____

_____

**5. Compare** How is fragmentation different from budding?

_____

_____

_____

CHAPTER 14 | Introduction to Animals

SECTION 2

# The Animal Kingdom

## BEFORE YOU READ

**After you read this section, you should be able to answer these questions:**

• What is diversity?

• What are vertebrates?

• What are invertebrates?

## What Is Diversity?

Insects, birds, and other animals look and are very different from one another. They also live in many different places. Scientists call this range of difference *diversity*.

Scientists have named more than 1 million species of animals. Some scientists estimate that more than 3 million species of animals live on Earth. That means many species that exist have not yet been discovered and named.

Animals that have been discovered and described are placed into groups. Grouping organisms makes it easier to study all of the different kinds of animals. The pie graph below shows the relative sizes of the main groups of animals in the animal kingdom.

### STUDY TIP

**Organize** As you read, make combination notes about each group of animals. Write descriptions in the left column of the notes. Draw pictures in the right column that will help you remember what each type of animal looks like.

### Makeup of the Animal Kingdom

Arthropods
Chordates
Echinoderms
Cnidarians
Sponges
Flatworms
Roundworms
Mollusks
Other
Annelids

## TAKE A LOOK

**1. Identify** Which group of animals has the most species?

_____

_____

## How Do Scientists Classify Animals?

Scientists organize animals into several groups. These groups are based on the characteristics the animals share and how closely they are related.

In the past, scientists grouped animals on the basis of only their structure or appearance. Today, scientists also use DNA, or genetic material, to group animals. There are two general groups of animals: invertebrates and vertebrates. ☑

## What Are Invertebrates?

Most of the animals on Earth are invertebrates. An **invertebrate** is an animal that does not have a backbone. In fact, invertebrates do not have any bones. Insects, snails, and worms are all invertebrates. Invertebrates can be found living in every environment on Earth. ☑

### SPONGES

Sponges are some of the simplest invertebrates. A sponge is a mass of specialized cells held together by a jelly-like material. Tiny, glassy structures in the sponge also provide support. Sponges are asymmetrical. Adult sponges generally do not move.

The body of a sponge has many tubes and thousands of small pores, or holes. Some cells sweep water into the pores. Other cells remove food particles from the water and digest them. Sponges can reproduce both asexually, by fragmentation, and sexually.

## CNIDARIANS

Cnidarians include jellyfish, sea anemones, and corals. Most cnidarians live in the ocean. Their simple bodies have radial symmetry. They have specialized stinging cells called *cnidocysts* on their tentacles. These cells help the animals stun and catch the tiny animals they eat. ☑

Cnidarians have one of two radially symmetrical body plans: a medusa form or a polyp form. These two body plans are shown below. Many cnidarians reproduce sexually. Some cnidarians can also reproduce asexually by budding and fragmentation.

**Jellyfish**

The jellyfish has the medusa body form. A medusa is a bell-shaped body with tentacles.

As adults, sea anemones and corals are polyps. The polyp body form looks like a cup on a base. A polyp attaches the base of the cup to a hard surface.

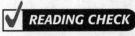

## FLATWORMS

Flatworms are the simplest worms. Many flatworms live in water or damp soils. Other flatworms are parasites. A *parasite* is an organism that invades and feeds on the body of another organism.

Flatworms are more complex than sponges or cnidarians. They are bilaterally symmetrical. Flatworms have heads and eyespots, which are sensitive to light. Every flatworm is both male and female. They can reproduce both asexually, by fragmentation, and sexually.

## ROUNDWORMS

Roundworms are cylindrical like spaghetti. They live in freshwater, in damp soils, and as parasites in the tissues and body fluids of other animals. Like flatworms, roundworms have bilateral symmetry. Unlike flatworms, roundworms are either male or female. They reproduce sexually. ☑

**TAKE A LOOK**

**5. Identify** What two body forms can cnidarians have?

_____

_____

**Flatworm**

**Roundworm**

Eyespot

Sensory lobe

This flatworm has a head with eyespots and sensory lobes. This kind of flatworm is often about 15 mm long.

## MOLLUSKS

Snails, slugs, clams, oysters, squids, and octopuses are mollusks. They live in water and on land. Mollusks have a specialized tissue called a *mantle*. The shells of snails, clams, and oysters are made by their mantles. A mollusk also has a muscular foot that helps it move. In some mollusks, the foot is modified into tentacles. ☑

Squids and octopuses use tentacles to capture prey, such as fish. Clams and oysters filter food from the water. Snails and slugs feed on plants and break down dead organisms. Mollusks reproduce sexually.

**Squid**

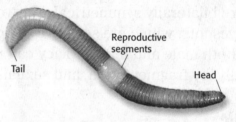

## ANNELIDS

Annelids are worms made of repeating body segments. For this reason, they are sometimes called *segmented worms*. Annelids have bilateral symmetry. Earthworms and leeches are types of annelids. ☑

Each annelid has both male and female sex organs. However, individuals must fertilize each other to reproduce sexually.

Reproductive segments

Tail

Head

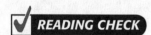

**READING CHECK**

**7. Identify** What specialized tissue makes a mollusk's shell?

_____

_____

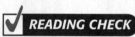

**READING CHECK**

**8. Compare** How are earthworms different from roundworms and flatworms?

_____

_____

_____

## ARTHROPODS

Arthropods are the most diverse group in the animal kingdom. Arthropods have bilateral symmetry and a strong, external armor called an **exoskeleton**. The exoskeleton protects arthropods from predators. The exoskeleton also keeps the animal from drying out. ☑

Insects are a familiar group of arthropods because they are often seen on land. An insect's body is clearly divided into three segments called the *head*, *thorax*, and *abdomen*. Millipedes, centipedes, spiders, and scorpions are also arthropods. Arthropods that live in the water include crabs and shrimp. Most arthropods are either male or female and reproduce sexually.

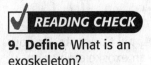

**READING CHECK**

**9. Define** What is an exoskeleton?

_____

_____

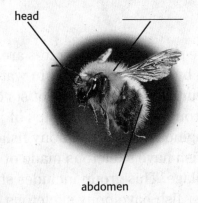

head

abdomen

**Say It**

**Describe** There are more arthropods on Earth than any other kind of animal! Describe to the class the last time you saw an arthropod. Where were you? What did the animal look like? What kind of arthropod was it?

## ECHINODERMS

Echinoderms live in the ocean. This group includes sea stars, sea urchins, and sand dollars. The name echinoderm means "spiny skinned." Echinoderms, like the sea urchins in the picture below, have exoskeletons covered in bumps and spines.

Echinoderms have a system of water pumps and canals in their bodies. This system, called the *water vascular system*, helps the animal move, eat, breathe, and sense its environment. Echinoderms usually reproduce sexually. Males release sperm as females release eggs into the water, where fertilization takes place. ☑

**READING CHECK**

**10. Define** What is the water vascular system?

_____

_____

_____

_____

_____

_____

Echinoderms have bilateral symmetry as larvae and radial symmetry as adults.

## What Are Vertebrates?

**Vertebrates** are animals that have backbones. The backbone is a strong but flexible column made of individual units called *vertebrae* (singular, *vertebra*). The backbone is a part of the endoskeleton of a vertebrate. An **endoskeleton** is an internal skeleton. It supports the body of the animal. It also provides a place for muscles to attach so that the animal can move.

Less than 5% of the known animal species are vertebrates. Vertebrates are divided into five main groups: fishes, amphibians, reptiles, birds, and mammals. Vertebrates are either male or female, and they reproduce mainly by sexual reproduction.

### FISH

Over half of the species of vertebrates are species of fish. Fish breathe by taking oxygen from water through specialized structures called gills. Scientists classify fishes into four groups: two small groups of jawless fishes plus cartilaginous fishes and bony fishes. ☑

Cartilaginous fish have skeletons made of a flexible tissue called cartilage. This group includes sharks and stingrays. All other fish have bony skeletons. Bony fish live in saltwater and freshwater environments all over the world. Trout, bass, and goldfish are all bony fishes.

### AMPHIBIANS

Salamanders, toads, and frogs are all amphibians. Because many amphibians spend part of their lives on land and part in the water, scientists say they have a two-part life cycle. Most amphibians live near fresh water because their eggs and young need water to survive.

*Critical Thinking*

**11. Apply Concepts** Do you have an exoskeleton or an endoskeleton?

_____

_____

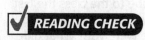

**12. Identify** What structure do fish use to breathe?

_____

_____

*Critical Thinking*

**13. Apply Concepts** How is the development of a tadpole into an adult frog an example of differentiation?

_____

_____

_____

_____

_____

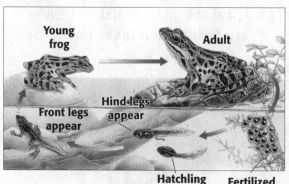

Young frog

Adult

Hind legs appear

Front legs appear

Hatchling tadpole

Fertilized eggs

As adults, most amphibians still need water. Salamanders and frogs have thin skin that must stay moist.

Young amphibians live in water and breathe with gills. As they develop, they grow legs and lungs that help them live on land.

## REPTILES

Reptiles include snakes, turtles, and alligators. Unlike amphibians, reptiles do not need to lay their eggs in water. Reptile eggs have membranes and a shell that protects them from drying out. Reptiles can live almost anywhere on land. They can also live in water. Reptiles generally reproduce sexually.

## BIRDS

Birds share many characteristics with reptiles, such as sexual reproduction, eggs with shells, and similar feet structures. However, birds are the only animals on Earth today that have feathers. Feathers are lightweight structures that help birds stay warm. They also help shape the body and wings for flying.

Some kinds of birds no longer use their wings to fly. The penguin, for example, uses its wings to swim. Birds such as ostriches and emus do not fly, but they have unique characteristics that help them run.

## MAMMALS

All mammals have hair at some time in their lives, and all female mammals can produce milk for their young. Mammals reproduce sexually.

Mammals are divided into three groups: monotremes, marsupials, and placental mammals.

### Three Kinds of Mammals

**Monotremes** are mammals that lay eggs. The echidna is a monotreme that lives in Australia.

**Marsupials** are mammals with pouches. Kangaroos are marsupials. Young marsupials develop inside the mother's pouch.

Most mammals are **placental mammals**. The placenta is a special organ that lets nutrients and wastes be exchanged between the mother and unborn young.

## Math Focus

**14. Calculate** A bird weighing 15 g eats 10 times its weight in food in a week. How much food does the bird eat in a day?

_____

## TAKE A LOOK

**15. List** What are the three groups of mammals?

_____

_____

_____

# Section 2 Review

7.5.a

## SECTION VOCABULARY

| | |
|---|---|
| **endoskeleton** an internal skeleton made of bone and cartilage | **invertebrate** an animal that does not have a backbone |
| **exoskeleton** a hard, external, supporting structure | **vertebrate** an animal that has a backbone |
| <u>Wordwise</u> The prefix *exo-* means "outside" or "external." Another example is *exotic*. | |

**1. Compare** What are two main differences between a sponge and a roundworm?

_____

_____

_____

**2. Describe** Describe the two cnidarian body plans.

_____

_____

_____

**3. Compare** What is the difference between an exoskeleton and an endoskeleton?

_____

_____

_____

**4. Explain** Why do most adult amphibians need to live near water or in a moist habitat?

_____

_____

_____

**5. Identify** What are two characteristics of mammals?

_____

_____

_____

**6. Explain** What is the function of a placenta?

_____

_____

_____

**CHAPTER 14** Introduction to Animals
**SECTION 3** Invertebrates

**BEFORE YOU READ**

After you read this section, you should be able to answer these questions:

• What structures and systems perform basic life functions in invertebrates?

• How do invertebrates reproduce and develop?

## What Are the Characteristics of Invertebrates?

Invertebrates are animals without backbones. They can be found in almost every environment on Earth. Invertebrates come in many different shapes and sizes. Some invertebrates have heads, and others do not. Some invertebrates eat food through their mouths. Others absorb food particles through their tissues.

**STUDY TIP**
**Underline** As you read, underline the characteristics of invertebrates.

### BODY SYMMETRY

Invertebrates have one of three basic body plans: irregular, radial, or bilateral. Sponges have irregular shapes. They are asymmetrical. Sea anemones have radial symmetry. That means that body parts extend from a central point. Animals with radial symmetry have only a top and a bottom that are very different from each other.

Most invertebrates have bilateral symmetry. This means the body can be divided into two mirror-image halves by one straight line. Animals with bilateral symmetry have a top and bottom that differ, as well as a front end and a back end that differ. The development of a head is seen only in organisms with bilateral symmetry.

*Critical Thinking*

**1. Predict** Would you expect a sea anemone to have a head? Explain your answer.

_____

_____

_____

_____

**TAKE A LOOK**
**2. Identify** What type of symmetry does the sea hare have?

_____

_____

## SEGMENTATION

The bodies of many animals are divided into **segments**, or sections. Segmentation in the body has many advantages. For example, each segment in an earthworm has a set of muscles that help the earthworm push through soil.

**Segmentation in Invertebrate Bodies**

**TAKE A LOOK**
**3. List** What are the three segments of an insect's body?

_____

_____

_____

The body of a marine worm has many segments that are almost equal in size.

The body of an insect has three unequal segments: a head, a thorax, and an abdomen.

## SUPPORT OF THE BODY

Invertebrate bodies need support and protection. Some invertebrates, like jellyfish and anemones, are supported by the water they live in. Others have structures in or on their bodies that support and protect them. The figure below shows the outer coverings of different invertebrates. Muscles attached to outer coverings in some invertebrates contract and relax to help the animals move.

**Support in Invertebrate Bodies**

**TAKE A LOOK**
**4. List** What are three types of support in invertebrate bodies?

_____

_____

_____

_____

A sponge is supported by jelly-like material and tiny glassy structures.

Some invertebrates, such as this roundworm, have thick skin as a tough outer covering.

Other invertebrates have tough outer coverings called exoskeletons.

SECTION 3 | Invertebrates *continued*

## RESPIRATION AND CIRCULATION

All animals take in oxygen and release carbon dioxide through respiration. Respiration is performed by the *respiratory system*. Different invertebrates have different structures for respiration. For example, lobsters have gills. Respiration in insects, however, is through a network of tubes, called *tracheae*, inside the body. ☑

Oxygen, carbon dioxide, and nutrients must circulate, or move around, within the body. The *circulatory system* moves these materials with blood through the body. Some invertebrates have an **open circulatory system**. In open circulatory systems, blood moves through open spaces in the body. Others have a **closed circulatory system**. In closed circulatory systems, blood moves through tubes that form a closed loop.

Trachea

This beetle moves air into and out of its body through small holes along the sides of its body.

**READING CHECK**

**5. Identify** Which body system takes in oxygen and releases carbon dioxide?

_____

_____

## DIGESTION AND EXCRETION

Animals get the energy they need by digesting food. Food is broken down and nutrients are absorbed by the *digestive system*. Invertebrates have relatively simple digestive systems. The mouth and anus form two ends of a tube called a *digestive tract*. Any material that is eaten but not digested is sent out of the body as waste. ☑

As cells in the body use up nutrients, another kind of waste forms. In many invertebrates, the digestive tract eliminates this kind of waste as well. Other invertebrates have a separate system, called the *excretory system*, that remove excess water and waste from cells.

**READING CHECK**

**6. Identify** Which body system breaks down food?

_____

_____

The digestive system in the snail is made up of a digestive tract that has four parts: a mouth, a stomach, an intestine, and an anus.

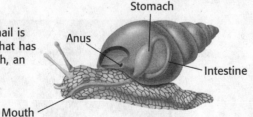

Stomach

Anus

Intestine

Mouth

## NERVOUS SYSTEM

The nervous system receives and sends electrical signals that control the body. The figure below shows the nervous systems of three invertebrates. The simplest invertebrates have only nerve cells. More complex invertebrates have brains and sense organs, such as eyes. ☑

**7. Describe** What is the function of the nervous system?

_____

_____

_____

_____

## TAKE A LOOK

**8. Compare** How do the nervous systems of a hydra and a grasshopper differ?

_____

_____

_____

_____

_____

_____

_____

*Critical Thinking*

**9. Apply Concepts** Are offspring produced in asexual reproduction genetically different from their parents? Explain your answer.

_____

_____

_____

_____

_____

_____

_____

### Invertebrate Nervous Systems

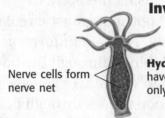

Nerve cells form nerve net

**Hydra** The simplest invertebrates have nervous systems made up of only nerve cells.

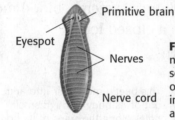

Primitive brain

Eyespot

Nerves

Nerve cord

**Flatworm** More complex nervous systems include sense organs, such as eyes or eyespots. They collect information such as sound and light.

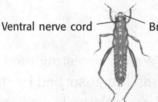

Ventral nerve cord

Brain

**Grasshopper** Many nervous systems have a specialized area called the brain. The brain acts as the control center.

## REPRODUCTION

Many invertebrates can reproduce both asexually and sexually. A hydra, for example, can reproduce asexually by budding. Budding happens when a part of the parent organism develops into a new organism. Other invertebrates can reproduce asexually by fragmentation. In fragmentation, parts of an organism break off and then develop into new individuals.

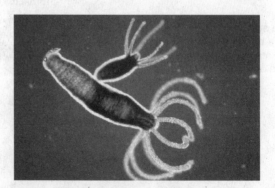

**SECTION 3** Invertebrates *continued*

## DEVELOPMENT

Some invertebrates, such as insects, change form as they develop. This change is called **metamorphosis**. Most insects, including butterflies, beetles, flies, bees, and ants, go through a complex change called *complete metamorphosis*.

### Stages of Complete Metamorphosis

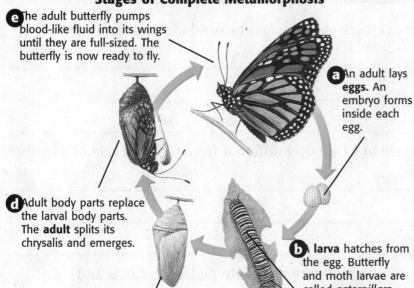

**e** The adult butterfly pumps blood-like fluid into its wings until they are full-sized. The butterfly is now ready to fly.

**a** An adult lays **eggs.** An embryo forms inside each egg.

**d** Adult body parts replace the larval body parts. The **adult** splits its chrysalis and emerges.

**b** A **larva** hatches from the egg. Butterfly and moth larvae are called *caterpillars*. The caterpillar eats leaves and grows rapidly. As the caterpillar grows, it sheds its outer layer several times. This process is called *molting*.

**c** After its final molt, the caterpillar makes a chrysalis and becomes a **pupa.** The pupal stage may last a few days or several months. During this stage, the insect is inactive.

### Stages of Incomplete Metamorphosis

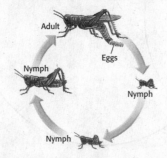

Adult

Eggs

Nymph

Nymph

Nymph

Some insects, such as grasshoppers and cockroaches, go through *incomplete metamorphosis*. Incomplete metamorphosis has three stages: egg, nymph, and adult.

Some nymphs shed their exoskeletons several times as they grow into adults. This shedding is called *molting*. In incomplete metamorphosis, nymphs look very much like small adults. ☑

## TAKE A LOOK

**10. List** What are the four stages of complete metamorphosis?

_____

_____

_____

_____

## TAKE A LOOK

**11. Compare** In which type of metamorphosis do more changes take place as the young develop?

_____

_____

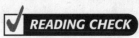

**READING CHECK**

**12. List** What are the three stages of incomplete metamorphosis?

_____

_____

_____

# Section 3 Review

7.2.a, 7.5.a, 7.5.b, 7.5.g

**SECTION VOCABULARY**

| | |
|---|---|
| **closed circulatory system** a circulatory system in which the heart circulates blood through a network of vessels that form a closed loop | **open circulatory system** a type of circulatory system in which the circulatory fluid is not contained entirely within vessels |
| **metamorphosis** a process in the life cycle of many animals during which a rapid change from the immature form of an organism to the adult form takes place | **segment** any part of a larger structure, such as the body of an organism, that is set off by natural arbitrary boundaries |

**1. Explain** What is the difference between open and closed circulatory systems?

_____

_____

_____

**2. Compare** How is the life cycle of a butterfly different from the life cycle of a hydra?

_____

_____

_____

**3. Compare** Use a Venn Diagram to compare complete metamorphosis and incomplete metamorphosis.

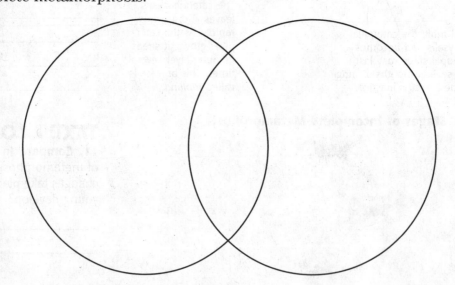

**4. Explain** Why are outer coverings important for movement in many invertebrates?

_____

_____

_____

**CHAPTER 14** Introduction to Animals

**SECTION 4** **Vertebrates**

**California Science Standards**

7.1.f, 7.2.a, 7.5.a, 7.5.b, 7.5.c, 7.5.g

---

**BEFORE YOU READ**

After you read this section, you should be able to answer these questions:

• How are vertebrates different from invertebrates?

• How do vertebrate organ systems work?

• How do vertebrate embryos develop?

---

## What Are the Characteristics of Vertebrates?

All vertebrates have a structure called a backbone. The backbone is part of a skeleton that is made of bone. Bone is a type of very hard tissue found only in vertebrates.

All vertebrates also have a head protected by a skull. The skull is made of either cartilage or bone. **Cartilage** is a flexible material made of cells and proteins. All vertebrate embryos have skeletons made of cartilage. However, as most vertebrates grow, bone replaces the cartilage. ☑

**BODY COVERINGS**

The bodies of vertebrates are covered with skin. Skin protects the body from the environment. The structure of skin is different in different vertebrates.

**STUDY TIP**

**Summarize** As you read, make an outline of the characteristics of vertebrates.

**READING CHECK**

**1. List** Name two characteristics of vertebrates.

_____

_____

_____

### Body Coverings in Vertebrates

**Scales** Reptiles and fish are covered with thin, small plates called scales.

**Feathers** Feathers on birds, like hairs on mammals, help keep the body temperature stable.

**Fur** Some body coverings have colors and patterns that help vertebrates hide from prey or predators.

**Skin** Skin protects the body from the environment.

**TAKE A LOOK**

**2. List** Name three different types of body coverings that protect vertebrate bodies.

_____

_____

_____

**SECTION 4** Vertebrates *continued*

## BODY SYMMETRY

All vertebrates have bilateral symmetry. A bilaterally symmetrical body has four main parts. (Though we are vertebrates, it helps to think of bilateral symmetry in an animal that walks on four legs.) The upper surface, or back, is the *dorsal* side. The lower surface, or belly, is the *ventral* side. The head is in the front of the body, or *anterior*. The tail is in the back of the body, or *posterior*.

## SUPPORT OF THE BODY

The body of a vertebrate is supported by an endoskeleton. An endoskeleton has three main parts: a skull, a backbone, and limb bones. Vertebrates need large bones and muscles for support and movement if they don't live in the water.

**Word Help: <u>framework</u>**
a basic structure that supports something

**3. Explain** How do bones and muscles work together to help vertebrates move?

_____

_____

_____

_____

_____

The backbone is made of smaller bones called *vertebrae* (singular, *vertebra*). Vertebrae surround and protect the spinal cord.

The skull surrounds and protects the brain.

Muscles attached to limb bones help the animal move.

## RESPIRATORY SYSTEM

The respiratory system in vertebrates brings oxygen into the body and takes carbon dioxide out. The main respiratory organs in vertebrates are either lungs or gills. ☑

Vertebrates that breathe air, rather than water, have their respiratory organs inside the body. This protects them from drying out.

✔ READING CHECK

**4. Identify** What are the two main respiratory organs in vertebrates?

_____

_____

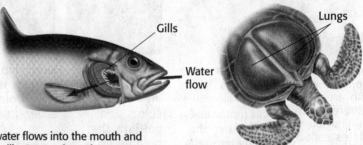

Gills

Water flow

Lungs

In fish, water flows into the mouth and over the gills. Oxygen from the water moves across the gills and into the blood. Carbon dioxide moves from the blood, across the gills, and into the water.

The inside surfaces of lungs have many small pockets. These pockets make more surface area for the exchange of oxygen and carbon dioxide.

**SECTION 4** Vertebrates *continued*

## CIRCULATORY SYSTEM

The circulatory system moves nutrients and other substances around the body. Vertebrates have closed circulatory systems made up of blood, blood vessels, and a heart. Arteries are vessels that carry blood away from the heart. Veins are vessels that carry blood to the heart. Tiny vessels called capillaries connect veins and arteries. ☑

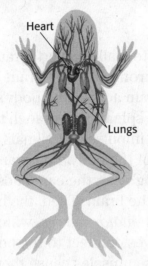

Heart

Lungs

## DIGESTIVE SYSTEM

Vertebrates have digestive systems to break down food and absorb nutrients. The digestive system is made up of a long tube called the *digestive tract*. Food moves through the digestive tract from the mouth to the anus. ☑

| Food passes from the mouth and into the stomach. |
| --- |

↓

| Chemicals in the stomach turn the food into a liquid. |
| --- |

↓

| The liquid moves into the **small intestine**, which absorbs nutrients. |
| --- |

↓

| Undigested material moves into the **large intestine**, which turns this material into feces. |
| --- |

↓

| The feces leave the body through the anus. |
| --- |

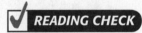 **READING CHECK**

**5. Identify** What kind of circulatory system do vertebrates have?

_____

_____

_____

**READING CHECK**

**6. Identify** What is the beginning and what is the end of the vertebrate digestive tract?

_____

_____

## EXCRETORY SYSTEM

The digestive system produces waste from the food that animals eat. However, cells also produce waste. In vertebrates, these wastes are removed by the *excretory system*. One of these wastes is ammonia. In mammals, the liver turns ammonia into urea. Then, the kidneys filter the urea from the blood. Urea combines with water to form urine.

## NERVOUS SYSTEM

The nervous system allows vertebrates to sense and respond to the environment. The brain is part of the spinal cord. The brain acts as the body's control center.

Nerves from the spinal cord branch throughout the body. Nerves carry impulses, or signals, between the brain and the rest of the body. For example, when a sound reaches a dog's ear, the ear sends a signal through *sensory nerves* to the brain. Then, the brain sends signals to the body through *motor nerves*, which cause the body to react. Some nerves connect to the body's muscles. Signals sent to these muscles cause them to contract.

Brain size is very different in different kinds of vertebrates. Although all vertebrates use instinct to react, those with larger brains depend more on learning. An *instinct* is a behavior or reaction that an animal is born with. *Learning* is a behavior in which new experiences change the way an animal reacts.

**Say It**

**Discuss** Work with a partner to discuss how the five senses—touch, taste, sight, hearing, and smell—are all important to animal survival. Prepare a short presentation to tell your classmates how an animal uses each sense.

## TAKE A LOOK
**7. Explain** Which of these animals probably relies more on learning than instinct? Explain your answer.

_____

_____

_____

_____

**Nervous Systems in Vertebrates**

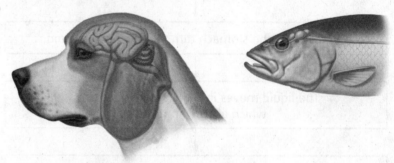

## REPRODUCTION

Most vertebrates reproduce sexually. Fertilization happens when the nucleus of a sperm cell joins with the nucleus of an egg cell. A fertilized egg cell divides many times. It becomes a multicellular embryo. As an embryo develops, its cells differentiate. That is, the cells develop different structures so that they can perform different functions.

**SECTION 4** Vertebrates *continued*

## DEVELOPMENT

Most fish and amphibians have a larval stage in their life cycles. A *larva* (plural, *larvae*) is a newly hatched animal that must go through metamorphosis to become an adult. The larvae of fish and amphibians usually hatch in the water and live on their own. Over time, larvae develop new structures or lose old structures to become adults.

Reptiles, birds, and mammals do not have a larval stage in their life cycles. These animals make eggs that are protected by special membranes. The eggs of reptiles, birds, and some mammals also have a shell. Shelled eggs are laid on land. However, most mammals do not lay eggs. Their embryos develop inside the female until the offspring are born. ☑

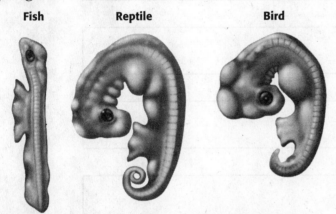

**Fish**      **Reptile**      **Bird**

Embryos of different species look similar at early stages of development. Embryos begin to look more like their own species as they develop.

## PARENTAL CARE

Human babies need a great deal of care from their parents for many years. However, not all vertebrates need as much parental care. Many fish, for example, simply lay their eggs and leave. These animals lay so many eggs that at least a few survive. Some fish and reptiles guard a nest until the young hatch. Usually, once they hatch, the young are on their own.

Birds and mammals generally show more parental care than other vertebrates. They have fewer offspring but spend more time feeding and protecting them. More parental care gives each offspring a better chance of survival.

---

✓ **READING CHECK**

**8. Identify** How do most vertebrates reproduce?

_____

_____

*Critical Thinking*

**9. Infer** Why are birds more likely to care for their young than frogs are?

_____

_____

_____

_____

_____

---

# Section 4 Review

7.1.f, 7.2.a, 7.5.a, 7.5.b, 7.5.c, 7.5.g

## SECTION VOCABULARY

| | |
|---|---|
| **cartilage** a flexible and strong connective tissue | **small intestine** the organ between the stomach and the large intestine where most of the breakdown of food happens and most of the nutrients from food are absorbed |
| **large intestine** the wider and shorter portion of the intestine that removes water from mostly digested food and that turns the waste into semisolid feces, or stool | |

**1. Summarize** Complete the Flow Chart to show how food passes through the digestive system.

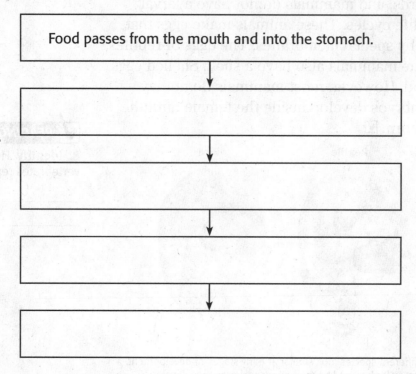

Food passes from the mouth and into the stomach.

**2. List** What are the three main parts of an endoskeleton?

_____

_____

_____

**3. Explain** Why do cells in a developing embryo differentiate?

_____

_____

**4. Compare** How does parental care differ in fish and mammals?

_____

_____

_____

CHAPTER 15 Body Organization and Structure
SECTION
1 **Body Organization**

 **California Science Standards**

7.1.f, 7.5.b

**BEFORE YOU READ**

After you read this section, you should be able to answer these questions:

• What is cell differentiation?

• What are the 11 different human organ systems?

• What is homeostasis?

## What Is Cell Differentiation?

Your cells must do many jobs. However, each of your cells does not have to do every job. Most cells in your body are *differentiated*. This means that each type of cell has a special structure that relates to its job in the body. For example, a muscle cell has special proteins that let the cell get shorter, or contract. Many muscles working together can make an entire organism move.

**STUDY TIP**

**Discuss** Read this section silently. When you finish reading, work with a partner to answer any questions you may have about the section.

### Examples of Differentiated Body Cells

**Muscle cells** have proteins that are specialized to make them shorter, or contract.

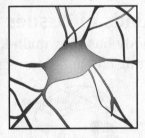

**Neurons** are nerve cells. Most neurons are long and thin.

**Red blood cells** have no nuclei but have a special pigment that picks up oxygen.

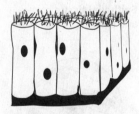

**Epithelial cells** have many jobs. They are found in skin and the linings of your organs.

**CALIFORNIA STANDARDS CHECK**

**7.1.f** Students know that as multicellular organisms develop, their cells differentiate.

**1. Define** What is cell differentiation?

_____

_____

_____

_____

_____

**TAKE A LOOK**

**2. Identify** One of these cells does not have a nucleus when it is mature. Name that cell.

_____

## How Do Cells Work Together?

Recall that there are four levels of organization in the body: cells, tissues, organs, and organ systems. Cells are the smallest level of organization in the human body. A group of similar cells working together forms a **tissue**.

_____ work together to form tissues.

Tissues work together to form _____

Organs work together to form organ systems.

Organ systems work together to form _____

## TAKE A LOOK

**3. Summarize** Complete
the chart to summarize the
levels of organization in the
human body.

# What Kinds of Tissues Are in the Body?

Your body has four main kinds of tissue: epithelial,
nervous, muscle, and connective.

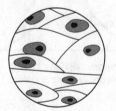

**Epithelial tissue** covers
and protects other tissues.

**Nervous tissue** sends
electrical signals through
the body.

## TAKE A LOOK

**4. List** What are the four
kinds of tissue found in the
human body?

_____

_____

_____

_____

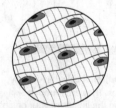

**Muscle tissue** is made
of cells that contract
and relax to produce
movement.

**Connective tissue** joins,
supports, protects, insulates,
nourishes, and cushions
organs. It also keeps organs
from falling apart.

# How Do Tissues Work Together?

An **organ** is two or more tissues working together to do a job. One kind of tissue alone cannot do all of the things tissues working together can do. For example, your stomach is made of connective tissue, nervous tissue, epithelial tissue, and muscle tissue. Your stomach works to digest food. However, none of the stomach's tissues could do that job alone. ☑

**READING CHECK**

**5. Define** What is an organ?

_____

_____

_____

**Four Kinds of Tissue in the Stomach**

Nervous tissue helps control all the movements of the stomach.

Epithelial tissue lines the stomach.

Blood is a **connective tissue** found in the wall of the stomach.

Muscle tissue mixes food and stomach acids.

# How Do Organs Work Together?

Organs work together to make up an organ system. For example, your stomach works with other organs in the digestive system, such as the intestines, to digest food. In the nervous system, the brain, spinal cord, nerves, and sense organs work together. Each of these organs helps the nervous system control body movements and other important functions.

Organ systems can also do jobs that one organ alone cannot do. Each organ is specialized to do part of the organ system's job. Each human organ system has a special function.

*Critical Thinking*

**6. Apply Concepts** How does the stomach work as part of an organ system?

_____

_____

_____

_____

# What Are the Organ Systems in the Human Body?

There are 11 different organ systems that make up the human body. None of the organ systems works alone. For example, the digestive system works with the muscular system to move food through your body.

**SECTION 1** Body Organization *continued*

**Say It**

**Discuss** Work with a partner and see how many organs you can name from each organ system.

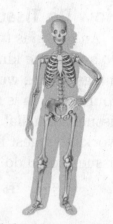

**Integumentary System** Your skin, hair, and nails protect the tissue that lies beneath them.

**Muscular System** Your muscular system works with the skeletal system to help you move.

**Skeletal System** Your bones provide a frame to support and protect your body parts.

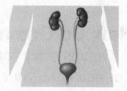

**Cardiovascular System** Your heart pumps blood through all of your blood vessels.

**Respiratory System** Your lungs absorb oxygen and release carbon dioxide.

**Urinary System** Your urinary system removes wastes from the blood and regulates your body's fluids.

## TAKE A LOOK

**7. Identify** Which organ system includes your skin?

_____

**8. Identify** Which organ system is different in males and females?

_____

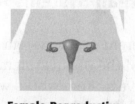

**Male Reproductive System** The male reproductive system produces and delivers sperm.

**Female Reproductive System** The female reproductive system produces eggs and nourishes and protects the fetus.

**Nervous System** Your nervous system receives and sends electrical messages throughout your body.

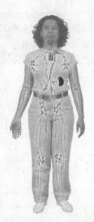

**Digestive System** Your digestive system breaks down the food you eat into nutrients that your body can absorb.

**Lymphatic System** The lymphatic system returns leaked fluids to blood vessels and helps get rid of bacteria and viruses.

**Endocrine System** Your glands send out chemical messages. Ovaries and testes are part of this system.

## How Do Organ Systems Work Together?

Each organ system has its own job. But your body's organ systems must work together to maintain homeostasis. For example, the respiratory system could not send oxygen through your body without the cardiovascular system.

Some organs have jobs that are important to more than one organ system. For example, the pancreas is an organ that makes fluids for digestion. But the pancreas is also part of the endocrine system. If the pancreas is damaged, it will affect both the digestive and endocrine systems. If one organ fails, it can affect more than one organ system and the whole organism.

## What Is Homeostasis?

Cells, tissues, and organs all work together to maintain, or keep, a stable environment. Your body works to keep itself stable even when things outside your body change. This is called *homeostasis*. Without homeostasis, you could not survive. Below is one example of how your body maintains homeostasis.

**TAKE A LOOK**
**9. Identify** Which organ system sends chemical messages through your body?

_____

_____

*Critical Thinking*
**10. Apply Concepts** Name five organ systems you would use to eat and digest a hamburger.

_____

_____

_____

_____

```
┌──────────────────┐     ┌──────────────────┐     ┌──────────────────┐
│ The temperature  │ →   │ You start to     │ →   │ Shivering makes  │
│ outside is       │     │ shiver.          │     │ heat for your    │
│ freezing.        │     │                  │     │ body.            │
└──────────────────┘     └──────────────────┘     └──────────────────┘
                                                            │
                   ┌──────────────────┐                    │
                   │ Your cells       │  ←─────────────────┘
                   │ don't freeze.    │
                   └──────────────────┘
```

# Section 1 Review

7.1.f, 7.5.a, 7.5.b

## SECTION VOCABULARY

| **organ** a collection of tissues that carry out a specialized function of the body | **tissue** a group of similar cells that perform a common function |
|---|---|

**1. List** What are the 11 organ systems?

_____

_____

_____

_____

**2. Apply Concepts** Can an organ do the same job as an organ system? Explain.

_____

_____

_____

**3. Predict** What would happen to your body if you could not maintain homeostasis?

_____

_____

_____

**4. Explain** Explain why differentiated cells are important for the human body.

_____

_____

_____

_____

**5. Explain** How is the lymphatic system related to the cardiovascular system?

_____

_____

_____

_____

CHAPTER 15 Body Organization and Structure
SECTION
2 **The Skeletal System**

---

 **California Science Standards**

7.5.a, 7.5.c, 7.6.h

**BEFORE YOU READ**

After you read this section, you should be able to answer these questions:

• What are the major organs of the skeletal system?

• What are the functions of the skeletal system?

• What are the three kinds of joints in the body?

## What Are Bones?

Bones may seem to be dry and brittle, but your bones are living organs. Bones are the major organs of the skeletal system. Connective tissues, such as cartilage and ligaments, are also part of the skeletal system. The adult human skeleton has 206 bones. ☑

## What Are the Functions of the Skeletal System?

Bones have many jobs. Bones help support and protect your body. They work with your muscles so you can move. Bones also help your body maintain homeostasis by storing minerals and making blood cells. The **skeletal system** has the following functions:

• It protects other organs. For example, your rib cage protects your heart and lungs.

• It stores minerals that help your nerves and muscles work properly. Long bones store fat that can be used as energy.

• Skeletal muscles pull on bones to cause movement. Without bones, you would not be able to sit, stand, or run.

• Some bones make blood cells. *Marrow* is a special material that makes blood cells.

**STUDY TIP**

**Organize** As you read this section, make a chart listing the functions of bones and the tissue or bone structure that does each job.

✓ **READING CHECK**

**1. Identify** What are the major organs of the skeletal system?

_____

_____

*Critical Thinking*

**2. Predict** Name one other organ system that would be affected if you had no marrow. Explain.

_____

_____

_____

_____

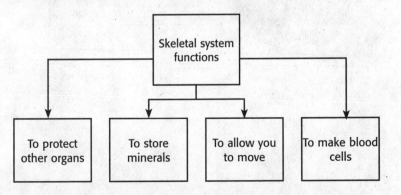

# What Is the Structure of a Bone?

A bone may seem lifeless. Like other organs, however, bone is a living organ made of several different tissues.

## BONE TISSUE

If you look inside a bone, you will see two kinds of bone tissue: compact bone and spongy bone. Compact bone has no large open spaces, but it does have tiny spaces filled with blood vessels. Spongy bone has many large open spaces that help the bone absorb shocks. ☑

## MARROW

Some bones contain a tissue called marrow. There are two types of marrow. Red marrow makes both red and white blood cells. Yellow marrow stores fat. ☑

## CARTILAGE

Did you know that most of your skeleton used to be soft and rubbery? Most bones start out as a flexible tissue called cartilage. When you were born, you didn't have much true bone. As you grew, most of your cartilage was replaced by bone. However, bone will never replace cartilage in a few small areas of your body. For example, the end of your nose and the tops of your ears will always be made of cartilage.

✓ **READING CHECK**

**3. Identify** What are the two kinds of bone tissue?

_____

_____

✓ **READING CHECK**

**4. Identify** What are the two kinds of marrow?

_____

_____

**TAKE A LOOK**
**5. Identify** Fill in the missing labels for tissues that are found in this bone

**Bone Tissues**

Blood vessels

Cartilage

Marrow

# What Is a Joint?

A place where two or more bones meet is called a
**joint**. Most joints, like your knees and elbows, let your
body move when your muscles contract, or shorten. Other
joints, called fixed joints, do not let bones move at all.
Many of the joints in the skull are fixed joints. Joints can
be grouped based on how the bones in the joint move.

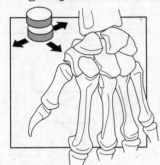

**Gliding Joint** Gliding joints let
bones in the wrist slide over each
other. This type of joint makes a
body part flexible.

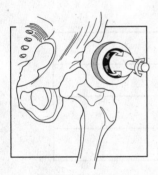

**Ball-and-Socket Joint** In the
same way that a video-game joy-
stick lets you move your character
around, the shoulder lets your
arm move freely in all directions.

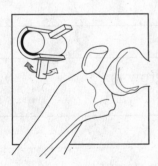

**Hinge Joint** A hinge lets a door
open and close. Your knee joint
lets your leg bend in only one
direction.

# What Is the Structure of a Joint?

Joints are often placed under a great deal of stress.
But joints can handle a lot of wear and tear because
of how they are made. Joints are held together by ligaments. *Ligaments* are strong bands of connective tissue.
Cartilage covers the ends of many bones and helps cush-
ion the areas where bones meet.

## TAKE A LOOK

**6. List** What are the three
types of joints in the human
body?

_____

_____

_____

### CALIFORNIA STANDARDS CHECK

**7.6.h** Students know how to
compare joints in the body (wrist,
shoulder, thigh) with structures
used in machines and simple
<u>devices</u> (hinge, ball-and-socket,
and sliding joints).

**Word Help: <u>device</u>**
a piece of equipment made
for a specific use

**7. Compare** How is a door
hinge like the joint in your
knee?

_____

_____

_____

_____

_____

_____

# Section 2 Review

7.5.a, 7.5.c, 7.5.h

## SECTION VOCABULARY

| | |
|---|---|
| **joint** a place where two or more bones meet | **skeletal system** the organ system whose primary function is to support and protect the body and to allow the body to move |

**1. Identify** What two things is the skeletal system made up of?

_____

_____

**2. List** What are four functions of the skeletal system?

_____

_____

_____

**3. Describe** Fill in the chart below to identify the three types of joints. Give an example of each.

| Type of joint | Example in your body |
|---|---|
| | wrist |
| | |
| Hinge | |

**4. Compare** What is the difference between red marrow and yellow marrow?

_____

_____

**5. Explain** What happens to the cartilage in your body as you grow up?

_____

_____

**6. Describe** What are the functions of ligaments and cartilage in a joint?

_____

_____

_____

_____

CHAPTER 15 Body Organization and Structure

SECTION 3 **The Muscular System**

**California Science Standards**

7.5.a, 7.5.c, 7.6.i

## BEFORE YOU READ

**After you read this section, you should be able to answer these questions:**

• What are the three kinds of muscle tissue?

• How do bones and muscles work like levers?

• What is mechanical advantage?

## What Is the Function of the Muscular System?

The **muscular system** is made up of the muscles that let you move. There are three kinds of muscle in your body: smooth muscle, cardiac muscle, and skeletal muscle.

Muscle action can be voluntary or involuntary. Muscle action that you can control is *voluntary*. Muscle action that you cannot control is *involuntary*. For example, cardiac muscle in your heart is involuntary and works on its own without your control. Skeletal muscle in your eyelids can be both voluntary and involuntary. You can blink your eyes when you want, but your eyes also blink automatically.

STUDY TIP

**Circle** As you read this section, circle any new science terms. Make sure you know what these words mean before moving to the next chapter.

| Kinds of muscle | Where in your body? | Voluntary or involuntary? |
|---|---|---|
| Cardiac | heart | involuntary |
| Smooth | digestive tract, blood vessels | involuntary |
| Skeletal | attached to bones, and other organs | both |

*Critical Thinking*

**1. Apply Concepts** Your diaphragm is a muscle that helps you breathe. Do you think this muscle is voluntary or involuntary? Explain.

_____

_____

_____

_____

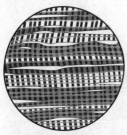

**Skeletal muscle** makes bones move.

**Smooth muscle** moves food through the digestive system.

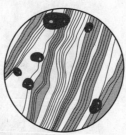

**Cardiac muscle** pumps blood around the body.

**Word Help:** <u>structural</u>
having to do with the arrangement of parts of a whole

**Word Help:** <u>framework</u>
a basic structure that supports something

**2. Explain** How do the muscular and skeletal systems work together?

_____

_____

_____

_____

_____

_____

_____

## How Do Muscles Work?

Skeletal muscles let you move. When you want to move, signals travel from you brain to your skeletal muscle cells. The muscle cells then contract. Mitochondria in muscle cells provide energy for the cells to contract.

## How Do Muscles and Bones Work Together?

Strands of tough connective tissue connect your skeletal muscles to your bones. These strands are called *tendons*. When a muscle that connects two bones contracts, the bones are pulled closer to each other. For example, tendons attach the biceps muscle to a bone in your shoulder and to a bone in your forearm. When the biceps muscle contracts, your forearm bends toward your shoulder.

| Bones are connected to other bones by ligaments. | Muscles are connected to bones by tendons. |
|---|---|

### MUSCLES IN PAIRS

Your skeletal muscles often work in pairs to make smooth, controlled motions. Generally, one muscle in the pair bends part of the body. The other muscle straightens that part of the body. A muscle that bends part of your body is called a *flexor*. A muscle that straightens part of your body is an *extensor*.

### TAKE A LOOK
**3. Identify** On the figure, write the words "flexor" and "extensor" next to the correct muscles.

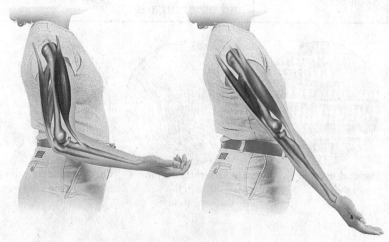

## What Is a Lever?

A muscle pulling on a bone works like a simple machine called a lever. A **lever** is a stiff bar that pivots, or turns, at a fixed point called a *fulcrum*. Any force put on the lever is called the *effort force*. A force that tries to keep a lever from moving, such as a weight on the bar, is called the *load*. Generally, levers let you do more work using less force. This increase in work is called **mechanical advantage**.

$$mechanical\ advantage = \frac{load}{effort}$$

## What Are the Different Kinds of Levers?

There are three classes of levers: first, second, and third class. Levers are grouped by where the fulcrum, load, and effect force are found.

### FIRST-CLASS LEVERS

First-class levers work like a car jack or seesaw.

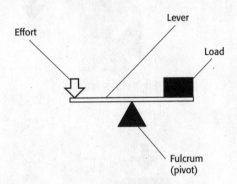

Effort    Lever    Load    Fulcrum (pivot)

**First Class Lever**

### SECOND-CLASS LEVERS

Second-class levers work like a shovel.

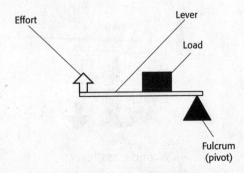

Effort    Lever    Load    Fulcrum (pivot)

**Second Class Lever**

## Math Focus

**4. Calculate** Force is measured using a unit called a newton (N). If a lever has a mechanical advantage of 8 and the load is 40 N, what is the effort?

## TAKE A LOOK

**5. Compare** How does a second-class lever differ from a first class lever?

_____

_____

_____

_____

### THIRD-CLASS LEVERS

Third-class levers work like a dolly used to carry heavy boxes.

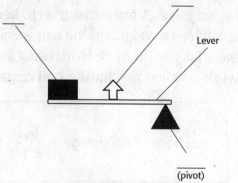

Third Class Lever

**6. Identify** Write the following words next to the correct parts of the drawing: fulcrum, effort, load.

## What Are Some Levers in Your Body?

In your body, a bone can be a lever. The effort force is applied by muscles. The fulcrum, where the bone pivots, is a joint. Most joints in the body move like third-class levers.

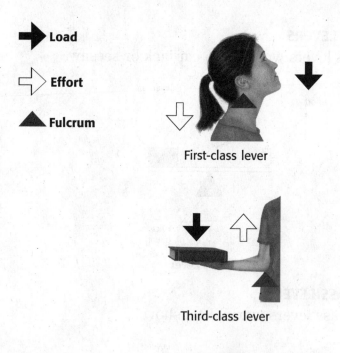

Load

Effort

Fulcrum

First-class lever

Third-class lever

**7. Identify** What type of lever is your neck?

_____

_____

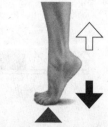

Second-class lever

# Section 3 Review

7.5.a, 7.5.c, 7.6.i

## SECTION VOCABULARY

| | |
|---|---|
| **lever** a simple machine that consists of a bar that pivots at a fixed point called a fulcrum<br>**mechanical advantage** a number that tells you how many times a machine multiplies force | **muscular system** the organ system whose primary function is movement and flexibility |

**1. List** What are the three kinds of muscle in the human body?

_____

**2. Explain** Describe how skeletal muscles work in pairs.

_____

_____

**3. Diagram** Draw a simple third-class lever. Label the lever, fulcrum, effort, and load in your diagram.

**4. Explain** What is mechanical advantage?

_____

_____

_____

**5. Describe** How are levers grouped?

_____

_____

**6. Compare** What is the difference between ligaments and tendons?

_____

_____

_____

CHAPTER 16 | Circulation and Respiration )
SECTION
1 **The Cardiovascular System**

**California Science Standards**

7.5.a, 7.5.b, 7.6.j

**BEFORE YOU READ**

After you read this section, you should be able to answer these questions:

• What is the cardiovascular system?

• What are some cardiovascular problems?

## What Is the Cardiovascular System?

Your heart, blood, and blood vessels make up your **cardiovascular system**. The word *cardio* means "heart." The word *vascular* means "blood vessels." *Blood vessels* are hollow tubes that your blood flows through. The cardiovascular system is sometimes called the *circulatory system*. This is because it circulates, or moves, blood through your body.

The cardiovascular system helps your body to maintain homeostasis. *Homeostasis* means "steady state." It occurs when all parts of your body are working properly. The cardiovascular system helps maintain homeostasis in the following ways:

• It carries oxygen and nutrients to your cells.

• It carries wastes away from your cells.

• It carries heat throughout your body.

• It carries chemical signals called *hormones* throughout your body. ☑

### HEART

Your heart is an organ that is about the same size as your fist. It is near the center of your chest. There is a thick wall in the middle of your heart that divides it into two halves. The right half pumps oxygen-poor blood to your lungs. The left half pumps oxygen-rich blood to the rest of your body.

Each side of your heart has two chambers. Each upper chamber is called an *atrium* (plural, *atria*). Each lower chamber is called a *ventricle*. These chambers are separated by flaplike structures called *valves*. Valves keep blood from flowing in the wrong direction. The closing of valves is what makes the "lub-dub" sound when your heart beats. The figure at the top of the next page shows how blood moves through your heart.

---

**STUDY TIP**

**Summarize** As you read, underline the main ideas in each paragraph. When you finish reading, write a short summary of the section, using the ideas you underlined.

---

**READING CHECK**

**1. Identify** What are two functions that the cardiovascular system does for your body?

_____

_____

_____

---

❶ Blood enters the atria first. The left atrium receives blood that has a lot of oxygen in it from the lungs. The right atrium receives blood that has little oxygen in it from the body.

❸ While the atria relax, the ventricles contract and push blood out of the heart. Blood from the right ventricle goes to the lungs. Blood from the left ventricle goes to the rest of the body.

# Math Focus

**2. Calculate** A person's heart beats about 70 times per minute. How many times does the person's heart beat in one day? How many times does it beat in one year?

_____

_____

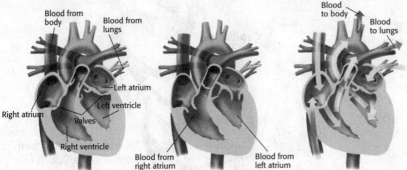

❷ When the atria contract, blood moves into the ventricles.

# TAKE A LOOK

**3. Identify** Where does the left ventricle receive blood from? Where does the right atrium receive blood from?

_____

_____

_____

_____

## BLOOD VESSELS

Blood travels throughout your body in your blood vessels. There are three types of blood vessels: arteries, capillaries, and veins.

An **artery** is a blood vessel that carries blood away from the heart. Arteries have thick walls that contain a layer of muscle. Each heartbeat pumps blood into your arteries. The blood is under high pressure. Artery walls are strong and can stretch to stand this pressure. Your *pulse* is caused by the pumping of blood into your arteries. ☑

A **capillary** is a tiny blood vessel. Capillary walls are very thin. Therefore, substances can move across them easily. Capillaries are very narrow. They are so narrow that blood cells have to pass through them in single file.

Nutrients and oxygen move from the blood in your capillaries into your body's cells. Carbon dioxide and other wastes move from your body's cells into the blood in your capillaries.

A **vein** is a blood vessel that carries blood toward the heart. Veins have valves to keep the blood from flowing backward. When skeletal muscles contract, they squeeze nearby veins and help push blood toward the heart.

✔ **READING CHECK**

**4. Describe** What causes your pulse?

_____

_____

_____

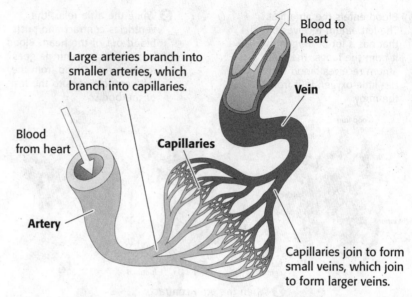

Blood to heart

Large arteries branch into smaller arteries, which branch into capillaries.

Vein

Blood from heart

**Capillaries**

**Artery**

Capillaries join to form small veins, which join to form larger veins.

## TAKE A LOOK

**5. Compare** What is one main difference between arteries and veins?

_____

_____

_____

**6. Define** What is pulmonary circulation?

_____

_____

## How Does Blood Flow Through Your Body?

Where does blood get the oxygen to deliver to your body? From your lungs! Your heart contracts and pumps blood to the lungs. There, carbon dioxide leaves the blood, and oxygen enters the blood. The oxygen-rich blood then flows back to your heart. This circulation of blood between your heart and lungs is called **pulmonary circulation**. ☑

The oxygen-rich blood returning to your heart from your lungs is then pumped to the rest of your body. This circulation of blood between your heart and the rest of your body is called **systemic circulation**. The figure below shows how blood moves through your body.

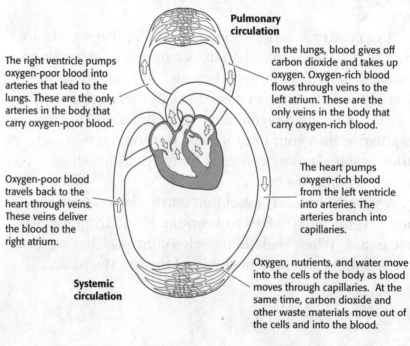

**Pulmonary circulation**

The right ventricle pumps oxygen-poor blood into arteries that lead to the lungs. These are the only arteries in the body that carry oxygen-poor blood.

In the lungs, blood gives off carbon dioxide and takes up oxygen. Oxygen-rich blood flows through veins to the left atrium. These are the only veins in the body that carry oxygen-rich blood.

Oxygen-poor blood travels back to the heart through veins. These veins deliver the blood to the right atrium.

The heart pumps oxygen-rich blood from the left ventricle into arteries. The arteries branch into capillaries.

**Systemic circulation**

Oxygen, nutrients, and water move into the cells of the body as blood moves through capillaries. At the same time, carbon dioxide and other waste materials move out of the cells and into the blood.

## TAKE A LOOK

**7. Color** Use a blue pen or marker to color the vessels carrying oxygen-poor blood. Use a red pen or marker to color the vessels carrying oxygen-rich blood.

# What Are Some Problems of the Cardiovascular System?

Problems in the cardiovascular system can affect other parts of your body. Your whole body can be harmed. Cardiovascular problems can be caused by smoking, too much cholesterol, stress, physical inactivity, or heredity. Eating a healthy diet and getting plenty of exercise can help to keep your cardiovascular system, and the rest of your body, healthy.

## ATHEROSCLEROSIS

Heart disease is the most common cause of death in the United States. One major cause of heart disease is atherosclerosis. *Atherosclerosis* is the narrowing of blood vessels when cholesterol and other fats build up inside them. This buildup causes the blood vessels to become narrower and less stretchy. When the pathway through a blood vessel is blocked, blood cannot flow through. ☑

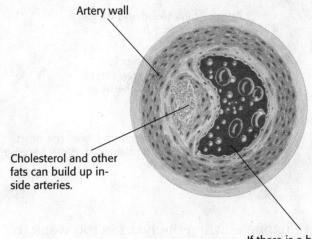

Artery wall

Cholesterol and other fats can build up inside arteries.

If there is a buildup of cholesterol, the artery becomes narrower. Not as much blood can flow through it at a time. If the cholesterol totally blocks the artery, no blood can flow through.

*Critical Thinking*

**8. Infer** How can a problem in your cardiovascular system affect the rest of your body?

_____

_____

_____

_____

**READING CHECK**

**9. Identify** What is the most common cause of death in the United States?

_____

_____

## TAKE A LOOK

**10. Explain** How can too much cholesterol cause problems in your cardiovascular system?

_____

_____

_____

**SECTION 1** The Cardiovascular System *continued*

## HIGH BLOOD PRESSURE

*Hypertension* is high blood pressure. Hypertension can make it more likely that a person will have cardiovascular problems. For example, atherosclerosis can be caused by hypertension.

High blood pressure can also cause a stroke. A *stroke* is a failure in the flow of blood to the brain cells. It happens when a blood vessel in the brain is blocked or breaks open. Without blood, the brain cells cannot get oxygen, so they die. ☑

## HEART ATTACKS AND HEART FAILURE

Hypertension can also cause heart attacks and heart failure. A *heart attack* is a failure in the flow of blood to the heart muscle cells. Arteries that deliver oxygen to the heart may be damaged. Without oxygen from the arteries, heart muscle cells can be damaged. If enough heart muscle cells are damaged, it is likely that the heart will stop.

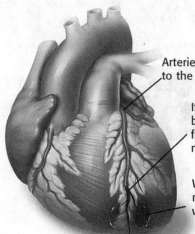

Arteries carry blood and oxygen to the heart muscle.

If an artery is blocked, blood and oxygen cannot flow to part of the heart muscle.

Without oxygen from blood, the heart muscle can be damaged. It can become weaker or die.

*Heart failure* happens when the heart is too weak to pump enough blood to meet the body's needs. Organs may not receive enough oxygen or nutrients to function correctly. It is also possible that waste products will build up in the organs and damage them.

---

✔ **READING CHECK**

**11. Identify** What is a stroke?

_____

_____

**TAKE A LOOK**

**12. Explain** How can blocking an artery in the heart cause heart damage?

_____

_____

_____

# Section 1 Review

7.5.a, 7.5.b, 7.6.j

## SECTION VOCABULARY

| | |
|---|---|
| **artery** a blood vessel that carries blood away from the heart to the body's organs | **pulmonary circulation** the flow of blood from the heart to the lungs and back to the heart through the pulmonary arteries, capillaries, and veins |
| **capillary** a tiny blood vessel that allows an exchange between blood and cells in tissue | |
| **cardiovascular system** a collection of organs that transport blood throughout the body | **systemic circulation** the flow of blood from the heart to all parts of the body and back to the heart |
| | **vein** in biology, a vessel that carries blood to the heart |

**1. Identify** What are the three main parts of the cardiovascular system?

_____

_____

_____

**2. Describe** Beginning and ending in the left atrium, describe the path that blood takes through your body and lungs.

_____

_____

_____

**3. Compare** How is a heart attack different from heart failure?

_____

_____

_____

**4. Explain** What is the function of valves in the heart and the veins?

_____

_____

**5. Compare** How are the arteries that lead from your heart to your lungs different from the other arteries in your body?

_____

_____

_____

CHAPTER 16 Circulation and Respiration
SECTION
**2** **Blood**

 **California Science Standards**

7.5.a, 7.5.b, 7.6.j

**BEFORE YOU READ**

After you read this section, you should be able to answer these questions:

• What is blood?

• What is blood pressure?

• What are blood types?

## What Is Blood?

Your cardiovascular system is made up of your heart, your blood vessels, and blood. **Blood** is a connective tissue made up of plasma, red blood cells, platelets, and white blood cells. It moves through miles of blood vessels to reach all the cells in your body. However, an adult human has only about 5 L of blood. Children have even less. That means that all the blood in your body would not even fill up two 3 L soda bottles! ☑

Blood carries important materials to all parts of your body. Your blood also helps to keep your body temperature constant. When you are hot, your blood vessels get bigger. Blood moves closer to the skin. Heat is released into the air, and your body cools. When you are cold, the blood vessels to the skin get narrower. Less blood flows to the skin. This means that less heat is lost through your skin.

**STUDY TIP**

**Ask Questions** As you read this section, write down the questions that you have. Then, discuss your questions with a small group.

**✓ READING CHECK**

**1. Define** What is blood?

_____

_____

_____

_____

**TAKE A LOOK**

**2. Identify** Fill in the blank lines to describe how blood vessels change when you are hot or cold.

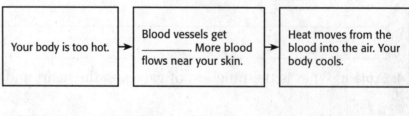

| Your body is too hot. | Blood vessels get _____. More blood flows near your skin. | Heat moves from the blood into the air. Your body cools. |

| Your body is too cold. | Blood vessels get _____. Less blood flows near your skin. | Less heat moves from the blood into the air. Your body gets warmer. |

### PLASMA

The fluid part of the blood is called plasma. *Plasma* is a mix of water, minerals, nutrients, sugars, proteins, and other substances. Red blood cells, platelets, and white blood cells are found in plasma, but they are not part of it.

**SECTION 2** Blood *continued*

## RED BLOOD CELLS

Most blood cells are *red blood cells*, or RBCs. RBCs carry oxygen to all the living cells in your body. Cells have to have oxygen to do their jobs for the body. RBCs use hemoglobin to carry oxygen. *Hemoglobin* is a protein that is found in all red blood cells. It attaches to the oxygen that you breathe into your lungs. RBCs can then move oxygen throughout the body. Hemoglobin is what makes RBCs look red. ☑

## PLATELETS

*Platelets* are pieces of larger cells. They last for only 5 days to 10 days, but they are an important part of blood. When you cut or scrape your skin, you bleed because blood vessels have been opened. As soon as bleeding starts, platelets clump together in the damaged area. They form a plug that begins to stop the blood loss. Platelets also give off chemicals that react with proteins in plasma to form tiny fibers. These fibers make a blood clot.

## WHITE BLOOD CELLS

Sometimes, pathogens get into your body. A *pathogen* is a virus, bacterium, or other tiny particle that can make you sick. When these things get into your body, they can meet *white blood cells*, or WBCs. The WBCs help you stay healthy by killing pathogens. WBCs also clean up wounds.

WBCs fight pathogens in many ways. Some WBCs squeeze out of blood vessels and move around in tissues, searching for pathogens. When they find a pathogen, they destroy it. Other WBCs release antibodies. *Antibodies* are chemicals that identify or destroy pathogens. WBCs also keep you healthy by destroying body cells that have died or been damaged.

Most WBCs are made in bone marrow. Some WBCs mature in another system in your body called the lymphatic system. ☑

| Component of blood | Function |
|---|---|
| Plasma | helps cells and other things flow |
| Red blood cells | carry oxygen |
| Platelets | help in clotting |
| White blood cells | help in defense |

✓ **READING CHECK**

**3. Explain** What does hemoglobin do for red blood cells?

_____

_____

_____

*Critical Thinking*

**4. Infer** Consider a person who does not have enough platelets in his or her blood. What will happen if the person gets a cut? Explain your answer.

_____

_____

_____

_____

✓ **READING CHECK**

**5. Identify** Where are most white blood cells made?

_____

_____

**Word Help: <u>generate</u>**
to bring about; to produce

**6. Explain** How is blood pressure produced?

_____

_____

_____

_____

**TAKE A LOOK**
**7. Identify** Fill in the blank spaces in the table to describe the two parts of blood pressure.

 **Say It**

**Discuss** Learn about two ways to maintain healthy blood pressure. In a small group, talk about how you can apply these ideas in your life.

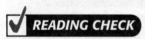 **READING CHECK**
**8. Identify** What determines your blood type?

_____

# What Is Blood Pressure?

Whenever your heart contracts, or squeezes, it pushes blood out of your heart and into your arteries. The force of the blood on the inside walls of the arteries is called **blood pressure**. Blood pressure is measured in millimeters of mercury (mm Hg).

Blood pressure is usually given as two numbers, such as 110/70 mm Hg. The first number is the systolic pressure. The *systolic pressure* is the pressure inside large arteries when the ventricles contract. The big push of blood causes the arteries to push out and produce a pulse. The second number is the diastolic pressure. *Diastolic pressure* is the pressure inside arteries when the ventricles relax.

| Type of pressure | What it is | Where it is found in a blood pressure measurement |
|---|---|---|
| Systolic | | It is the top number. |
| | pressure in the arteries when ventricles relax | |

For adults, a blood pressure of 120/80 mm Hg or less is healthy. Remember that hypertension, or high blood pressure, can cause problems in the cardiovascular system. High blood pressure can make a person more likely to have a heart attack or stroke. It can also cause damage to other parts of the body. For example, high blood pressure can cause heart or kidney damage.

# What Are Blood Types?

There are special particles on the surface of your RBCs called *antigens*. There are different kinds of antigens, and they determine your blood type. People with different blood types have different antigens on their RBCs. They also have different antibodies in their plasma. These antibodies react against the antigens of other blood types as if the antigens were pathogens. ☑

There are two main systems for grouping blood types. One is the ABO system. The other is the Rh system.

**SECTION 2** Blood *continued*

## ABO SYSTEM

The ABO system is one way of classifying blood. Every person has one of four blood types: A, B, AB, or O. Type A blood has A antigens; type B has B antigens; and type AB has both A and B antigens. Type O blood has neither A antigens nor B antigens. ☑

Each blood type also has different antibodies. For example, type A blood has antibodies that react against type B antigens. If a person with type A blood is injected with type B blood, the type B antibodies attach themselves to the type B red blood cells. These RBCs begin to clump together. The clumps can block blood vessels. A reaction to the wrong blood type may be fatal.

✓ **READING CHECK**

**9. Describe** What kinds of antigens are found on the RBCs of a person with type AB blood?

_____

_____

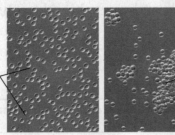

This picture shows RBCs in a mixture of blood from two people. Both people have the same blood type. Notice that the RBCs are not clumped together.

This picture shows RBCs in a mixture of blood from people with different blood types. The _____ in the blood have reacted with the _____ on the surface of the RBCs. The RBCs have formed clumps.

**TAKE A LOOK**
**10. Identify** Fill in the blank lines to explain what has happened in the right-hand picture.

## Rh SYSTEM

Another antigen that may be on the surface of RBCs is the Rh antigen. A person with the Rh antigen is considered Rh-positive ($Rh^+$). A person without the Rh antigen is Rh-negative ($Rh^-$). If an $Rh^-$ person receives a blood transfusion of $Rh^+$ blood, antibodies may react and cause the blood to clump.

Usually, the ABO system and the Rh system are combined. People with $AB^+$ blood type have A, B, and Rh antigens on their RBCs. People with $O^-$ blood have no antigens on their RBCs.

*Critical Thinking*

**11. Apply Concepts** What kinds of antigens are found on the RBCs of a person with $A^+$ blood?

_____

_____

| Blood type | Antigens | Antibodies |
|---|---|---|
| A | A antigens | B antibodies |
| B | B antigens | A antibodies |
| AB | A and B antigens | neither A nor B antibodies |
| O | neither A nor B antigens | A and B antibodies |
| $Rh^+$ | Rh antigens | no Rh antibodies |
| $Rh^-$ | no Rh antigens | Rh antibodies |

## Why Are Blood Types Important?

A person can lose blood from an injury or because of surgery. If a person loses too much blood, the person may go into shock. *Shock* happens when a person's cells do not get enough blood. Without blood, the cells do not get enough oxygen and nutrients. Wastes build up. After a time, cells may die. If too many of a person's cells die, the person can die, too. ☑

In order to replace the blood that was lost, a person can receive a blood transfusion. A *transfusion* is placement of someone else's blood into a person's blood vessels. The person receiving blood cannot use blood from just anyone. Remember that antibodies in blood can react with antigens on RBCs and cause blood to clump. If a person receives blood with the wrong antibodies in it, the person could die. The table below shows blood transfusion possibilities.

| Blood type | Can receive blood from | Can donate blood to |
|---|---|---|
| A | types A and O | types A and AB |
| B | types B and O | types B and AB |
| AB | types A, B, AB, and O | type AB only |
| O | type O only | types A, B, AB, and O |

## What Are Some Blood Disorders?

Sometimes, a person's blood may not be able to do everything it is supposed to do. The person is said to have a *blood disorder*. Two of the most common blood disorders are hemophilia and leukemia.

A person with *hemophilia* is missing a protein that helps blood to clot. Blood clots form in healthy people when a blood vessel has been damaged. A person with hemophilia does not form blood clots normally. Even a small cut can cause a person with hemophilia to lose a lot of blood. ☑

*Leukemia* is a type of cancer that affects blood cells. A person with leukemia may not be able to make enough healthy WBCs or RBCs. Leukemia may be treated with bone marrow transfusions. Bone marrow is taken from the hip bones of donors and given to the sick person.

---

✔ **READING CHECK**

**12. Define** What is shock?

_____

_____

_____

**TAKE A LOOK**

**13. Identify** Which blood type can receive blood from the most other blood types? Which type can donate blood to the most other types?

_____

_____

✔ **READING CHECK**

**14. Explain** Why can even small cuts be dangerous for people with hemophilia?

_____

_____

_____

# Section 2 Review

7.5.a, 7.5.b, 7.6.j

## SECTION VOCABULARY

| | |
|---|---|
| **blood** the fluid that carries gases, nutrients, and wastes through the body and that is made up of platelets, white blood cells, red blood cells, and plasma | **blood pressure** the force that blood exerts on the walls of arteries<br>**Wordwise** The root *press* means "to press." |

**1. Identify** What are two functions of white blood cells?

_____

_____

**2. Describe** How is systolic blood pressure different from diastolic blood pressure?

_____

_____

**3. List** What are three functions of blood?

_____

_____

_____

**4. Draw Conclusions** Why does your face get redder when you are hot?

_____

_____

_____

**5. Explain** Why is it important that a person with type O blood only receive a blood transfusion from another person with type O blood?

_____

_____

_____

_____

**6. Predict Consequences** A person has a disease that causes hemoglobin to break down. What will happen to the person's RBCs?

_____

_____

_____

_____

**SECTION**
**3** The Respiratory System

**California Science Standards**

7.5.a, 7.5.b

**BEFORE YOU READ**

After you read this section, you should be able to answer these questions:

• What is the respiratory system?

• What are some respiratory disorders?

## What Is the Respiratory System?

Breathing—you do it all the time. You're doing it right now. You probably don't think about it unless you can't breathe. Then, it becomes very clear that you have to breathe in order to live. Why is breathing important? Breathing helps your body get oxygen. Your body needs oxygen in order to get energy from the foods you eat.

The words *breathing* and *respiration* are often used to mean the same thing. However, breathing is only one part of respiration. **Respiration** is the way the body gains and uses oxygen and gets rid of carbon dioxide and water. ☑

Respiration is divided into two parts. The first part involves inhaling and exhaling, or breathing. The second part is cellular respiration. *Cellular respiration* involves the chemical reactions that let you get energy from food.

The **respiratory system** is the group of organs that take in oxygen and get rid of carbon dioxide. The nose, throat, lungs, and passageways that lead to the lungs make up the respiratory system.

**STUDY TIP**

**Compare** Make a chart showing the features of the different parts of the respiratory system.

**READING CHECK**

**1. Define** What is respiration?

_____

_____

_____

_____

**Parts of the Respiratory System**

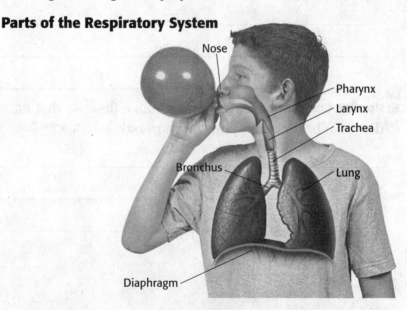

**TAKE A LOOK**
**2. Identify** What are the parts of the respiratory system?

_____

_____

_____

_____

## NOSE, PHARYNX, LARYNX, AND TRACHEA

Your *nose* is the main passageway into and out of the respiratory system. You breathe air in through your nose. You also breathe air out of your nose. Air can also enter and leave through your mouth. ☑

From the nose, air flows through the **pharynx**, or throat. Food and drink also move through the pharynx on the way to the stomach. The pharynx branches into two tubes. One tube, the *esophagus*, leads to the stomach. The other tube leads to the lungs. The larynx sits where the two tubes branch.

The **larynx** is the part of the throat that contains the vocal cords. The *vocal cords* are bands of stretchy tissue that stretch across the larynx. Muscles connected to the larynx control how much the vocal cords are stretched. When air flows between the vocal cords, the cords vibrate. These vibrations make sound.

The larynx guards the entrance to a large tube called the **trachea**, or windpipe. The trachea is the passageway for air traveling from the larynx to the lungs. ☑

## BRONCHI AND ALVEOLI

Inside your chest, the trachea splits into two branches called **bronchi** (singular, *bronchus*). One bronchus connects to each lung. Each bronchus branches into smaller and smaller tubes. These branches form a series of smaller airways called *bronchioles*. In the lungs, each bronchiole branches to form tiny sacs called **alveoli**.

✔ **READING CHECK**

**3. Describe** What is the main function of the nose?

_____

_____

✔ **READING CHECK**

**4. Identify** What is the trachea?

_____

_____

Inside your lungs, the bronchi branch into bronchioles.

Trachea

Bronchus

Lung

Bronchiole

Alveoli

Capillary

The bronchioles branch into tiny sacs called alveoli. Gases can move between the alveoli and the blood that is in the capillaries.

**TAKE A LOOK**

**5. Infer** Which do you have the most of in your lungs: bronchi, bronchioles, or alveoli?

_____

## How Does Breathing Work?

Your lungs have no muscles of their own. Instead, your diaphragm and rib muscles do the work that helps you breathe. The *diaphragm* is a dome-shaped muscle underneath the lungs. When the diaphragm contracts and moves down, you inhale. At the same time, some of your rib muscles contract and lift your rib cage. The volume of your chest gets larger. As a result, air is sucked in.

Exhaling is this process in reverse. Your diaphragm relaxes, your rib muscles relax, and air moves out.

## How Are Breathing and Cellular Respiration Related?

In *cellular respiration*, cells use oxygen to release the energy that is stored in molecules of a sugar. This sugar is called *glucose*. When cells break down glucose, they give off carbon dioxide.

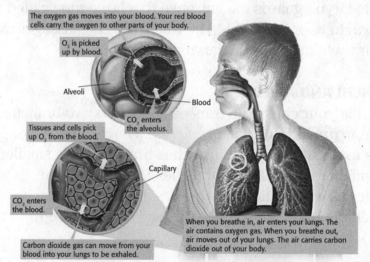

The oxygen gas moves into your blood. Your red blood cells carry the oxygen to other parts of your body.

$O_2$ is picked up by blood.

Alveoli

Blood

$CO_2$ enters the alveolus.

Tissues and cells pick up $O_2$ from the blood.

Capillary

$CO_2$ enters the blood.

Carbon dioxide gas can move from your blood into your lungs to be exhaled.

When you breathe in, air enters your lungs. The air contains oxygen gas. When you breathe out, air moves out of your lungs. The air carries carbon dioxide out of your body.

## What Are Some Respiratory Disorders?

People who have *respiratory disorders* have trouble getting the oxygen they need. Their cells cannot release all of the energy in the food they eat. Therefore, these people may feel tired all the time. They may also have problems getting rid of carbon dioxide. The carbon dioxide can build up in their cells and make them sick.

| Respiratory disorder | What it is |
|---|---|
| Asthma | a disorder that causes bronchioles to narrow, making it hard to breathe |
| Emphysema | a disorder caused when alveoli are damaged |

# Section 3 Review

7.5.a, 7.5.b

## SECTION VOCABULARY

| | |
|---|---|
| **alveoli** any of the tiny air sacs of the lungs where oxygen and carbon dioxide are exchanged | **respiration** the exchange of oxygen and carbon dioxide between living cells and their environment; includes breathing and cellular respiration |
| **bronchus** one of the two tubes that connect the lungs with the trachea | **respiratory system** a collection of organs whose primary function is to take in oxygen and expel carbon dioxide |
| **larynx** the area of the throat that contains the vocal cords and produces vocal sounds | |
| **pharynx** the passage from the mouth to the larynx and esophagus | **trachea** the tube that connects the larynx to the lungs |

**1. List** What are three respiratory disorders?

_____

_____

**2. Identify** What is cellular respiration?

_____

_____

**3. Compare** How is respiration different from breathing?

_____

_____

_____

**4. Explain** The nose is the main way for air to get into and out of your body. Why can you still breathe if your nose is blocked?

_____

_____

_____

_____

**5. Describe** How do vocal cords produce sound?

_____

_____

_____

**6. Explain** What are two ways that a respiratory disorder can make a person sick?

_____

_____

_____

# The Nervous System

**California Science Standards**

7.5.a, 7.5.b

**BEFORE YOU READ**

After you read this section, you should be able to answer these questions:

• What does the nervous system do?

• What is the structure of the nervous system?

---

**STUDY TIP** ⟨

**Organize** As you read, make a chart that describes different structures in the nervous system.

## What Are the Two Main Parts of the Nervous System?

What is one thing that you have done today that did not involve your nervous system? This is a trick question! Your nervous system controls almost everything you do.

The nervous system has two basic functions. First, it collects information and decides what the information means. This information comes from inside your body and from the world outside your body. Second, the nervous system responds to the information it has collected.

The nervous system has two parts: the central nervous system and the peripheral nervous system. The **central nervous system** (CNS) includes the brain and the spinal cord. The CNS takes in and responds to information from the peripheral nervous system. ☑

The **peripheral nervous system** (PNS) includes all the parts of the nervous system except the brain and the spinal cord. The PNS connects all parts of the body to the CNS. Special structures called *nerves* in the PNS carry information between the body and the CNS.

---

✓ **READING CHECK**

**1. Identify** What are the two main parts of the nervous system?

_____

_____

_____

_____

**TAKE A LOOK**

**2. Summarize** Complete the chart to describe the main parts of the nervous system.

| Part of the nervous system | What it includes | What it does |
|---|---|---|
| Central nervous system (CNS) | | takes in and responds to messages from the PNS |
| Peripheral nervous system (PNS) | | |

---

# How Does Information Move Through the Nervous System?

Special cells called **neurons** carry the information that travels through your nervous system. Neurons carry information in the form of electrical energy. These electrical messages are called *impulses*. Impulses may travel up to 150 m/s!

Like any other cell in your body, a neuron has a nucleus and organelles. The nucleus and organelles are found in the *cell body* of the neuron. However, neurons also have structures called dendrites and axons that are not found in other kinds of cells.

*Dendrites* are parts of the neuron that branch from the cell body. Most dendrites are very short compared to the rest of the neuron. A single neuron may have many dendrites. Dendrites bring messages from other cells to the cell body.

*Axons* are longer than dendrites. Some axons can be as long as 1 m! Axons carry information away from the cell body to other cells. The end of an axon is called an *axon terminal*.

## Math Focus
**3. Calculate** To calculate how long an impulse takes to travel a certain distance, you can use the following equation:

$$time = \frac{distance}{speed}$$

If an impulse travels 100 m/s, about how long will it take the impulse to travel 10 meters?

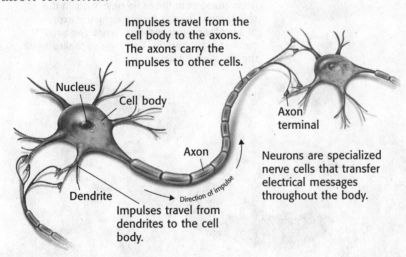

Impulses travel from the cell body to the axons. The axons carry the impulses to other cells.

Nucleus

Cell body

Axon terminal

Axon

Dendrite

Direction of impulse

Impulses travel from dendrites to the cell body.

Neurons are specialized nerve cells that transfer electrical messages throughout the body.

**TAKE A LOOK**
**4. Identify** Add an arrow to the diagram that shows the direction of impulses at the dendrites.

## SENSORY NEURONS

Some neurons are sensory neurons. *Sensory neurons* carry information about what is happening in and around your body. Some sensory neurons are called receptors. *Receptors* can detect changes inside and outside your body. For example, receptors in your eyes can sense light. Sensory neurons carry information from the receptors to the CNS.

**Say It**

**Name** With a partner, or in small groups, name parts of the body that have sensory receptors.

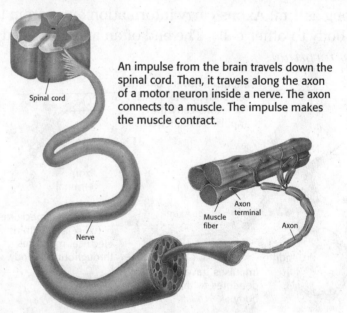

## MOTOR NEURONS

*Motor neurons* carry impulses from the CNS to other parts of your body. Most motor neurons carry impulses to muscle cells. When muscles cells receive impulses from motor neurons, the muscle cells contract. Some motor neurons carry impulses to glands, such as sweat glands. These messages tell sweat glands when to make sweat.

## NERVES

In many parts of your body, groups of axons are wrapped together with blood vessels and connective tissue to form bundles. These bundles are called **nerves**. Your central nervous system is connected to the rest of your body by nerves.

Nerves are found everywhere in your PNS. Most nerves contain axons from both sensory neurons and motor neurons. Many nerves carry impulses from your CNS to your PNS. Other nerves carry impulses from your PNS to your CNS.

An impulse from the brain travels down the spinal cord. Then, it travels along the axon of a motor neuron inside a nerve. The axon connects to a muscle. The impulse makes the muscle contract.

Spinal cord

Axon terminal

Muscle fiber

Axon

Nerve

## What Are the Parts of the Peripheral Nervous System?

Recall that the PNS connects the CNS to the rest of the body. Sensory neurons and motor neurons are both found in the PNS. Sensory neurons carry information to the CNS. Motor neurons carry information from the CNS to the PNS. The motor neurons in the PNS make up two groups: the somatic nervous system and the autonomic

---

**5. Predict** What would happen if your nerves stopped working?

_____

_____

_____

_____

_____

✓ **READING CHECK**

**6. Identify** What are the two main groups of motor neurons in the PNS?

_____

_____

_____

_____

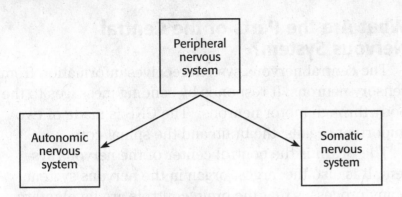

## THE SOMATIC NERVOUS SYSTEM

The *somatic nervous system* is made up of motor neurons that you can control. These neurons are connected to skeletal muscles. They control voluntary movements, or movements that you have to think about. These movements include walking, writing, and talking.

## THE AUTONOMIC NERVOUS SYSTEM

The *autonomic nervous system* controls body functions that you do not have to think about. These include digestion and the beating of your heart. The main job of the autonomic nervous system is to keep all of the body's functions in balance.

The autonomic nervous system has two divisions: the *sympathetic nervous system* and the *parasympathetic nervous system*. These two divisions work together to maintain a stable state inside your body. This stable state is called *homeostasis*. The table below shows how the sympathetic and parasympathetic nervous systems work together. ☑

| Organ | Effect of sympathetic nervous system | Effect of parasympathetic nervous system |
|---|---|---|
| Eye | makes pupils larger so it is easier to see | returns pupils to normal size |
| Heart | raises heart rate to increase blood flow | lowers heart rate to decrease blood flow |
| Lungs | makes bronchioles larger to get more oxygen into the blood | returns bronchioles to normal |
| Blood vessels | makes blood vessels smaller to increase blood pressure | has little or no effect |
| Intestines | reduces blood flow to stomach and intestines to slow digestion | returns digestion to normal |

*Critical Thinking*

**7. Explain** How does eating a hamburger involve both the somatic and autonomic nervous systems?

_____

_____

_____

_____

_____

**✓ READING CHECK**

**8. Identify** What are the two divisions of the autonomic nervous system?

_____

_____

## What Are the Parts of the Central Nervous System?

The central nervous system receives information from sensory neurons. It responds by sending messages to the body through motor neurons. The CNS is made of two important organs: the brain and the spinal cord.

The **brain** is the control center of the nervous system. It is also the largest organ in the nervous system. Many processes that the brain controls are involuntary. However, the brain also controls many voluntary processes. The brain has three main parts: the cerebrum, the cerebellum, and the medulla. Each part of the brain has its own job.

### THE CEREBRUM

The *cerebrum* is the largest part of your brain. This dome-shaped area is where you think and where most memories are kept. The cerebrum controls voluntary movements. It also lets you sense touch, light, sound, odors, taste, pain, heat, and cold. ☑

The cerebrum is made up of two halves called *hemispheres*. The left hemisphere controls most movements on the right side of the body. The right hemisphere controls most movements on the left side of the body. The two hemispheres also control different types of activities, as shown in the figure below. However, most brain activities use both hemispheres.

**READING CHECK**

**9. Identify** What kind of movements does the cerebrum control?

_____

_____

**TAKE A LOOK**

**10. Explain** Which hemisphere of your brain are you mainly using as you read this book? Explain your answer.

_____

_____

_____

_____

_____

_____

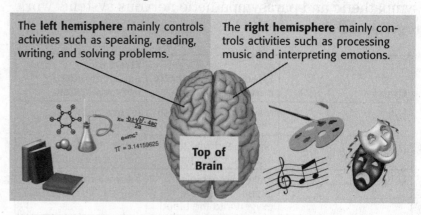

The **left hemisphere** mainly controls activities such as speaking, reading, writing, and solving problems.

The **right hemisphere** mainly controls activities such as processing music and interpreting emotions.

Top of Brain

**SECTION 1** The Nervous System *continued*

### THE CEREBELLUM

The *cerebellum* is found under and beneath the cerebrum. The cerebellum receives and processes information from your body, such as from your skeletal muscles and joints. This information lets the brain keep track of your body's position. For example, your cerebellum lets you know when you are upside-down. Your cerebellum also sends messages to your muscles to help you keep your balance. ☑

### THE MEDULLA

The *medulla* is the part of your brain that connects to your spinal cord. It is only about 3 cm long, but you cannot live without it. It controls involuntary processes, such as breathing and regulating heart rate.

Your medulla is always receiving sensory impulses from receptors in your blood vessels. It uses this information to control your blood pressure. If your blood pressure gets too low, your medulla sends impulses that cause blood vessels to tighten. This makes your blood pressure rise. The medulla also sends impulses to the heart to make it beat faster or slower.

✓ **READING CHECK**

**11. Identify** What are two functions of the cerebellum?

_____

_____

_____

_____

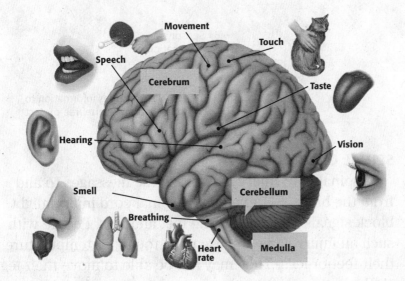

**TAKE A LOOK**

**12. Identify** Which part of the brain controls breathing?

_____

**13. Identify** Which part of the brain processes odors?

_____

## THE SPINAL CORD

Your spinal cord is part of your central nervous system. It is made up of neurons and bundles of axons that send impulses to and from the brain. The spinal cord is surrounded and protected by bones called *vertebrae* (singular, *vertebra*).

The axons in your spinal cord let your brain communicate with your PNS. The axons of sensory neurons in your skin and muscles carry impulses to your spinal cord. The impulses travel through the spinal cord to your brain. The brain then processes the impulses and sends signals back through the spinal cord. The impulses travel from the spinal cord to motor neurons. The axons of motor neurons carry the signals to your body.

*Critical Thinking*

**14. Explain** What is one way your nervous system and skeletal system work together?

_____

_____

_____

_____

_____

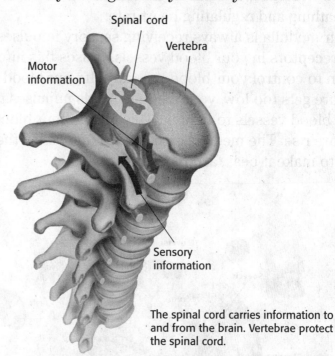

Spinal cord

Vertebra

Motor information

Sensory information

The spinal cord carries information to and from the brain. Vertebrae protect the spinal cord.

## SPINAL CORD INJURIES

A spinal cord injury may block the messages to and from the brain. For example, a spinal cord injury might block signals to and from the feet and legs. People with such an injury cannot sense pain, touch, or temperature in their feet or legs. They may not be able to move their legs.

Each year, thousands of people are paralyzed by spinal cord injuries. Most spinal cord injuries in young people happen during sports. You can prevent these injuries by wearing proper safety equipment. ☑

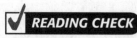 **READING CHECK**

**15. Identify** How can you help prevent spinal cord injuries while playing sports?

_____

_____

_____

# Section 1 Review

7.5.a, 7.5.b

## SECTION VOCABULARY

| | |
|---|---|
| **brain** the organ that is the main control center of the nervous system | **neuron** a nerve cell that is specialized to receive and conduct electrical impulses |
| **central nervous system** the brain and the spinal cord | **peripheral nervous system** all of the parts of the nervous system except for the brain and the spinal cord |
| **nerve** a collection of nerve fibers through which impulses travel between the central nervous system and other parts of the body | **Wordwise** The root *peri* means "around" or "near." The root *pher* means "to bear" or "to go." |

**1. Compare** How do the functions of the CNS and the PNS differ?

_____

_____

_____

**2. Summarize** Complete the diagram below to show the structure of the nervous system.

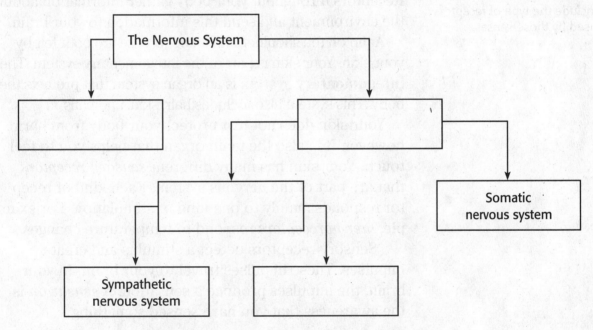

**3. Compare** How do the functions of dendrites and axons differ?

_____

_____

**4. Explain** What can happen to someone with a spinal cord injury?

_____

_____

_____

_____

**CHAPTER 17** | Communication and Control

**SECTION 2** **Sensing the Environment**

**California Science Standards**

7.5.a, 7.5.b, 7.5.g, 7.6.b

**BEFORE YOU READ**

After you read this section, you should be able to answer these questions:

• How do the integumentary system and nervous system work together?

• What is a feedback mechanism?

• How do your five senses work?

**STUDY TIP**

**List** As you read, make a list of the five senses. In your list, include the type of receptors used by those senses.

## How Does Your Sense of Touch Work?

When a friend taps you on the shoulder, or you feel a breeze, how does your brain know what has happened? Receptors throughout your body gather information about the environment and send this information to your brain.

A tap on the shoulder and a cool breeze are both felt by your skin. Your skin is part of the integumentary system. The **integumentary system** is an organ system that protects the body. This system also includes hair, skin, and nails.

Your skin does not just protect your body from harm, however. It is also the main organ that helps you to feel touch. Your skin has many different *sensory receptors* that are part of the nervous system. Each kind of receptor responds mainly to one kind of stimulation. For example, *thermoreceptors* respond to temperature changes.

Sensory receptors detect a stimulus and create impulses. These impulses travel to your brain. In your brain, the impulses produce a sensation. A *sensation* is the awareness that you have sensed something.

## TAKE A LOOK

**1. List** What are three types of sensations that your skin can detect?

_____

_____

_____

Different kinds of receptors in your skin can sense different things.

## REFLEXES

When you step on something sharp, do you stand still? Of course not! You move your foot right away without thinking about it. This reaction is called a reflex. A **reflex** is an action that happens very fast and that you cannot control.

Reflexes help protect your body from getting hurt. For example, if you step on something sharp, pain receptors in your foot send messages to your spinal cord. The spinal cord sends a message back to move your foot. Messages that cause reflexes don't even travel all the way to your brain. If you had to wait for your brain to act, you could be badly hurt.

## FEEDBACK MECHANISMS

Reflexes are helpful to your body. However, most of the time, the brain decides what to do with the messages from the skin receptors. Your brain helps to control many of your body's functions by using feedback mechanisms. A **feedback mechanism** is a cycle of events in which one step controls or affects another step. ☑

Feedback mechanisms help to keep your body functioning. Below is an example of how a feedback mechanism helps to keep your body temperature stable.

**Say It**

**Discuss** With a partner, name some other examples of reflexes. What part of the body is involved? When does the reflex happen? How does the reflex protect your body?

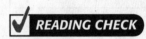

**READING CHECK**

**2. Complete** Feedback mechanisms in your nervous system are controlled by the

_____.

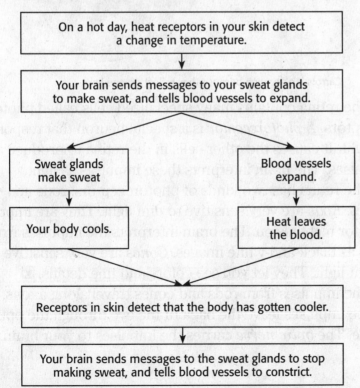

On a hot day, heat receptors in your skin detect a change in temperature.

↓

Your brain sends messages to your sweat glands to make sweat, and tells blood vessels to expand.

Sweat glands make sweat | Blood vessels expand.

Your body cools. | Heat leaves the blood.

Receptors in skin detect that the body has gotten cooler.

↓

Your brain sends messages to the sweat glands to stop making sweat, and tells blood vessels to constrict.

SECTION 2 Sensing the Environment *continued*

## How Does Your Sense of Sight Work?

Sight is the sense that lets you know the size, shape, motion, and color of objects around you. You see an object when light bounces off the object and enters your eyes. The light produces impulses in your eyes. These impulses travel to the brain and produce the sensation of sight.

The eyes are complex sensory organs. A clear membrane called the *cornea* covers the front of the eye. The cornea protects the eye but lets light enter. Light from an object enters the front of your eye through an opening called the **pupil**. Then, the light travels through the lens to the back of the eye. There, the light hits the **retina**, a layer of light-sensitive cells.

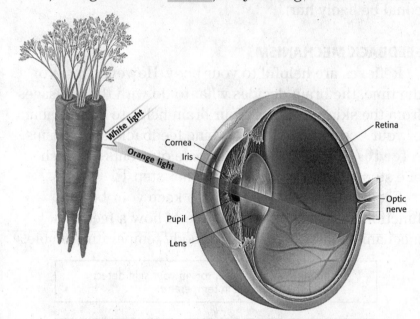

Carrots look orange because they reflect orange light.

The retina contains many specialized cells called photoreceptors. A *photoreceptor* is a special neuron that responds to light. It causes the other cells in the retina to produce impulses. The brain interprets these impulses as light.

The retina has two kinds of photoreceptors: rods and cones. *Rods* are very sensitive to dim light. They are important for night vision. The brain interprets the impulses from rods as black-and-white images. *Cones* are very sensitive to bright light. They let you see colors and fine details. ☑

The impulses from rods and cones travel along axons. These impulses leave the back of the eye through the optic nerve. The *optic nerve* carries the impulses to your brain.

---

### CALIFORNIA STANDARDS CHECK

**7.5.g** Students know organ systems function because of the contributions of individual organs, tissues, and cells. The failure of any part can <u>affect</u> the entire system.

**Word Help: <u>affect</u>**
to change; to have an effect on; to influence

**3. List** Name three parts of the eye and list their functions.

_____

_____

_____

_____

_____

_____

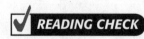
**READING CHECK**

**4. Identify** What are the two kinds of photoreceptors in the retina?

_____

---

**SECTION 2** Sensing the Environment *continued*

## REACTING TO LIGHT

Your pupil looks like a black dot in the center of your eye. Actually, it is an opening that lets light enter the eye. Around the pupil is a ring of muscle called the **iris**. The iris controls how much light enters your eye. It also gives your eye its color.

In bright light the iris *contracts*. This makes the pupil smaller.

In dim light the iris relaxes. This makes the pupil *dilate*, or get larger

## FOCUSING LIGHT

The lens focuses light onto the retina. The *lens* is an oval-shaped piece of clear, curved material behind the iris. The lens *refracts*, or bends, light. Muscles in the eye change the shape of the lens in order to focus the light on the retina. When you look at something that is close to your eye, the lens becomes more curved. When you look at objects that are far away, the lens gets flatter.

Some people have vision problems because their eyes cannot focus light correctly. The figure below shows the causes of some common vision problems.

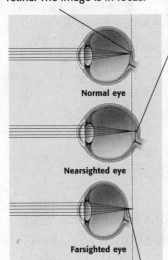
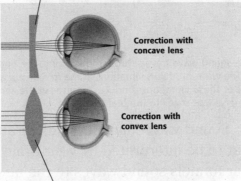

In a normal eye, light focuses onto a point on the retina. The image is in focus.

Normal eye

Nearsighted eye

Farsighted eye

In a nearsighted eye, the light focuses on a point in front of the retina. The image looks blurry.

A lens that is thinner in the middle than at the edges is a *concave* lens. Concave lenses bend light outward and help to correct nearsightedness.

Correction with concave lens

Correction with convex lens

In a farsighted eye, the light focuses on a point behind the retina. The image looks blurry.

A lens that is thicker in the middle than at the edges is a *convex* lens. Convex lenses bend light inward to help correct farsightedness.

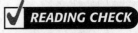

**READING CHECK**

**5. Identify** What is the function of the iris?

_____

_____

_____

## TAKE A LOOK

**6. Explain** Why do some images look blurry to people who are nearsighted and farsighted?

_____

_____

_____

_____

_____

_____

_____

# How Does Your Sense of Hearing Work?

Sound is produced when something *vibrates*. A drum, for example, vibrates when you hit it. Vibrations produce waves of sound energy. Hearing is the sense that lets you experience sound energy. ☑

Ears are the organs used for hearing. The ear has three main parts: the outer ear, middle ear, and inner ear. The chart below shows the structures that make up each part.

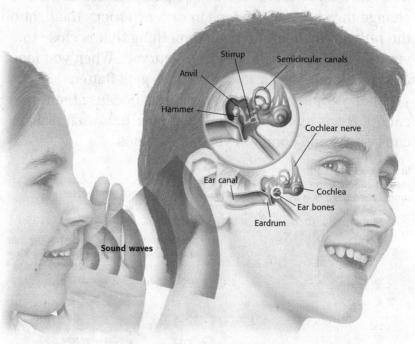

| Part of ear | Main structures |
|---|---|
| Outer ear | ear canal |
| Middle ear | *tympanic membrane*, or eardrum; three ear bones: hammer, anvil, and stirrup |
| Inner ear | cochlea and auditory nerve |

A sound wave travels through the air into the outer ear. The wave produces vibrations in the middle ear and inner ear. These vibrations produce impulses in the cochlear nerve that travel to the brain

Sound waves must create vibrations throughout your ear to be interpreted by your brain as sound. The outer ear funnels sound waves to the middle ear. Sound waves hit the eardrum and make it vibrate. These vibrations make the hammer, anvil, and stirrup vibrate. The stirrup vibrates against the **cochlea**, an organ filled with fluid. The vibrations make waves in the fluid. This causes neurons in the cochlea to send impulses to the brain.

**READING CHECK**

**7. Complete** Sound energy is produced by

_____.

**TAKE A LOOK**

**8. Color** Use colored pencils to color the outer ear blue, the middle ear green, and the inner ear red.

## THE EXTERNAL EAR

The part of the ear that you can see is called the *external ear*. It collects sound waves and sends them into your ear canal. In humans, the external ear is fixed in place. However, many animals can move their external ears around. This helps them hear sounds that are very quiet. Moving the external ear helps some animals, such as rabbits, know which direction a sound is coming from.

## KEEPING YOUR BALANCE

Your ears let you hear, but they also help you keep your balance. The *semicircular canals*, special fluid-filled canals in your inner ear, are filled with tiny hair cells. Fluid bends the hair cells when you move your head. This sends impluses to your brain. The brain then uses these impulses to figure out the position of your head. ☑

# How Does Your Sense of Taste Work?

Taste is the sense that lets you detect chemicals and tell one flavor from another flavor. Your tongue is covered with tiny bumps called *papillae* (singular, *papilla*). Most papillae contain taste buds. Taste buds have groups of *taste cells*, which are the receptors for taste. Taste cells respond to dissolved food molecules in your mouth. Taste cells react to five basic tastes.

| Taste | Example |
|-------|---------|
| Sweet | sugar |
| Sour | lemons, vinegar |
| Salty | potato chips |
| Savory | meats, cheeses |
| Bitter | coffee, unsweetened chocolate |

# How Does Your Sense of Smell Work?

Receptors for smell are located on olfactory cells in your nasal cavity. An *olfactory cell* is a nerve cell that senses the molecules in the air. You smell something when the receptors react to molecules you have inhaled.

*Critical Thinking*

**9. Explain** How is the external ear different from the outer ear?

_____

_____

_____

_____

_____

☑ **READING CHECK**

**10. Identify** What are two functions of the ear?

_____

_____

_____

**TAKE A LOOK**

**11. List** Give two examples of foods that have a mainly salty taste. Do not use the example in the table.

_____

_____

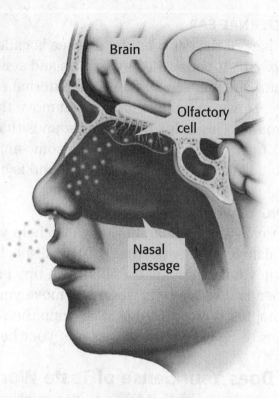

Brain

Olfactory cell

Nasal passage

Olfactory cells line the nasal cavity. These cells are sensory receptors that react to chemicals in the air and produce the sensation of smell.

Inhaled molecules dissolve in the moist lining of the nasal cavity and trigger an impulse. Olfactory cells send the impulses to the brain. The brain interprets the impulses as the sensation of smell.

Taste buds and olfactory cells both sense dissolved molecules. Your brain combines the information from your taste buds and your nose to let you sense flavor.

*Critical Thinking*

**12. Apply Concepts** Why do you have a hard time tasting things when you have a cold?

_____

_____

_____

_____

_____

**TAKE A LOOK**

**13. Summarize** Complete the chart to summarize the major senses and sense receptors.

| Sense | Receptors | What the receptors respond to |
|-------|-----------|-------------------------------|
| Touch | many different kinds | |
| Sight | | |
| | neurons in the cochlea | |
| Taste | | dissolved molecules |
| | olfactory cells | |

# Section 2 Review

7.5.a, 7.5.b, 7.5.g, 7.6.b

## SECTION VOCABULARY

**cochlea** a coiled tube that is found in the inner ear and that is essential to hearing

**feedback mechanism** a cycle of events in which information from one step controls or affects a previous step

**integumentary system** the organ system that forms a protective covering on the outside of the body

**iris** the colored, circular part of the eye

**pupil** the opening that is located in the center of the iris of the eye and that controls the amount of light that enters the eye

**reflex** an involuntary and almost immediate movement in response to a stimulus

**retina** the light-sensitive inner layer of the eye that receives images formed by the lens and transmits them through the optic nerve to the brain

**1. List** What are the five senses?

_____

**2. Explain** How do the integumentary system and nervous system work together?

_____

_____

_____

**3. Explain** Why are reflexes important for the body?

_____

_____

_____

_____

**4. Describe** What are the functions of rods and cones in the retina?

_____

_____

**5. Describe** How do the lenses in your eyes change when you look at things that are close and things that are far away?

_____

_____

_____

_____

**6. Explain** How do your ears help you keep your balance?

_____

_____

_____

SECTION
1 **Human Reproduction**

**California Science Standards**

7.2.b, 7.5.a, 7.5.d

BEFORE YOU READ

**After you read this section, you should be able to answer these questions:**

- How are sperm and eggs made?
- How does fertilization occur?
- What problems can happen in the reproductive system?

## What Happens in the Male Reproductive System?

The male reproductive system has two functions:

- to make sperm
- to deliver sperm to the female reproductive system

To perform these functions, organs in the male reproductive system make sperm, hormones, and fluids. The **testes** are a pair of organs that hang outside the body covered by a skin sac called the *scrotum*. They make sperm and *testosterone*, the main male sex hormone.

A male can make millions of sperm each day. Immature sperm cells divide and change shape as they travel through the testes and epididymis. The *epididymis* is a tube attached to the testes that stores sperm as they mature. ☑

Mature sperm pass into the *vas deferens*, which connects the epididymis and urethra. The *urethra* is a tube that runs from the bladder through the penis. The **penis** is the male organ that delivers sperm to the female. Before leaving the body, sperm mixes with a fluid mixture to form *semen*.

**Summarize** As you read, create two process charts. In the first, describe the path an egg takes from ovulation to fertilization. In the second, describe the path of an egg that does not get fertilized.

**1. Identify** How many sperm can a male make in one day?

_____

_____

### The Male Reproductive System

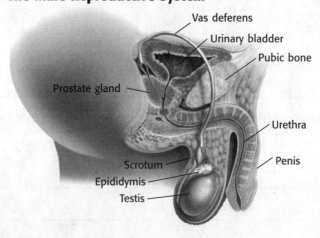

- Vas deferens
- Urinary bladder
- Pubic bone
- Prostate gland
- Urethra
- Penis
- Scrotum
- Epididymis
- Testis

**TAKE A LOOK**
**2. Circle** On the diagram, circle the structure that makes sperm.

## How Are Sperm Delivered to the Egg?

Most sperm leave the penis during ejaculation. *Ejaculation* is the sudden discharge of semen during sexual activity. However, some sperm may leave the penis without the male's knowing. In both cases, sexual activity that results in the release of sperm may lead to fertilization and pregnancy. *Fertilization* happens when one sperm penetrates, or enters, an egg.

## What Happens in the Female Reproductive System?

The female reproductive system has three functions:

• to produce eggs
• to protect and nourish fertilized eggs
• to give birth

Unlike males, who produce new sperm throughout their lives, females have all their eggs when they are born. Eggs are produced in an **ovary**. Ovaries also release the main female sex hormones: estrogen and progesterone. These hormones control the release of eggs from the ovaries and the development of female characteristics. Females generally have two ovaries.

### THE EGG'S JOURNEY

During *ovulation* an ovary releases an egg. The egg passes into a *fallopian tube*. The fallopian tube leads from the ovary to the uterus. Fertilization usually takes place in the fallopian tube.

If fertilization takes place, the fertilized egg enters the uterus and may embed in the thick lining. A fertilized egg develops into a baby in the **uterus**. When the baby is born, it passes from the uterus into the vagina. The **vagina** is the canal between the outside of the body and the uterus.

### THE MENSTRUAL CYCLE

From puberty through her late 40s or early 50s, a woman's reproductive system goes through the *menstrual cycle*. This cycle of about 28 days prepares the body for pregnancy. An ovary releases an egg at *ovulation*. This happens at around the 14th day of the cycle. If the egg is not fertilized, menstruation begins. *Menstruation* is the monthly discharge of blood and tissue from the uterus.

---

**CALIFORNIA STANDARDS CHECK**

**7.5.d.** Students know how the reproductive organs of the human male and female generate eggs and sperm and how sexual activity may lead to fertilization and pregnancy.

**Word Help: generate**
to bring about; to produce

**3. Explain** Why can fertilization happen during sexual contact without ejaculation?

_____
_____
_____
_____

**Math Focus**
**4. Calculate** The average woman ovulates each month from about the age of 12 to about the age of 50. How many mature eggs does she release from age 18 to age 50?

_____

---

## The Female Reproductive System

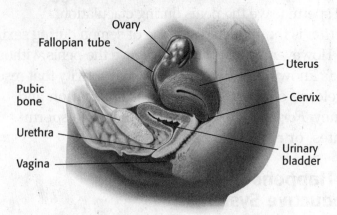

**TAKE A LOOK**

**5. Identify** On the diagram, put a circle around the structure that produces eggs. Put a square around the structure where a baby develops.

## What Happens During Fertilization?

If there are sperm in the female reproductive system within a few days of ovulation, the egg can become fertilized. During fertilization, a single sperm enters an egg.

Recall that chromosomes carry genetic information for each of your cells. Most body cells have two copies of each chromosome, one from each parent. An egg and sperm each carry only one copy of each chromosome. After fertilization, the fertilized egg, or *zygote*, has two copies of each chromosome. ☑

✓ **READING CHECK**

**6. Identify** How many copies of each chromosome do sperm and eggs carry?

_____
_____
_____

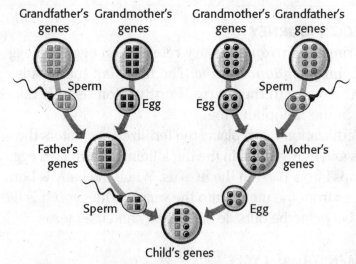

Eggs and sperm contain chromosomes. You inherited half of your chromosomes from each parent.

**TAKE A LOOK**

**7. Identify** What fraction of your genes did you inherit from each grandparent?

_____
_____
_____

# What Problems Can Happen in the Reproductive System?

Problems such as disease can cause the reproductive system to fail. Reproductive problems are commonly caused by sexually transmitted diseases and cancers.

## SEXUALLY TRANSMITTED DISEASES

A *sexually transmitted disease* (STD) is a disease that can pass from one person to another during sexual contact. They are also called *sexually transmitted infections* (STIs). Sexually active young people have the highest risk for STDs.

One example of an STD is human immunodeficiency virus (HIV), the virus that leads to AIDS. HIV destroys the immune system of the infected person. People with AIDS generally die from infections that are not fatal to people with healthy immune systems. Below is a table showing the most common STDs and how fast they are spreading in the United States.

| STD | Approximate number of new cases each year |
|---|---|
| Chlamydia | 3 to 10 million |
| Genital HPV (human papilloma virus) | 5.5 million |
| Genital herpes | 1 million |
| Gonorrhea | 650,000 |
| Syphilis | 70,000 |
| HIV/AIDS | 40,000 to 50,000 |

## CANCER

Sometimes cancer happens in reproductive organs. *Cancer* is a disease in which cells grow at an uncontrolled rate. In men, the two most common cancers of the reproductive system happen in the testes and prostate gland. In women, the two most common reproductive cancers are breast cancer and cancer of the cervix.

*Critical Thinking*

**8. Infer** In women, some untreated STDs can block the fallopian tubes. How would this affect fertilization?

_____

_____

_____

_____

_____

## TAKE A LOOK

**9. Identify** Which STD has the most number of new cases in the U.S. each year?

_____

 **Say It**

**Research** Use your school library or the internet to research one of the STDs in the chart. What organism or virus causes it? How does it affect the body? What treatments are available? Present your findings to the class.

# Section 1 Review

7.2.b, 7.5.a, 7.5.d

## SECTION VOCABULARY

| | |
|---|---|
| **ovary** an organ in the female reproductive system of animals that produces eggs | **uterus** in female mammals, the hollow, muscular organ in which a fertilized egg is embedded and in which the embryo and fetus develop |
| **penis** the male organ that transfers sperm to a female and that carries urine out of the body | **vagina** the female reproductive organ that connects the outside of the body to the uterus |
| **testes** the primary male reproductive organs which produce sperm and testosterone (singular, *testis*) | |

**1. Explain** What is the purpose of the menstrual cycle?

_____

_____

**2. Organize** Complete the chart below to describe the functions or characteristics of structures in the female reproductive system.

| Structure | Characteristic or function |
|---|---|
| | produces eggs and releases female sex hormones |
| Uterus | |
| Fallopian tube | |
| | connects uterus to the outside |

**3. Explain** What is fertilization and how does it occur?

_____

_____

_____

**4. Apply Concepts** Fraternal twins are created when two sperm fertilize two different eggs. Paternal, or identical, twins are created when a single egg divides after fertilization. Why are fraternal twins not identical?

_____

_____

_____

_____

SECTION
## 2 Growth and Development

**California Science Standards**

7.1.f, 7.5.d, 7.5.e

### BEFORE YOU READ

**After you read this section, you should be able to answer these questions:**

• What happens after an egg is fertilized?

• How does a fetus develop?

• How does a person develop after birth?

## How Does Fertilization Occur?

A man can release millions of sperm at once. However, only one sperm can fertilize an egg. Why are so many sperm needed?

Only a few hundred sperm survive the journey from the vagina to the uterus and into a fallopian tube. In the fallopian tube only a few sperm find and cover the egg. Once one sperm enters, or *penetrates*, the egg, it causes the egg's covering to change. This change keeps other sperm from entering the egg. When the nucleus of the sperm and egg join, the egg is fertilized.

**Fertilization and Implantation**

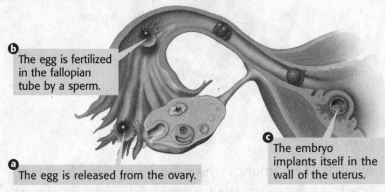

**b** The egg is fertilized in the fallopian tube by a sperm.

**c** The embryo implants itself in the wall of the uterus.

**a** The egg is released from the ovary.

## What Happens After Fertilization?

At fertilization, the egg is only a single cell. At this stage, the fertilized egg is called a *zygote*. As the zygote moves down the fallopian tube, it divides many times. After about a week the zygote is a ball of cells. This ball of cells implants in the uterus and is called an **embryo**. ☑

As the cells of the embryo continue to divide, some cells start to *differentiate*. They develop special structures for certain jobs in the body. After week 10 of the pregnancy, the embryo is called a **fetus**.

### STUDY TIP

**Summarize** As you read, make your own timeline that shows the stages an egg goes through as it is fertilized and develops into a baby.

## Critical Thinking

**1. Form Hypothesis** Why do you think millions of sperm are released to fertilize one egg?

_____

_____

_____

_____

## TAKE A LOOK

**2. Identify** Where does fertilization usually take place?

_____

_____

### ✓ READING CHECK

**3. Identify** What is the egg called right after fertilization?

_____

## TAKE A LOOK

**4. List** List the three stages a fertilized egg goes through as it develops.

_____

_____

_____

| The cells of the *zygote* divide and become a ball of cells | → | The ball of cells implants in the uterus and becomes an *embryo* | → | The cells of the embryo divide and differentiate; the embryo becomes a *fetus* |

## How Does an Embryo Develop?

A woman's **pregnancy** starts when an egg is fertilized, and ends at birth. Pregnancy is measured from the starting date of a woman's last period. This is easier than trying to determine when fertilization took place.

After a zygote implants in the uterus, the placenta forms. The **placenta** is an organ used by the embryo to exchange materials with the mother. The placenta has many blood vessels that carry nutrients and oxygen from the mother to the embryo. They also carry wastes from the embryo to the mother.

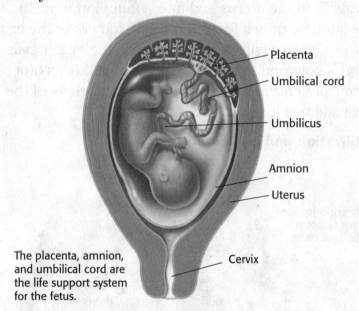

- Placenta
- Umbilical cord
- Umbilicus
- Amnion
- Uterus
- Cervix

## TAKE A LOOK

**5. Identify** What structure surrounds the fetus?

_____

_____

The placenta, amnion, and umbilical cord are the life support system for the fetus.

In week 5 of pregnancy, the **umbilical cord** forms. It connects the embryo to the placenta. The umbilical cord is attached to the fetus at the *umbilicus*. Between weeks 5 and 8, a thin membrane called the amnion develops. The *amnion* surrounds the embryo and is filled with fluid. This fluid cushions and protects the embryo. ☑

At weeks 37 to 38 the fetus is fully developed. A full pregnancy is usually 40 weeks. As birth begins, the muscles of the uterus begin contractions called *labor*. These contractions push the fetus out of the mother's body through the vagina. Once the baby is born, the umbilical cord is tied and cut.

## ✓ READING CHECK

**6. Explain** What is the function of the umbilical cord?

_____

_____

_____

## Pregnancy Timeline

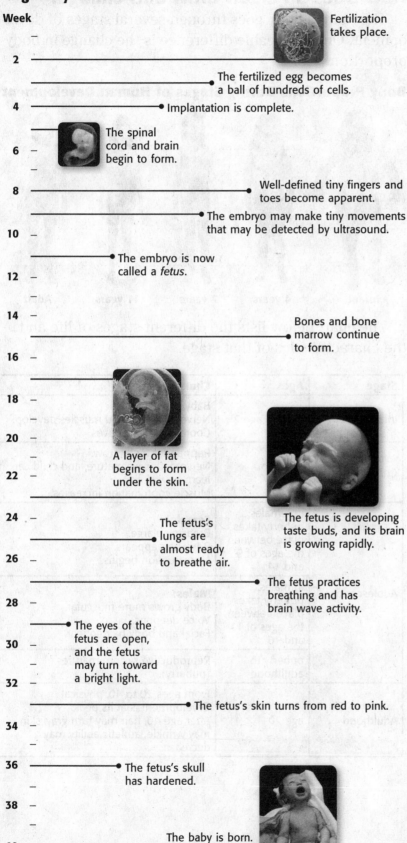

Week

**2** — Fertilization takes place.

The fertilized egg becomes a ball of hundreds of cells.

**4** — Implantation is complete.

**6** — The spinal cord and brain begin to form.

**8** — Well-defined tiny fingers and toes become apparent.

The embryo may make tiny movements that may be detected by ultrasound.

**10** —

The embryo is now called a *fetus*.

**12** —

**14** —

Bones and bone marrow continue to form.

**16** —

**18** —

**20** —

A layer of fat begins to form under the skin.

**22** —

**24** — The fetus's lungs are almost ready to breathe air.

The fetus is developing taste buds, and its brain is growing rapidly.

**26** —

The fetus practices breathing and has brain wave activity.

**28** —

The eyes of the fetus are open, and the fetus may turn toward a bright light.

**30** —

**32** —

The fetus's skin turns from red to pink.

**34** —

**36** — The fetus's skull has hardened.

**38** —

The baby is born.

**40** —

## TAKE A LOOK

**7. Identify** By what week has the brain of the embryo started to form?

_____

_____

**8. Identify** At around what week does the fetus start to develop taste buds?

_____

_____

**SECTION 2** Growth and Development *continued*

## How Does a Person Grow and Change?

The human body goes through several stages of development. One noticeable difference is the change in body proportion.

**Body Proportions During Stages of Human Development**

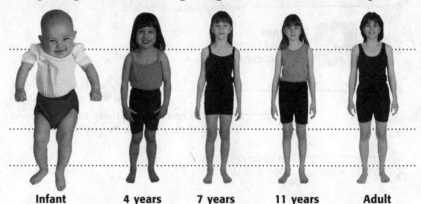

| Infant | 4 years | 7 years | 11 years | Adult |

### TAKE A LOOK
**9. Identify** At which stage or age is the head largest in proportion to the rest of the body?

_____

The chart below lists the different stages of life and the characteristics of that stage.

### Math Focus
**10. Calculate** Alice is 80 years old. She started puberty at age 12. Calculate the percentage of her life that she has spent in each stage of development.

_____

_____

_____

| Stage | Ages | Characteristics |
|---|---|---|
| Infancy | birth to age 2 | Baby teeth appear.<br>Nervous system and muscles develop.<br>Coordination improves. |
| Childhood | age 2 to puberty | Permanent teeth grow.<br>Nerve pathways mature, and child can learn new skills.<br>Muscle coordination increases. |
| Adolescence | in females, puberty takes place between the ages of 9 and 14 | **Females:**<br>Breasts enlarge.<br>Body hair appears.<br>Menstruation begins. |
| | in males, puberty takes place between the ages of 11 and 16 | **Males:**<br>Body grows more muscular.<br>Voice deepens.<br>Facial and body hair appear. |
| | puberty to adulthood | Reproductive system matures (puberty). |
| Adulthood | age 20+ | From ages 20 to 40, physical development is at its peak.<br>After age 40, hair may turn gray, skin may wrinkle, athletic ability may decrease. |

### TAKE A LOOK
**11. Identify** Which stage of development are you in?

_____

# Section 2 Review

7.1.f, 7.5.d, 7.5.e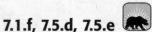

## SECTION VOCABULARY

| | |
|---|---|
| **embryo** a developing human, from fertilization through the first 8 weeks of development (the 10th week of pregnancy)<br><br>**fetus** a developing human from the eighth week after fertilization until birth<br><br>**placenta** the partly fetal and partly maternal organ by which materials are exchanged between the fetus and the mother | **pregnancy** the period of time between the first day of a woman's last menstrual period and the delivery of her baby (about 280 days, or 40 weeks)<br><br>**umbilical cord** the ropelike structure through which blood vessels pass and by which a developing mammal is connected to the placenta |

**1. Define** What is fertilization?

_____

_____

**2. Explain** Why can only one sperm enter an egg?

_____

_____

**3. Explain** What does it mean that cells differentiate?

_____

_____

**4. Identify** What is the function of the amnion?

_____

**5. Explain** Why is the placenta important to a developing embryo?

_____

_____

_____

**6. Define** What is the umbilicus?

_____

_____

**7. List** What are the four stages of human development?

_____

**8. Identify** What is the main characteristic of adolescence?

_____